SLAVES TODAY

A Story of Liberia

BY

GEORGE S. SCHUYLER

McGrath Publishing Company
College Park, Maryland

Reprint McGrath Publishing Company 1969

Library of Congress Catalog Card Number: 70-76120

Manufactured in the United States of America
by Arno Press, Inc., New York

FOREWORD

Slavery, in the form of forced labor with little or no compensation, exists under various euphemisms today in practically all parts of Africa, the East Indies and the South Seas. It is found as well in the colonies of European powers as in the Negro-ruled states of Abyssinia and Liberia. Regardless of the polite name that masks it while bloody profits are ground out for white and black masters, it differs only in slight degree from slavery in the classic sense, except that the chattel slaves' lives were not held so cheaply.

In Liberia this modern servitude is strikingly ironic because this black republic was founded by freed Negro slaves from the United States a century ago as a haven for all oppressed black people. Its proud motto reads, "The Love of Liberty Brought Us Here," but the aborigines find little liberty under their Negro masters.

The material for this narrative was gathered during a three-month sojourn on the

West Coast of Africa in the early part of 1931. All of the characters are taken from real life. Zo, Soki, Pameta, Big Georgie and Chief Bongomo answer to those names in Liberia today. The author is personally acquainted with them, as he is with most of the Americo-Liberian characters who appear under fictitious names.

If this novel can help arouse enlightened world opinion against this brutalizing of the native population in a Negro republic, perhaps the conscience of civilized people will stop similar atrocities in native lands ruled by proud white nations that boast of their superior culture.

GEORGE S. SCHUYLER

NEW YORK, N. Y.
October 6, 1931

SLAVES TODAY

SLAVES TODAY

CHAPTER ONE

STANDING on a prominent corner of Ashman
Street, the unpaved principal thoroughfare of
Monrovia, capital city of the West African
Negro republic of Liberia, is the Executive
Mansion. It is a three-storied balconied white
house, its roof relieved by dormer windows.
Before it is a strip of cement sidewalk with
curbstone, one of a dozen such in the strag-
gling, trash-ridden town of six thousand souls.
Surrounding it is an iron fence with an im-
pressive concrete gateway leading to the front
door.

Before it paces a tall, black, barefoot soldier
of the Liberian Frontier Force proudly carrying at correct angle an obsolete type of rifle
with gleaming bayonet fixed. Clad in khaki
shirt, shorts and wrap leggins, a wide dark
leather belt is drawn tightly about his narrow
waist while a red fez with a tassel sits jauntily
over one eye. On one side of the verandah
are a number of his comrades, lolling on the

benches and smoking cigarettes; on the other side sit dignified native chiefs from the far hinterlands in their picturesque robes and accompanied by their servants and advisers. They are awaiting an audience with the President of Liberia. From each side of the verandah a machine gun points threateningly across the street at the Department of State, a three-storied, square, cement structure done in the Moorish style. From a pole on the second balcony of the Executive Mansion, the lone-starred Liberian flag hangs lazily, occasionally swayed to and fro by the vagrant breezes that for a fugitive minute relieve the great heat of the African midday.

Upstairs in a high ceilinged office with French windows, red carpet, mahogany furnishings and an atmosphere of importance and tradition sat Sidney Cooper Johnson, President of Liberia, before a large flat-top desk. He was a dark brown man, past middle age, slightly plump, with piercing eyes and a cunning, calculating expression. He seemed worried as he toyed with his gold fountain pen. Occasionally he would stroke his long nose and chin in apparent quandary only to smile craftily a minute later.

President Johnson was a Liberian aristo-
crat. He seemed to belong in rooms like this
one from which he could look from the French
windows down upon the sprawling capital he
ruled. Three generations before, his ancestors,
Philadelphia freedmen, had helped found the
republic with the assistance of American
philanthropists and perturbed slaveholders.
They had fought off the aboriginal inhabitants, battled white-slave raiders, and cut
farms out of the virgin jungle. The tropical
climate to which they were unused had not
made life easy but they had persevered with
the true pioneer spirit.

Like most of his contemporaries, His Excellency was not of the material of his pioneer
grandparents. Educated in the United States
and trained in the law, he preferred a life of
ease, political intrigues and polite conversation to the worries and rigors of tropical agri-
culture. He loved to wander through the
mazes of legalism and enjoyed a reputation for
his ability to win cases by resurrecting mouldy
precedents. After a career as Judge and Attorney General, he had become Secretary of
State where he won international fame for
saying nothing adroitly. The long, involved
sentences which characterized his diplomatic

notes had caused the foreign ministers of great powers to scratch their heads in puzzlement and admiration. His state papers were always masterpieces because they could be interpreted in many ways, but they seldom contained anything definite.

The President was worried now because, like all successful candidates for office, he was finding it easier to promise than to pay off. The Conservative Party had remained in office continuously for thirty or more years, and so when he was elected there were few offices to parcel out because none of the Conservative officeholders ever quit except upon death or promotion. He now lamented the fact that few Liberians had any occupation other than practicing law and holding office. Each year a larger and larger number of the civilized population left farming with disgust and turned to politics with relief. The number of offices remained almost stationary while the pack of officeseekers steadily grew.

His Excellency frowned as he considered this dilemma. Then he turned momentarily to a problem even more ticklish. For a decade imports had exceeded exports. Spurred by necessity he had as Secretary of State negotiated a loan in Europe. This loan had made conditions in the country worse because the money was squandered and more of the civilized folk deserted farms and came to town in the hope of sharing in the reported holiday. Now the annual payments took a greater part of the national revenue. Sometimes even he could not get all of his salary while his subordinates were often not paid for months. White loan officials, saddled upon the country, deducted what was coming to the bankers first, leaving little in the treasury.

Lucky for Liberia, the President thought, that it had the missionaries and the natives. The former furnished education and brought into the country a half million dollars a year while from the latter came food and taxes. A ruling class, he observed to himself, must be supported in leisure by those whom it ruled. The unwritten law of Liberia decreed that the President be responsible for this support. He must select officials of slight scruples who would keep the flow of food and taxes coming down from the hinterland to Monrovia and at the same time permit certain money-making, if questionable practices, to be carried on by prominent citizens for the sake of party harmony.

Well, what was he to do now? President

Johnson asked himself. First, he concluded,
he'd have to get rid of Smith, the Commissioner in the First District. Too lazy and
soft. A hard man was needed up there. . . .
What about Jackson? Yes, he was the type
exactly. Was mighty active in the campaign,
too. Certainly have to do something for him.
Smith had little party influence. Jackson
could not be ignored. He was the man to de-
liver the goods without pushing the natives
too hard. . . . He'd recruit a lot of "boys"
for Fernando Po, too.

The President smiled cunningly at the
thought of Fernando Po. Much money
could be made from that business. They had
plenty of labor and the Spanish wanted it for
their cocoa plantations. Each man sent meant
fifty dollars split three ways between the re-
cruiter, the agent and His Excellency. The
income from the business increased, naturally,
with the growth of the traffic.

Of course, the Attorney General, a young
fellow with foolish ideas garnered abroad,
would denounce the business as a menace to
native life and all that sort of thing. He
would strenuously object to the exportation
of this labor from the prohibited area of Monrovia. That fellow was too honest for his own

good—only put in the cabinet to make it appear more respectable. Well, thought His Excellency, the Conservative Party had always managed to find ways and means to bring such fellows down to earth.

President Johnson straightened with sudden resolution and tapped a bell on his desk. The outer door flew open and a tall, black man in the uniform of a Colonel entered. He was the President's aide-de-camp. "Fitzsimmons," the President snapped, "get out an order relieving Smith as Commissioner of the First District and appointing David Jackson in his stead. Make it effective at once and send a fast runner up country tonight with it."

"Yes sir," replied the colonel, retiring.

His Excellency rose, stretched, and walked to the French windows. In the distance he could see his half-completed new residence upon which no workmen could be discerned. Shoving his hands into his pockets and rocking back and forth on his heels, he observed, "Probably I can get that finished now."

CHAPTER TWO

A CIRCLE of giant cottonwood trees hemmed
in the sleeping village of Takama. They
waved their umbrellalike tops to and fro in
the midnight breeze. In back of them
stretched the low, black wall of the jungle.
Within their circle some fourscore palm-
thatched African huts, resembling overgrown
hat boxes with conical tops, were planlessly
scattered about.

The night was moonless. Here and there
an isolated star kept watch in the heavens only
to disappear before the advancing banks of
heavy clouds which had mobilized to the north
and were moving slowly toward the little Gola
town. The giant trees grew more restless as
the wind increased. They bent lower and then
straightened up as if searching for something
in the lanes of the village.

Great flashes of lightning, three- and four-
pronged spears, darted across the heavens the
entire length of the big mountain range, il-
luminating every ridge, tree and valley.

It was late March and the first of the

torrential, tropical rains was approaching.
Weeks would pass before the rainy season set
in in earnest. This approaching storm was
but a warning, a prelude to the inevitable
deluge that would confine Africa to the interior of its huts for long months with few
respites.

The big trees bowed lower. The forks of
lightning shot across the sky more frequently
until Takama was as light as day. The booms
and rolls of thunder were like the climax of a
decisive battle.

Now came the hurried raindrops, small and
spaced far apart at first but growing quickly
larger and more frequent until they joined
together in a vertical deluge. Water streamed
off the thatched roofs and converted the wind-
ing lanes of the village into turbulent brooks.

The other forces of nature retreated before
this flood of water. After a few desultory
demonstrations, the north wind stopped blow-
ing, the thunder declined to a murmur and
the spectacular lightning flashes died with
equal dispatch. As if celebrating its victory,
the rain outdid itself in the black darkness
unrelieved by a single star.

There is no rain like the tropical rain. The
best built habitations cannot altogether with-

stand its insistent, prolonged pounding. It beats down irresistibly for days and weeks with slight intermission, making huts leak, drenching the best protected pedestrians, destroying trails and roads, swelling streams dangerously to twice or thrice their normal size.

Takama slept on. Even the heaviest rain could not be expected to disturb the slumbers of the inhabitants. They had risen at daybreak and been engaged all day in clearing the matted jungle for new farms, planting crops, repairing bridges and performing other more or less strenuous duties. Heavy with their evening meal of rice, fish and palm oil —the only meal of the day—they had taken to their sleeping mats with the coming of darkness that they might be fresh and strong with the dawn.

Two men in Takama did not sleep. Through the storm they sat huddled in a small hut on the edge of the village. The walls and rafters above them were hung with skin pouches, dried carcasses of small animals, bundles of twigs and herbs, bones of animals and men darkened by smoke from the central fire, and other strange articles of curious shape and purpose.

A small iron pot bubbled astraddle of two logs which hemmed in the small fire. It gave forth a queer, spicy, but not unpleasant odor.

Before this cauldron sat Tolo, the witch doctor, wrinkled, white-haired, stooped. A fleshless ancient, his bones protruded from every point and his aged black skin covered them but loosely. About him there was an immense dignity born of long and assured position in the little world which held him and his magic in awe. For eighty years Tolo had dwelt here protecting the people from the spirits of evil. He it was who uncovered the wrongdoers in Takama; it was to him the simple folk came to rid themselves of every malady of the flesh and spirit. Every resident of Takama was sure that Tolo could peer into the future and tell them of love, birth and death. If his magic failed to work, then it was not his fault but due to the machinations of an evil spirit some culprit was harboring.

Naked except for a piece of the coarse native cloth about his waist, his bony feet thrust into the warm ashes, a well-filled pouch of gri gri hanging from his withered neck and the glow of the fire lending his shrewd old face a satanic expression, he indeed looked like a devil man. Occasionally he tossed something

from a basket at his side into the iron pot
which strengthened the odd, spicy odor or he
would pass another stick of wood into the fire.
Once or twice he dipped a large spoon into the
concoction, tasted it, shook his wooly head and
murmured to himself.

Chief Bongomo of Takama sat on the hardened clay sleeping-platform across from Tolo.
Elbows on knees and cheeks in hands, he steadily and wonderingly watched the ancient before him. He was middle-aged, tall and muscular, his strong face reflecting some anxiety
as the witch doctor slowly went about his aba-
cadabra. The chief was garbed in a long robe
of blue-striped native cloth with flowing
sleeves and a rectangular pocket over the
breast, while on his feet were a pair of gaudy
Mandingo slippers. A straggling mustache
and a whispy beard added to his appearance of
authority.

Tomorrow Pameta, the chief's youngest and
favorite daughter, must undergo the supreme
test of marriage. For three years she had
gone to the gri gri bush, the native school,
where girls learned all that was necessary to
know in preparation for marriage and mother-
hood. Tonight she had gone to the hut of
her husband. Would all go well? Bongomo

wondered. He was naturally eager to know
for the revelations of the marriage bed might
bring joy or sorrow. The storm thus early
in the season seemed to him a bad sign, a probable augury of evil. So he had left his sleeping mat and come to Tolo. Like his people,
he had confidence in Tolo, much more in fact
than Tolo had in himself. Now he sat anxiously and respectfully awaiting the ancient's
verdict.

At last the witch doctor tasted again the
concoction and nodded his head in approval.
Murmuring with satisfaction he reached into
his gri gri pouch and pulled forth an oddly
shaped object. He straightened up his
rounded shoulders, his face grew animated and
he rubbed the object in his bony palms until
it was reduced to powder.

The chief leaned forward, his hands trembling slightly, his eyes wide open. Now he
would know that for which he had come.
Again the wizardry of Tolo would reveal the
future that the ruler of Takama might be reassured.

Holding the powder in his left hand, Tolo
added another stick to the fire with his right.
The blaze leaped higher and the pot bubbled
more actively. He cast the handful of pow-

der into the boiling liquid. Instantly a great
column of greenish steam rose into the rafters
of the hut and the concoction boiled over and
almost extinguished the fire.

The old man sat impassively watching the
phenomenon, his arms crossed like an old Bud-
dha, but Bongomo slunk back against the wall
of the hut, his eyes starting from his head in
fright, one sleeve shielding his face from this
hellish demonstration. An acrid, unpleasant
odor filled the hut. Finally Tolo removed the
pot from the fire and replenished the dying
embers with several small sticks. Again the
hut was illuminated so the two men could
plainly see each other. His temporary fright
gone, Bongomo moved again to the edge of the
sleeping platform.

"Well?" he inquired respectfully breaking
the long silence.

"Marriage good," observed Tolo without
hesitation.

Grinning with satisfaction, the chief arose
and reaching into the pocket of his gown withdrew some silver coins.

"But," added the witch doctor, "pot spill
over and that's bad. I don't understand yet.
Tomorrow start good, maybe end bad."

Tolo liked to add disturbing touches to his

prophecies. Like those of his craft the world
over, he had found it advisable to surround
all of his findings with an aura of mystery and
uncertainty, the better to hold the respect and
confidence of his clients.

Bongomo, somewhat disturbed by Tolo's
final words, placed three of the coins in the
ancient's clawlike hand. Then removing his
gown, folding it up tightly and placing it under his arm, he ran naked through the pouring
rain to his compound.

Daybreak. Only little pools of water here
and there like broken mirrors scattered about
gave proof that there had been a rain. A
foggy haze dimmed all objects into unreality.
Trees and huts were indistinct as if seen
through gray spectacles. Persons stirring
about at first resembled wraiths. The surrounding jungle was alive with the amazing
chorus of thousands of birds and insects. At
times the sound grew deafening. Then, as
the sun appeared and the first heat of day descended, the chorus grew fainter until only the
twittering of a few birds, the complaints of
monkeys from the high treetops and the
steam-enginelike swishing of the hornbills'
wings could be heard. A fresh, clean, washed

odor pleasing to the nostrils filled the air,
while from the jungle a scent of perfume was
wafted to the village.

Doors creaked open in Takama and people
began to stir about. Cocks crowed, goats
raced up and down the lanes exuberantly kicking up their heels, while women emerged with
pails on the way to the nearby stream. They
hailed each other and in groups descended the
hill talking loudly.

No one was going to the farms or forest today. There would in all probability be big
times in Takama with much eating of good
roast meat, huge quantities of rice and palm
oil and many big, fat fish from the river. Boys
would go out early into the jungle trails and
return with numbers of huge snails that appear by scores after a heavy rain. Of course
everything depended on the outcome of the
first night together of Zo and Pameta.

Zo had watched the chief's beautiful daughter ever since she was a very small girl and
desired her. As she grew older his desire increased. Three years before he had taken several articles of value to her father and mother,
telling them he wanted the girl. Having ascer-
tained the approximate value of the gifts, they
had agreed to the marriage after Pameta came

out of "the bush," or school. This had proved satisfactory to Zo and he had placed the betrothal rings on the girl's fingers. In accordance with the Gola custom, he had for the three years of school paid all of her necessary expenses.

Yesterday she had formally graduated from "the bush," a tall, ripe, brown beauty, painted with red clay and loaded down with many ropes of multicolored necklaces, her arms encircled with bracelets made by the village blacksmith. Strong, black, and sixteen, with pearly white teeth usually exposed in laughter—Zo had waited impatiently for her. His new hut, which the entire village had helped to build, was in readiness.

Around noon her parents had made the formal call and invited him to go to the compound and see his wife. He had returned with them, in accordance with the ancient custom. This done he had gone to his hut and waited. Shortly afterward Pameta's sister, brother and aunt had brought the bride. They had also brought a large white cloth which they spread over the sleeping-mat. The two were then left to themselves.

Now, as the sun rose higher and Takama became more animated, Pameta's sister, brother

and aunt returned to Zo's hut with a small
crowd in their wake. From a distance Bongomo and Pameta's mother, Badé, watched
anxiously. Their anxiety was justified for
very soon they and their little world would
know whether or not Pameta had been proved
a virgin. If she had there would be feasting, drinking and dancing such as Takama had
not seen in many moons; if not, there would be
sorrow and lamentation. Her family would
have to retire precipitously to the jungle, the
gifts of Zo would have to be returned and
he could walk up and down the lanes of Takama and revile the girl and her family, while
Pameta would never be able to get a husband
in her village. She would have to repay her
parents for their material loss by serving as a
sort of village prostitute for men whose wives
were temporarily unfitted by nature for the
most intimate of the marital duties. Such was
the ancient and honorable law of the Golas.

The trio knocked at the door of Zo's hut.
It was opened and they entered. The crowd,
increasing in size, waited expectantly outside.
Almost immediately the three returned.
Standing on the broad ledge outside the door,.
Pameta's aunt, who bore the white cloth, tri-
umphantly unfurled it for all to see. In its

center was a large irregular red spot, the proof of virginity. A great shout went up from the onlookers. Bongomo and Badé sighed with relief and did not conceal their joy. Immediately the chief ordered six goats to be killed and large quantities of other food to be prepared. He sent several youths after palm wine. The stage was being set for a mighty celebration.

Everyone felt a certain unexpressed gratefulness to Pameta. Only because she had proved herself a virgin were they having such a feast.

Morning cooking is unusual in African villages. It was different this day in Takama. The cook shacks gave forth clouds of wood smoke mingled with the odors of roasting flesh. Goatskins and chicken feathers lay all about. Great pans of steaming rice were soon in evidence. The women preparing the food chattered excitedly while the men lazed around the palaver house enjoying their vacation.

Old Tolo sat on the steps of his hut quite satisfied with himself. All had happened as he prophesied. The marriage was good indeed. His usual luck had been with him. Much palm wine would be brought to him today. It would warm his old bones and send the blood coursing more swiftly through his withered frame. Soon the good food would be before him. Almost toothless, he would have to cut the delicious goat and chicken into small pieces and gulp it down. The rice saturated with palm oil would present less difficulty. He scratched his arms and legs contentedly and switched his clay pipe to the other side of his mouth.

While Tolo was not by any means as gullible as his flock about the efficacy of his witchcraft, he still believed there was something unknown and malignant surrounding all people, ready to take its toll. He could hardly avoid being superstitious in such an environment. For example, he was somewhat worried over whether the boiling over of his iron pot the night before had meant anything. His long experience told him it meant nothing; but then, he argued, everything meant something. He scanned the sky somewhat anxiously—it was a cloudless blue. He glanced toward the surrounding jungle—it was a brilliant green. He shook his wooly head and sucked strongly on his pipe. He felt in his bones that something was going to happen today. What could it be? Quite as ignorant of the future as the others, he yet had a foreboding of evil.

Sitting on his verandah, a little unsteady from palm wine, a red fez cocked sidewise over his braids, Bongomo was the happiest of men. He was arrayed in his most elaborate gown, wearing his Mandingo slippers and swinging at his side the sword of authority encased in an ornate leather scabbard. He was thinking of his good fortune. When the ancients of the village came to offer their congratulations, he beamed as though he were the bridegroom.

High noon. The sun hurled its penetrating rays upon Takama. The air was hot and breathless. No breeze stirred. Village lanes were deserted. Even goats and chickens had sought the shelter of shade. Inside the huts where it was cool and pleasant the families had gathered to consume the feast. From each habitation issued talk and laughter. Outside all was silent and no sound came from the jungle.

There is no heat like that of the African midday. It is humid and withering. Unable to stand against it, both man and beast seek the shade until the cooler hours. On the jungle trail the pedestrian is often saved from prostration by the sheltering trees and bushes. At this hour the word "tropics" assumes added significance.

Inside their new hut Zo and Pameta lay in each other's arms, giggling, playful, happy. To one side in basins and pans were the remnants of their feast; beside them stood a large gourd half filled with palm wine. This was their day. To them the future seemed brilliantly golden as to all newlyweds. They had youth and love, plenty of food and leisure, so they played and laughed, buoyant and content.

"When are you going to buy another wife?" asked Pameta jokingly.

"Oh, not for a long, long time," Zo replied. "I must pay back father first."

"That's good," the young wife declared emphatically. "I do not want anyone else to have you yet."

"When I do get other wives," said the husband, "you will always be my head wife," he announced.

"Are you sure?" she queried.

"Quite sure," he answered, "because I wanted you more than I can ever want anyone else."

"That's what you say now," she remarked coquettishly, pretending to move away.

"No, I mean it, Pameta," he said soberly.

They clung closer.

Again Takama slept, sated with the prodigious repast Bongomo had provided. When had there been such a feast; when such floods of palm wine? There was not a palm tree for three miles around that had not been tapped for the precious fluid. No wonder the folk were happy and listless and slept through the heat of midday. Doors stood open. No smoke arose from the village. Here and there a chicken saved from the feast pecked away in search of food.

It was midafternoon when Chief Bongomo emerged from his big hut, stretching his arms and rubbing his eyes. He sat down in his chair for a minute or two as if to clear his head. Then he rose, arranged his gown and fez and walked majestically to the other end of the village and entered the hut of the witch doctor.

Tolo did not relish this disturbance of his siesta. He, too, was heavy with food and sleep. Had the intruder been anyone except the chief he would have loudly upbraided him and driven him from the place. Bongomo greeted him with a sort of grunt which elicited a similar reply from the witch doctor.

"No evil spirits come, Tolo," the chief declared. "Tonight we have a big dance in the moonlight, eh?"

"Day's not over," mumbled Tolo. "Plenty time for spirits. Hold dance now."

Tolo knew that daylight dances were unusual but as a shrewd student of humanity he also knew that it is the unusual that disarms and mystifies. Moreover, he wanted to sleep tonight instead of being kept awake by the drums.

Bongomo pondered Tolo's advice for a few moments. To dance under the sun was very unusual but if Tolo said now, it would be now. Who knew better than Tolo what should be done to ward off evil. Some of the ancients might object but what of it? Was he not the chief? At the thought of his importance, he straightened up to his full height, arranged one or two of his braids behind his ears, announced his departure with a grunt and strode back to his compound, his sword flapping at his side.

Africa loves to dance. Almost every night when the tropical moon illumines village streets as if they were lighted by arc lights, the variously pitched drums tap out their intricate rhythm and the close-packed crowd shuffles, leaps and hops to exhaustion.

Few forms of entertainment prove superior to the African dance in all of its variations. The roll-tap-and-boom of the drums sends peculiar tingles over the body. The inhibitions of industrial society drop gradually from even the most civilized person until he also wants to join the gyrating, stamping black folk. The dance, the drums, the horns—these musical instruments are ages old. They have come down from the dawn of humanity. They are a part of our heritage. No wonder all humans are drawn to them.

When Bongomo reached his hut, he went to a large drum on the verandah. It was made from the trunk of a tree, well carved and painted. He tapped upon it a peculiarly intricate syncopated staccato. It was not loud but it was penetrating. First he used one hand, then two; striking the drum head with an alternation of finger, center of palm and wrist.

In answer to this summons, the first to emerge from the huts was the chief's messenger, a plump, round-faced man of medium height, his mouth yet greasy from the feast; his eyes still full of sleep. He ran uncertainly to the verandah and relieved the chief at the drum. Bongomo reclined in his chair and watched the people assemble. He made mental notes and comments as various ones appeared.

There was the blacksmith, a short fellow with powerful arms and shoulders, who made excellent tools and ornaments, but was always having trouble with his three wives. Coming yonder was the weaver, a tall, silent, surly fellow, who made fine cloths and had manufactured the beautiful gown the chief wore. Trotting along with two or three of his young friends came a big sturdy black fellow just returned with many shillings from the big rubber plantation. With an appraising eye Bongomo scrutinized a group of young girls, ripe young things, laughing and giggling. He sighed as he thought of his loss of prowess with the fair sex and recalled with a frown that he had five other wives besides Badé.

Bongomo's messenger announced to the assembled folk that a dance was to be held. A murmur of surprise ran through the crowd. Like human beings everywhere they were greatly surprised by anything unusual. They had always been told that moonlight nights were best for dancing, but when it was explained that the change was necessary to ward off spirits of evil all objections were withdrawn.

The African lives in a spirit world where every object, animate and inanimate, has a soul and is related to him. The very atmosphere is, to him, filled with lost souls and at every step he may offend some spirit. Against this ever-present evil he must always be prepared. Sometimes an offering of food will suffice but more often powerful medicine is necessary.

To all parts of the village the people ran to get musical instruments: horns, pipes, drums, harps and gourds. When again assembled, the chief's messenger loudly addressed them. Bongomo, he declared, was a great man with no superior anywhere. His ancestors had also been noted personages who had led the Golas to victory over their traditional enemies, the Vais. Reclining in his chair, Bongomo affected an air of bored indifference but he was listening intently and proudly to every word.

When the tale was told, the village women came forward bearing pebble-filled gourds. They were led by a strong, middle-aged woman armed with an enormous gourd covered with a network of French coins. She had

about her an air of authority and command.
The village folk deferred to her in such a
way that you knew instinctively she was a person of importance. She had, indeed, a wide
reputation as a witch through the Gola country. During the three years of the girls'
school she taught young virgins what they
should know. In addition she headed the
women's secret society.

She stepped now to the center of the crowd
of women and they withdrew slightly to give
her the room she needed. She leaned back,
one hand on her hip, and began a song about
Bongomo, telling what a great and good chief
he had been. The chorus accompanied her
softly with their rattles. Then she sang more
softly and the other women joined her. Her
strong voice now rose until it seemed to carry
far into the surrounding jungle. As a stanza
was ended she would raise her muscular bare
arm and begin manipulating the huge gourd.
If there had been syncopation and intricate
rhythm before, they were nothing compared
to that she added. She threw herself into the
business with an energy that brought streams
of perspiration off her dark face, neck, arms
and bare breasts. Song followed song about
great lovers, hunters and fighters, all legend-

ary heroes of the Gola people, whose history embraced five thousand years.

At last the chorus retired and the orchestra took its place. The weaver had a large V-shaped drum decorated gaudily with paint and a leather fringe about the head hanging from his neck; the brawny little blacksmith came with a huge horn tucked under his arm; another villager brought a smaller drum seven inches in diameter and hung in horizontal position from his neck. This drum was played with two sticks struck on the sides instead of the ends. It gave forth a lighter, higher tone to contrast with the boom of the big drum which was played with the hands. A dozen other people with horns, pipes and harps joined the group.

This orchestra made fascinating, bloodstirring music as it executed a preliminary march from one end of Takama to the other. Naked little boys and girls followed it yelling and capering. When they returned a great circle was made by the people with the orchestra opposite the chief. There was now to be individual dancing. Rival experts would display remarkable exhibitions of intricate footwork and gymnastics. Lithe girls would twist and kick up their heels. Youngsters not yet in

their 'teens would leap practically nude into
the ring, flashing like animated ebony in the
afternoon sun.

But first the great Bongomo himself must
start the solo dancing. So with a deprecating
smile, he came down from his chair on the
verandah. The music grew livelier. He
leaped into the circle, paused as if listening for
a sound from afar and raced around the ring,
his long robe floating out behind him. Following some clever footwork, he ended in a
toplike whirl. Puffing and sweating, he returned amid the plaudits of his people to his
chair.

Now one after another the best dancers of
the village bounded into the ring emulating
and surpassing their chief. Then suddenly Zo,
clad in a fine homespun jacket that reached
almost to his knees, shot into the open space
with a handspring and stopped still while the
orchestra played softly. As the drums
speeded up the tempo with savage intensity
punctuated by weird blasts from the horns and
squeals from the pipes, he became a whirlwind
of arms and legs. He sprang high into the
air, moving his legs as if running. He executed the heel-and-toe dance, which is as swift

as it is graceful. Then, turning another handspring, he flashed out of the circle.

The excitement of the crowd grew. Calls
were made for certain well-known dancers.
Reluctantly, these experts were pushed into
the human circle where, despite their hesitancy,
they gave a good account of themselves. Next
came the women and among them Pameta.
The bride was greeted with a shout as with
eyes coquettishly lowered, she moved with the
grace of a bacchante, smoothly, sensuously.

The players sweated profusely but seemed
not to tire. The sun sank a little lower and the
air grew cooler. Now the crowd itself wanted
to dance *en masse*. The orchestra began to
march backward down the lane from Bongomo's compound. Following it came the crowd,
singing and dancing. The basic step was a
heel-and-toe movement executed in unison.
Then at intervals and as if by command, the
entire group executed a comical little jump to
one side and a rocking back on the heels. The
march continued through all the lanes of Takama with the folk growing more hilarious.
With considerable difficulty Chief Bongomo
held himself from participating in the dance.
He knew the act would be a serious breach

of etiquette. Not that he cared particularly, but the people themselves, especially the ancients, would frown upon it. So he sighed in resignation, watching the gyrating crowd enviously and accompanying the music with a shuffling of his slippered feet and tosses of his head.

Well satisfied with the events of the day, Bongomo took a long drink from his gourd of cool palm wine and settled back lazily to watch his people disport themselves.

CHAPTER THREE

THE rays of the sinking sun were filtering fit-
fully through the forest screen as a long column of men toiled at their utmost speed to
reach Takama before dark. The harsh voice
of a Frontier Force sergeant urged them on.
First came the carriers with their heavy trunks
and hampers. Almost naked the streams of
perspiration ran off them as if they were under
a shower bath. They were weary and bent
low with their heavy loads: trunks, hampers,
beds and the like. They were quite as eager
as the sergeant to reach the village that they
might lie down like cattle to rest.

After the carriers came three two-carrier
hammocks each occupied by a young and hand-
some girl. Behind them in a four-carrier hammock lolled an important-looking Liberian
official, while a small detachment of Frontier
Force soldiers brought up the rear. The hammock carriers puffed, panted and perspired as
they staggered along. Frequently they read-
justed the poles which, despite protective pads,
cut cruelly into their shoulders. They too were

eager for the rest soon to come when their
aching muscles and bruised feet would have a
night's relief and they could prepare themselves for the morrow's task by gorging great
handfuls of palm oil and rice.

The important official was David Jackson,
Commissioner of the First District, with over
a half a million natives under his jurisdiction.
A scion of an old pioneer Liberian family, a
graduate of a missionary college and a power
in politics, he was a mahogany-brown man of
medium size with a square, brutal face, a sneering, sensual mouth and little piggish eyes under which depended the telltale pouches of
dissipation.

In the hammock beside him was a half-filled
bottle of Scotch whiskey. Now and then he
refreshed himself with a drink. From one corner of his mouth hung a cold, stringy, half-
smoked cigar. His olive drab army service
hat was jammed on the back of his head and
his khaki suit was spattered with liquor and
sprinkled with cigar ashes.

"Sergeant!" he yelled. "Where the hell are
you?"

"Right here, sir," said the sergeant appearing at his side.

"By God, sergeant," Jackson shouted for

the tenth time that afternoon, "get some more speed out of these 'boys' or I'll give them all the whip. We're going too slow, understand, we're going too slow. Pretty soon we'll be caught in the dark. Make 'em hurry up, sergeant."

"Yes, sir," replied the noncommissioned officer. He and the men who overheard and could understand the conversation, knew that Commissioner Jackson would flog every carrier if darkness overtook the column.

Jackson leaned back in his hammock and the sergeant went about his task of hurrying up men who were almost exhausted. He yelled, shouted and cursed at them until they moved just a little faster than before.

Finally the column emerged from the jungle trail, crossed the swift little stream that was Takama's water supply and toiled up the incline to the town. A welcome sight it was to porters and carriers weary from ten hours' journey. These huts meant food, shelter and rest. With a sigh of relief and renewed energy they bore their burdens to the center of the village and stopped in front of the palaver kitchen.

At this time of the day there would normally have been quite a group of village men sitting

around resting after the day's work, but the
place seemed almost deserted. From the messenger of the District Commissioner sent on
ahead to notify townspeople of the great man's
coming, the people had heard the unwelcome
announcement and fled to the jungle or in-
doors. Only five or six ancients, including old
Tolo, surrounded Chief Bongomo to receive
their ruler whom they knew to be more important than six paramount chiefs. Gone were
the skipping children, the exuberant dancers
and the gay musicians. A certain air of omi-
nous expectancy pervaded the place.

Somewhat apprehensive, Bongomo strode
to the District Commissioner's hammock and
paid his respects through Joe, the official's interpreter and general handy man. To this little speech the Commissioner replied with an
indifferent salute and a grunt. He stepped
unsteadily out of his hammock, straightened
his hat on his head, adjusted his black necktie. Joe handed the half-filled whiskey bottle
to one of the girls.

"Everything fixed, Joe?" asked the Commissioner, shooting a glance at Bongomo and
his senile staff.

"No sah, massah," the man replied. "Chief

say have plenty big feast today. Eat up most everything. Chief ask massah to wait small. Pretty soon plenty chop."

Jackson's little eyes grew smaller with sudden rage as he eyed the perturbed Bongomo. The chief began to stammer out duly interpreted apologies. They seemed to anger the Commissioner. The latter was outraged that all preparations had not been made for his coming. Was he not the District Commissioner? He swelled up more at the thought and became doubly indignant. He began to see this delay as an affront to the authority of the Liberian government.

"Goddam you," he shouted, shaking his finger in the face of the amazed chief, "don't you try to fool me! You get plenty rice, palm oil, goat, fish, chicken or I'll fix you so you won't forget it."

In his anger he forgot that the chief could not speak English, but Joe acquainted Bongomo immediately with the import of his threat. The chief was in a dilemma. Threshed rice and palm oil were to be obtained only from the agricultural half towns a distance of two or three miles. As for palm wine which Joe had said was required in large quantities, there was

not a tree within an hour's walk that had not
been tapped for its day's supply of the cool,
heady fluid.

Bongomo clapped his hands and his messenger appeared only to be sent to tell the people to leave their huts and get the needed food
supplies. Several women were ordered to
prepare at least a half dozen huts for the
guests, which meant ousting the present occupants. Excitedly the chief ordered them
about, urging them to make haste as he
watched the increasingly hard expression on
the Commissioner's face.

Carriers, porters, concubines and soldiers
sat around awaiting the enforced hospitality
of Takama while Jackson, hands on hips,
angry and half drunk, cursed none too softly.
Bongomo and his elderly cabinet stood apprehensive and uneasy at a respectful distance
awaiting they knew not what.

Suddenly Jackson had an inspiration that
brought a grim smile to his face. He was
deeply offended that everything should not
have been in readiness upon his arrival but
realized that the chief had a good excuse and
was doing the best he could. His new idea
might give him a reason for inflicting some
punishment. He turned to Joe and asked:

"Have we been getting stuff from this place regularly, Joe?"

"Yassah, massah," his man replied, "but he late this time. Last time he short on rice they tell me."

Jackson turned and glared balefully at the unfortunate Bongomo, and demanded, through Joe, why the monthly requisition of rice and palm oil had not been sent. Bongomo stammered an apology, swearing the requisition would be delivered to Boloba the next day. It was this food, requisitioned from each town for the maintenance of the Commissioner and his staff, that had been consumed that day in the joyous feast.

The women came announcing that the huts were ready and all of the newcomers except the Commissioner, Joe, the sergeant and the soldiers moved off to get settled for the night. Hammocks, trunks, beds and hampers were carried away, thus clearing the square in front of the palaver kitchen.

In drunken persistence Jackson kept balefully glaring at the chief. He was getting too damn uppity, thought the Commissioner. Couldn't let natives disobey orders. . . . Requisition should have been sent to Boloba. . . . He'd teach this fellow a lesson!

"Sergeant!" he yelled, "get your whip and put it on this fellow."

Unable to understand the Commissioner's order, Bongomo and his followers were nevertheless alarmed at its tone. Only the gathering crowd of villagers behind them bearing the ordered food somewhat reassured them.

It was now almost dusk. In a great red blaze the sun sat on the green horizon of the jungle. Already the crickets, toads and frogs were quietly rehearsing for their deafening evening chorus. It had grown much cooler and a breeze blew through the village lanes making old Tolo shiver under his cloth.

The sergeant and his six, red-fezzed soldiers approached Bongomo. Two of them seized him, bound him securely with a rope handed to them by the sergeant and threw him to the ground. The chief struggled and yelled in vain. His people could not help him in the face of the threatening rifles. Their only weapons were spears, jungle knives, bows and arrows. Of what avail would they be against rifle bullets? Increasing now in number they stood angrily, impotently and watched the outrage. Again and again the sergeant, his right arm bared, brought down the bull whip on the squirming body of Bongomo.

The African chief is the father of his village. To him the simple folk defer and pay homage. His word is law. Parents point to him as an example their children should follow if they also would become great. That he should be humiliated by a public whipping before his people is unthinkable to them. And yet there was the beloved chief of Takama writhing in the dirt being flogged by an inferior and no one dared go to his assistance.

Jackson watched the spectacle with apparent satisfaction as he puffed on a fresh cigar. The six soldiers, their bayoneted rifles raised and pointed at the horrified villagers, stood ready and eager for the order to fire.

"That's about enough, sergeant," ordered Jackson. "Let him up now."

"Yes, sir," replied the perspiring sergeant.

Bongomo's bonds were cut and he rose slowly to his feet. He was hurt in body but more so in soul. He had always striven to maintain the dignity befitting a chief. Thereby he had won his people's respect and admiration. Now he had been beaten like a thief before them. The thought of what had happened enraged him. Without considering the consequences, he yanked his sword from its decorated scabbard and with a yell to his people leaped toward Jackson. The villagers drew their knives and followed him, emboldened by his courage.

The attack ended almost as quickly as it began but it lasted long enough for Jackson to be badly scared. The sergeant's automatic pistol spoke twice and Bongomo staggered back, the sword dropped from his hand and he fell sprawling, his left hand clutching his breast, his mouth foaming blood.

The soldiers fired a volley into the advancing crowd, then another. Seven or eight natives lay dead and wounded at their feet. The remainder fled, terrified and demoralized, to their huts.

"After them!" yelled the sergeant, excited by the sight of blood.

"Aye, yah!" cried the soldiers, following the crowd with fixed bayonets.

They had overtaken and clubbed two or three of the less fleet villagers when Jackson, somewhat sobered by his narrow escape, countermanded the order. It would be best not to go any further. As it was there would perhaps be complaints to Monrovia though nothing would ever really be done about it. Had he not been given a free hand a year ago?

It was almost dark. As he turned to go to
his hut with Joe, old Tolo, almost deranged
with anger over the outrageous proceedings,
ran up cursing and waving his bag of gri gris
in the Commissioner's face. Jackson leaped
back in fear, for everybody in Africa, civilized
and uncivilized, respects the witch doctors,
even if sceptical of their many claims.

By the time Jackson recovered his poise the
old man was halfway to his hut and moving
with surprising speed. Two soldiers ran after
him to bring him back for a whipping but Tolo
reached the hut before they did, entered, and
barred the door. Finally, forcing the door, the
soldiers rushed in the place to find the back
door wide open and the magician gone to the
jungle.

Darkness fell with dramatic suddenness.
The dead and wounded had been removed.
Relatives of the unfortunates were wailing
over the bodies in the huts. Others armed with
long torches were escaping to the safety of the
jungle half towns. Jackson sat in a camp
chair outside the door of his hut while his
dinner was being prepared. Porters and carriers were cooking their food and that for the
soldiers. Joe came out of the hut and handed

the Commissioner a tall glass of whiskey and
soda.

He returned to the hut and began setting
up the folding camp table. This done, a white
cloth was spread upon it and silver, china and
glassware arranged. The service sparkled
brightly in the light of the two big lanterns
hanging from rafters.

The District Commissioner lived well even
if he was in the hinterland. He insisted on
having his Scotch and soda, his favorite pickles
and cheese, ham and eggs every morning, the
best of native food and plenty of palm wine
to wash it down. Each of his meals had
to end with coffee and a cigar. Why rule
a half a million natives unless you were to
live well?

For over a year now he had ruled this district and ruled it satisfactorily according to
his way of thinking. He was sending more
requisitioned food to Monrovia than Smith
had ever dreamed of. His messengers and
soldiers had gone to the isolated villages un-
visited for years to get food and taxes and, as
Jackson said, "to put the fear of God in their
hearts." Every one of these towns knew now
that they must obey orders promptly or punishment would be swift and severe. However,

he advised his soldiers to avoid shedding blood
except when necessary. He had the district
well in hand and was proud of his accomplishment.

"Dinner ready, massah," Joe announced
grinning mechanically from the doorway.

"It's about time," said the Commissioner,
rising. "I'm starving."

On the table he found tender young chicken
cooked in palm butter, a plate heaped with
steaming rice, a small saucer of the powerful
Liberian peppers, a jar of pickles, a small
plate of sliced Swiss cheese, half of a large
pawpaw sprinkled with lime juice, a gourd
of palm wine taken from one of the huts and
a small pitcher of coffee. Jackson's little eyes
glowed with satisfaction as he pulled up his
chair and unfolded his napkin. His friends
were not doing any better than this in Monrovia, he observed to himself. With the exception of women, there was nothing he liked
better than eating and drinking.

"All right, Joe," he said irritably. "Hurry
up."

"Yassah," replied the servant, coming with
plate, fork and spoon.

Jackson had a deep respect for the African
knowledge of poisons and willingness to use

them, so at each meal he must be reassured.
Going from dish to dish of the freshly cooked
food, Joe took a small amount from each
and ate it before the Commissioner's eyes. This
precautionary measure completed, Jackson attacked the meal like a starved lumberjack.

The dinner disappeared rapidly and the
diner smacked his thick lips with satisfaction
when the dishes were empty. The attentive
Joe brought the box of cigars and the Commissioner thrust in a pudgy hand. Joe cleared
the table while the official sank back in his
camp chair filling the hut with cigar smoke.
His necktie was off, his collar open, his belt
loosened and a sated expression on his face.
On a small tin trunk at his side sat a tall glass
of strained palm wine. Several times Joe re-
filled it.

Outside the blood-red moon rolled across the
tops of mountains and jungles, brilliantly
lighting the lanes of Takama. There was no
breeze now to sway the circle of cottonwood
trees. Still and straight they stood like old
friends at a funeral service. For a century
they had looked down upon Takama. They
had found the village here. Gola tradition did
not tell of the time when Takama was not here
surrounded by its jungle wall. Ancient it

was, like the Gola nation; ancient and dignified with the pride of long tradition. But tonight it lay shamed, hurt and resentful.

Loud lamentations rose from the compound of the dead chief where wives, sisters and daughters wept around the bier. All night the village women would bemoan the loss of their dear ones. The day which had begun with feasting, joy and happiness had ended with hatred, sorrow and death.

Zo lay sleepless on his mat. Pameta had gone to wail with the other women over the body of her father. Zo, son of laughter, was now solemn and thoughtful. A dozen times he asked himself what it all meant. How could a day that had begun so auspiciously end so tragically? What had Takama done to merit such treatment? Was there no way to punish men like this District Commissioner? Had the natives no redress?

He felt like going out and avenging the death of Bongomo by sending an arrow through Jackson but a voice within restrained him. Such a step would surely mean death, and what of the beautiful Pameta whom he had held in his arms but one night? No, he must never lose Pameta. Since she was a little girl he had been attracted to her and wanted

her. He remembered with his first smile of
the evening how he had saved, scrimped and
borrowed from his father and relatives to get
together the Bindele Bi Kukwela, the "Bundle"
or pledge to her parents. How glad he was
that he had done so. What better wife could
one have?

Commissioner Jackson was far too practical
to bring three women along merely to cook
and be gazed at. With both cigar and wine
gone, he walked unsteadily over to his camp
bed, sat down on the edge of it and concluded
that the night was far too young for him to
go to sleep.

"Joe!" he shouted.

"Yassah, massah," the man replied, running
into the hut.

"Tell Gonda to come here, quick," he ordered.

"Gonda she make chop," said Joe.

"I don't give a damn if she is eating, tell
her to come here. What the hell does she think
I'm dragging her around the country for? Tell
her to get here in a hurry."

Joe rushed out. In five minutes Gonda, the
favorite, entered. She was a very attractive,
semi-civilized girl with Cupid's bow lips and
big brazen black eyes.

"You want Gonda?" she asked cajolingly, seating herself on the bed beside Jackson.

"What the hell do you think I called you for?" he snarled.

"Gonda make massah mad too much?" she lisped, placing her little hand on his shoulder and letting it descend slowly to his thigh.

"Well," he grumbled, "I want you around when I call you."

"Ooh!" she exclaimed. "Massah want Gonda pretty quick." She threw both arms about his neck and kissed him lengthily, while her quick fingers unbuttoned his shirt. Crickets in the thatch were soon chirping an accompaniment to an ages-old pastime.

Outside, a tall black sentry who was not deaf smiled to himself and slowly walked his post. The red moon hung like a bronze plaque behind a cluster of palm trees. From the blackness of the jungle issued a piteous squeal as a stealthy leopard downed its prey.

Takama, with the exception of its vociferous mourners, again slept, but Tolo did not sleep. Two miles in the depths of the jungle in a small hut where he prepared his medicines, he sat before a bright fire. His wrinkled old face was contorted by hatred. Bits of cloth and strips of skin were beside him. One by one he was busily sewing them into a shape —the shape of a man. He was very intent on his work. Leopards, bush cats and other nocturnal prowlers attracted by the light might sniff about the place and even come to the door and look in, but he did not fear them. He believed they were his friends.

The little image Tolo was busily sewing together would, when finished, represent District Commissioner Jackson. Tomorrow, when the Liberians had gone he would enter Jackson's hut and search for a hair, a fingernail paring, anything that had come from the Commissioner's body. Tolo had implicit faith in this particular form of magic. There could be no mistake about its efficacy. Had it not been proved for centuries? It was only necessary that something from the body of the intended victim be placed inside the little image and evil would befall him with each puncturing of the effigy by pin or thorn. The end would be death. The old man puckered up his face in a grim smile. Like all delvers in magic he possessed a certain gullibility.

Again with the customary haziness and tropical unreality, the dawn arrived. From the houses of sorrow and death still rose the

lamentations of the living. Sore and stiff from
yesterday's grueling trip, the carriers and
porters awoke to pound and rub each other
into suppleness and to consume the remnants
of their supper. Hardy fellows, they had slept
without mats or blankets about the central
fire on the cement-hard earth like so many
goats. Jackson's two lesser concubines went
for pails of water. Some of the soldiers
yawned and stretched while others slept on.
All of them had done guard duty during the
night, watching their arms and the Commissioner's hut. The officious sergeant was
already bustling about seeing that everyone
rose and kept sufficiently quiet to permit the
big man to sleep on until seven o'clock.
A few chickens ventured out to pick up
their breakfast. The villagers kept to their
huts.

A half hour later Gonda emerged from the
guest house carrying two folding canvas buckets with which she descended to the stream.
The watchful Joe immediately went inside
with a "Mo'nin', massah!" and prepared a
Scotch and soda for the haggard Commissioner. He then set up the folding bathtub.
Having once represented the Liberian government as a consul in England (being removed

for his refusal to send any consular fees back
to Monrovia), Jackson insisted on his morning
tub. He had also fallen into.the habit of five
o'clock tea and dressing for dinner.

His ablutions completed and another
whiskey and soda consumed, the Commissioner
sat down before a great slab of ham surrounded by a half a dozen golden eggs, a smoking plate of rice, fried plantains and a pot of
steaming coffee. He could barely wait until
Joe had finished tasting each dish before he
sailed into the breakfast as though famished.
Nearby, a towel thrown smartly over one arm,
stood Joe.

A clever fellow was this Bassa man, Joe.
As a small child he had been pawned by his
father to a Liberian farmer in payment of a
debt of ten pounds and never redeemed. He
had resolved, at adolescence, to change his
status. One evening when his owner was
asleep he had gone about his business at full
speed. Eventually he had reached Monrovia.
There he had wormed his way into the good
graces of the agent of an English steamship
company and became its messenger. A disagreement with the agent about whether a silk
shirt of the latter had been stolen or misplaced
ended with Joe's discharge.

Then came a woman explorer to town. Learning that she wanted a steward he had boldly represented himself to her as perhaps the best steward in the country. He got the job and traveled across the hinterland with the lady, managing not to steal enough to arouse her suspicions. Joe had soon learned that a perpetually smiling countenance, speedy service, and unfailing courtesy very effectively cover a multitude of sins. He knew enough not to steal more than one of the Commissioner's cigars a week or more than one drink of whiskey a day. It was Joe who had impressed upon the suspicious and scary Mr. Jackson that his meals should always be tasted by another in his presence before consumption. Thus, Joe and his master ate the same food.

Cigar in mouth, the Commissioner had his camp chair moved to the outside of the hut that he might recline at ease during his morning smoke. The soldiers and carriers were sitting about ready to go. The women were washing the dishes and packing them away. The sun was out but not high enough to be unpleasant. A deep blue sky contrasted with the bright green of the encircling jungle wall. A few village women emerged furtively from their huts to go for water. A goat munched

leaves 'from a low bush. A hornbill's wings
swished enginelike overhead.

Pameta had dearly loved her father and all
night she had observed the customary rites in
company with her mother, Bongomo's other
wives, and her sisters and aunts. Yet she
loved Zo quite as much and was eager to get
back to him. It was therefore with some im-
patience that she had alternately dozed, wailed
and waited for the dawn. At daybreak her
eagerness to depart grew irresistible. She
must see after her husband. So, when no one
was looking but the understanding Badé, she
arranged her headkerchief, drew her cloth
about her and sidled out of the door. It was
a decided relief to leave behind the depressing
atmosphere of the death chamber. Like virile
youth the world over, Pameta was more interested in life than in death.

She made hurriedly for the bridal hut, presenting a striking picture with her splendid
carriage, erect breasts and slender hands and
feet. Soldiers and carriers sat up to watch
her and make admiring comments. The sergeant called Joe's attention to her. Joe ran
to the Commissioner whose little eyes nar-

rowed and a sensual smile curled his lips as the girl drew nearer.

"Bring her here!" he ordered out of the corner of his mouth.

Joe sprang to do his bidding. The girl had almost reached the bridal hut when the Bassa grasped her by one hand and speaking rapidly in Gola said that one of the women in the party wanted to speak to her. Frightened, Pameta struggled to get away but Joe was an old hand at the business. He had not been David Jackson's right-hand man for over a year without learning a thing or two. Placing one hand across her mouth, he picked her up and swiftly ran with her into the guest house where the sergeant was waiting with a handkerchief to gag her. It all went off very neatly.

Jackson came in and eyed her expertly. He often boasted that he was the best picker of women in Liberia. While Joe held her hands behind her, Jackson passed his hand over her satiny skin and patted her plump breasts approvingly. Yes, he would take her. She would be a relief from Gonda and the other two. He was a little tired of them. This girl was young and fresh and would give him added vitality. He nodded knowingly to his man and stepped outside the hut. The sergeant, chuckling, produced a cord from his pocket and bound Pameta's wrists and ankles. A pretty neat job and a rich prize. No villager had seen the kidnapping and no one else dared to warn Takama.

As the sergeant emerged from the hut, Jackson halted him with "Go tell whoever is chief now to come here." The Commissioner had decided to give the inhabitants of Takama a final lesson. The authority of the central government must be recognized and established. Attacking soldiers and officials could not be tolerated.

The sergeant returned with Takama's acting chief, Bongomo's brother, a tall, black, surly fellow in a short ragged jacket. The two stopped within a respectful distance of the Commissioner. For some moments Jackson eyed the acting chief sharply without speaking. The latter shifted from foot to foot uneasily, wondering what was going to happen now.

"You remember last night?" asked Jackson, the sergeant interpreting.

"Yes sir," replied Bongomo's brother.

"You don't want any more trouble, eh?" persisted the Commissioner.

"No sir!" answered the man uneasily.

"You're going to be chief now, eh?" inquired the official.

"Maybe so," said the other. "I act as chief now."

"You understand this town must send eight kainjis of rice and five big gourds of palm oil to Boloba every moon?" Jackson went on.

"Yes sir," replied the chief, wondering what was coming.

"Well, you must send ten kainjis of rice and six gourds of palm oil from now on or soldiers come. Understand?" ordered Jackson.

"I understand, sir," said the chief, "but we are only a small town and that is a great deal of rice and oil. We work here from sun to sun. So much must we raise for the government that we have little time to do anything for ourselves. Now we shall have less time. It is very hard."

"Oh, so you think it's hard, eh," sneered Jackson. "Well, it's going to be harder from now on. How many huts here?"

"The government man last time count eighty-five," answered the chief.

"How many new huts you build after the man counted them?" pursued the District Commissioner.

"We build five huts," the man replied.

"That makes ninety," Jackson remarked. "Well, let's see. . . . Five times ninety is four fifty. Four hundred and fifty shillings that's twenty-two pounds, ten shillings. All right, you go to your people and tell them the town is fined twenty-five pounds. Understand?"

"But where would we get such a sum, sir?" the chief remonstrated.

"Don't argue with me," the Commissioner snapped. "Or I'll make it fifty pounds. You do as you're told. Understand?"

"I hear what you say," replied the man obediently yet sullenly.

"You better do what I say, too," added the Commissioner. "And do it right now."

"Today?" asked the chief in surprise and consternation.

"Yes, today," echoed Jackson. "We sit down here until Takama pays its fine. Understand?"

"Yes sir."

The acting chief departed hurriedly. Soon a crowd of the elders gathered at the palaver kitchen and began jabbering earnestly with Bongomo's brother. The sun moved higher. Other village men joined the crowd of old fellows and the talk grew more animated. The gathering soon dispersed and the men scattered to their respective huts.

There was frenzied digging up of buried sixpenny pieces and shillings from out-of-the-way places. In a half hour the rangy chief returned with a pouch full of dirty, discolored coins. From the doors of huts many heads appeared to see what was taking place. The District Commissioner looked up coldly at the village head and then nodded to Joe.

"Count it," he commanded.

"Yassah," replied Joe, taking the pouch and dumping its contents on the ledge which ran around the guest house. Soldiers, porters and carriers looked on from a respectful distance. Here was more money than they would ever possess. Even the soldiers were paid but twelve pounds a year—when they were paid.

"Twenty-five pounds, massah," announced Joe, straightening up from the pile of coins.

"All right, put it away," ordered Jackson, "and tell this fellow to clear out."

The acting chief retired. The District Commissioner rose and the sergeant stepped forward and folded up his chair. The packing proceeded inside and one by one the trunks were brought outside and turned over to the porters. Everything was ready for the start.

One of the lesser concubines walked and Pameta, still bound, was placed in her hammock. The sergeant strode through the village ordering the people to stay inside their huts.

At last the porters lifted the trunks to their heads and the kainjis (hampers) to their backs, the carriers straightened up under the poles of the hammocks and the soldiers formed in twos in the rear. Walking briskly, the little column soon passed out of the village and the jungle swallowed them up.

Takama immediately opened its doors and poured into the lanes to angrily discuss the events of the preceding twenty-four hours. Zo had no sooner emerged from his new hut than, turning, he found himself face to face with Badé, Pameta's mother, her eyes swimming in tears.

"They've taken her," she wailed.

"Who?" he shouted, alarmed. "Pameta?"

"Yes, Pameta," she answered, while a sympathetic group gathered around. "My baby! They've taken her. Oh, what shall we do? What shall we do?"

Leaning on Zo's shoulder the mother sobbed hysterically. He was stunned by this totally unthought of, incredible tragedy. The bottom seemed to drop out of everything. For a minute he just looked at Badé and the others blankly, almost uncomprehendingly. Yesterday afternoon and the night before she had lain on his strong right arm; now she was gone!

The news of Pameta's disappearance spread with the usual rapidity of bad news. Folk gathered around the palaver kitchen and seriously discussed the kidnapping. What could they do about it? They were disarmed; the government was armed. They could not fight rifle bullets with bows and arrows, spears and bush knives. Enraged young bucks, led by Zo, wanted to catch up with the column and attempt to rescue the girl but more conservative counsel prevailed. Did the youngsters so easily forget the happenings of yesterday? And if they were successful, would not the government send more troops to punish the people of Takama?

Everybody but Zo finally agreed that nothing could be done. And, yet, because something just had to be done about such a series of outrages, regardless of their impotence, many began to talk of the catastrophe as the work of an evil spirit. Someone must have

offended an evil spirit. Who could it be?
Someone in Takama must be guilty. There was
a cause for every happening. The thought
took hold. People began glancing suspiciously
at each other. The psychology of the mob was
asserting itself. Unable to punish the real
culprit, it must find a scapegoat within its
ranks.

Just at this time old Tolo, smiling tri-
umphantly, stepped from the guest house.
After a minute examination of the hut he had
found several hairs and some fingernail parings. The witch man believed that the District Commissioner was now in his power.
These hairs and nail parings would be stuffed
inside the effigy of Jackson. Each day a certain poisonous thorn would be thrust into the
little image, and each day Jackson would be
nearer death. When the image was full of
thorns, the great man would pass to his reward. Such was the theory and Tolo, cynical
as he might be about much of his craft, believed it would work.

As the old wizard approached the palaver
kitchen, he was surrounded by the villagers
and told of their suspicions. They begged for
a trial that the guilty one might be found.
Old Tolo hesitated a moment then, push-

ing his way through the people, went into the palaver kitchen and sat alone in one corner. The crowd stood at a respectful distance awaiting his decision.

It was foolish to stage a trial when the real culprit was the District Commissioner whose life, the witch man felt sure, would soon be terminated. And yet, not to hold a trial when the people wanted it might prove a grave error, as he would always be blamed. His prestige must be maintained. The people must always respect and fear him. It would never do for them to lose confidence in him. Tolo was a shrewd old fellow and knew well the fickleness of the public. After all, he argued, a trial could do little harm and would place the villagers in a frame of mind to return to their daily pursuits, which was the really important thing. In spite of murder, fines and kidnappings life must go on.

Zo stood around frowning and impatient. He wanted to be off; to follow the Commissioner's party; to rescue Pameta, if possible, either on the trail or after reaching Boloba, the headquarters of District No. 1. How he would do it single-handed with only his primitive weapons, he did not know and had thought little of it. He might be killed, but why

should one live after suffering such an outrage?

Yet Zo could not leave now. Suspicion
would be directed toward him. No power on
earth would be able to convince them that he
had not offended some spirit and brought on
the calamitous happenings if he left the village now. He knew that the real culprit was
the government official, but he knew also that
it would do little good to express his opinion
when the people had set their minds on a victim close at hand. What the crowd might
think held him as securely to the spot as it
would any human anywhere. Takama was his
home. Here he was known and loved; in the
outer world he was unknown. Within this
jungle-bordered clearing was his universe. It
held all of the ties dear to his memory except
Pameta, and even the thought of her being
carried down the green-lined trail could not
budge him. He dared not risk dishonor and
the curse of the village. So, against his will,
he remained for the ordeal.

Tolo arose and raising his bony arm beck-
oned the people to him. He announced dramatically that there would be an ordeal—the
ordeal of the whip. A murmur rose from the
assemblage. It was more an expression of

surprise than satisfaction. The ordeal of the whip was most often resorted to in cases of theft. They had hoped for something more exciting, more spectacular, the placing of lives at stake, but Tolo had spoken and the whip it would be.

The witch doctor strode through their ranks and made for his mysterious hut of which it was rumored among the simple folk that no uninvited person could enter and live very long. The crowd waited. There was excited talk among women and old people; low, earnest conversation among the elders. An electric feeling was in the air. Everyone except Zo and Badé was eager for the ordeal, even though any one person might be selected as the culprit, the cause of all the trouble.

Tolo emerged from his hut, his body streaked with white clay put on in vertical stripes that gave him a peculiar, elongated appearance and went very well with his headdress of feathers and horns, his necklace of leopard's teeth and his bracelets and anklets of human knuckle bones. He bore a black clay bowl containing a strange-smelling concoction in which leaves and herbs appeared, and a stout black whip. He solemnly approached the palaver house with the dignity becoming the high priest and physician of a proud and ancient people.

The crowd parted at his approach and he placed the bowl on the waist-high wall of the palaver kitchen. He called for a small boy and promptly a little black youngster was led whimpering to him. Not a sound came from the surrounding villagers engrossed in the proceedings. Tolo placed the whip in the child's hand, rubbed the little wrists with the mess from the bowl and liberally applied the same to the handle and thongs of the lash.

Having completed the applications, the witch doctor then commanded the whip to go all over Takama, to search among the people, locate the person who had in some way offended the spirits and brought on the catastrophe suffered by the village and flog him until he confessed his guilt. The small boy was now identified with the whip. Indeed, he was now the whip.

Through the lanes of Takama the youngster sped, looking into first this hut and then that, and inspecting every shed and granary. In a short time he came back to the crowd about the palaver house. No one had said a word during his absence. There they all stood as if hypnotized awaiting his return. He had not found the culprit.

Now he wended his way in and out of the crowd, crouching low and straightening up alternately, mumbling to himself as if under a spell while the people held themselves taut with fear and expectancy. Each person in turn shivered as he thought "It might be me!" Tolo, standing alone, apart from the crowd, a sort of gruesome majesty about him, watched the proceedings with a weary, professional lack of interest.

Suddenly everyone gasped incredulously and simultaneously. The boy had stopped in front of Zo, who was speechless with dismay, surprise and shame. Up went the whip and was held for a moment poised in the air. Down it came across the flawless skin of the bereaved bridegroom. Zo winced slightly. The whip stung more than one would have imagined being wielded by a mere child. Again and again it rose and whistled down to Zo's skin. The villagers leaned forward, surprised at the unexpected turn of events and yet convinced of Zo's guilt. They had been made to believe since infancy that the ordeal was always right in its findings. How could they question it now? Welts rose on the young man's body as the child continued to tirelessly apply the whip. Tolo, himself also secretly surprised at the turn of events, remained impassive, arms folded, staring blankly ahead.

Bewildered, uncertain of just what to do, surrounded by a thick wall of relatives and lifelong friends who expected him at any moment to admit his guilt, and himself convinced of the power of the witch doctor, the existence of evil spirits and the necessity for appeasing them, Zo argued to himself with each blow of the whip that perhaps, after all, some act of his *had* brought catastrophe to Takama. And yet something prevented him from unsealing his lips and proclaiming his guilt.

He held out stoically, biting his lips to keep from crying aloud as the blows of the whip fell with what seemed increasing rapidity and force. He held his head high while all about him the silent assemblage seemed to be crying "Confess!" Cold perspiration gathered on his brow, his hands began to tremble. It was not the whipping but the accusing eyes and the unsympathetic expressions on the faces of his friends and relatives that finally weakened him. It was intolerable, unbearable. He could stand it no longer. Man is a gregarious animal. The disapproval of those about him is one condition he cannot tolerate because it takes from him all the things he holds most dear. Zo felt that. "Yes! Yes! I am the one," he cried and fell swooning to the ground.

A great sigh of mingled relief and satisfaction came now from the crowd. As if Zo's admission had unlocked their tongues, the people began to talk loudly and rapidly. The little boy, immensely proud of himself, returned to the witch doctor. Tolo took the proffered whip and wiped the concoction off the lad's wrists. The boy immediately joined his elders. Tolo walked over to the prostrate form of the young man, bent over him, mumbled a few words over him to impress the crowd with his powers and then slapped Zo sharply on the cheek. Zo opened his eyes wide and looked about him wildly. Then he remembered and rising slowly to his feet, walked alone to his hut. No one spoke to him; no one offered a word of sympathy for on his shoulders now rested a great guilt.

The assembled natives now began to disperse. A culprit had been found, a victim discovered, and human beings everywhere like nothing better than to have someone on whom to blame their troubles. Almost contented, they returned to their habitations. Shortly the dead would be buried, the wounded healed and life would go on much as it had before—with only an additional anecdote to hand down to the next generation. Evil spirits had visited Takama with disastrous results. Now they had been discovered within the body of Zo and driven out by the whip of the ordeal as signified by his admission of guilt. For many, many moons there would again be peace, security and plenty in Takama.

Lying in his hut with the door tightly closed, Zo was wracked with doubts. He did not wish to be sceptical and question the beliefs of his people, and yet he somehow could not understand how he could have been guilty of causing the death of Chief Bongomo and the other evils following in its train. He could not understand why he had confessed a guilt which he knew in his heart was not his.

Puzzled, he passed his hand again and again over his honest, open face and broad forehead, as he tried to comprehend it all. Of one thing he was sure: he must leave Takama at once and find his bride. He could not stand the glances of the villagers nor tolerate their remarks. Pameta was all he had now. With her he could go to some other village or to the coast region about which he had heard and settle down. As long as he stayed in Takama, there would always be a shadow of guilt upon him. Better it would be to go where he was not known.

A sudden resolution made him jump up from his mat and hastily gather together some personal effects. Wrapping them in a big handkerchief bought from a traveling Mandingo peddler, he fastened his long knife to his red leather belt and hooked it around his slender waist. Thrusting his arm into a hole in a corner of the hut, he extracted a small pouch containing some British coins. He ate a few mouthfuls of rice, fish and palm oil from a pan, washed it down with a copious draught of palm wine and was ready to go.

He knew it would not be easy to go—it never is. There were many near and dear to him whom he must and should bid farewell. He approached this task with distaste, but the majority of the people made it easy for him. Like most human beings the world over, they wanted nothing to do with one who was, at least for the time being, so unpopular, and those who would ordinarily have speeded him on his way with a good word were afraid of what the rest might think or say. He went to his father's hut and there the old man gave him advice and offered a bundle of the iron strips that serve as money in the hinterland of Liberia. Zo refused to take them, saying he had money and was traveling light. In another hut his mother bewailed his going and insisted that he take a powerful gri gri along to ward off evil. Then, without further delay, he strode hurriedly through the village and thence into the cool, green tunnel of the trail.

Sitting on the step in front of his hut, his regalia removed, Tolo was explaining with a certain condescension the meaning of the outcome of the ordeal to three old men who squatted before him.

"Evil spirits made Zo want Pameta long ago. When Pameta came from the bush they married. Chief Bongomo gave plenty good chop and much wine. Not much left when the people were full. Liberians come and want food, wine, house. Food and wine not handy. Big man got mad because he must wait. Then trouble started. If Zo had not married Pameta, there would have been no feast. When Liberians came there would have been plenty food and wine. They would have liked it much, praised Chief, and so, no trouble. Now you see? . . . Good!"

"Good!" the old men echoed. The trio rose with somewhat impolite haste and returned to the palaver kitchen to explain the mysterious workings of magic to their cronies. They could scarcely find time to express their thanks to Tolo.

The witch man was not at all offended. He had dealt with people a long time and knew them well. He smiled sardonically. Then he remembered that he had a duty to perform. He rose as quickly as his age would permit and entered his hut. Going to a basket he took from it a long thorn, chuckling the while, and then drew from under a cloth the little image representing the District Commissioner. Holding the thorn between thumb and forefinger, he thrust it clear through the effigy. This he considered the first step in the destruction of the man who had brought sorrow and shame to Takama. Tolo believed that before the next full moon, Jackson would be dead.

Seven or eight miles away the District Commissioner's little column sped along the jungle trail. Mr. Jackson lolled contentedly in his hammock quite unaware of Tolo's black magic. He was in excellent spirits, humming to himself a tune from a phonograph record he had recently purchased. Twenty-five pounds and a pretty girl was not bad, he surmised, for a morning's work.

A few paces back of him Pameta, her gag removed but her ankles still bound, rocked to and fro in her hammock. To her the end of the world had come. There was nothing ahead now but a life of shame. She dismissed rescue or escape as impossible. Her tears streamed down her cheeks and dampened the bridal necklaces.

CHAPTER FOUR

Zo hurried along the trail and for the first time since the occurrences in Takama actually felt light of heart. Was he not free of the shackles of society and about to rescue his Pameta?

It was noon. It was also very warm although the screen of leaves, branches, vines and creepers only permitted the sunshine to pepper the trail with spots of golden light. The jungle was silent.

The heat meant nothing to Zo as he almost ran along the trail, his tough, bare feet striking against tree roots and stones; but sometimes there were steep hills to climb that taxed even a youngster's limbs and lungs, and descending them required a clear eye and ready footwork lest a misstep plunge one down the tortuous trail perhaps to the bottom. The occasional little brooks of cool water were very welcome to one exhausted by exertion, heat and thirst. When Zo wanted to drink, he would deftly make a small cone of a broad green leaf; at other times, when unusually winded, he fell upon his stomach and drank like the animals of the forest.

He knew that eyes were watching him from the branches of trees and the tangled underbrush and vines that laced them together. But he had no fear of the animals, as they seldom attack human beings unless molested. Like his black brethren, Zo did not look upon reptiles, or four-footed or feathered animals as his inferiors, or think their only purpose.on earth was to be driven and exploited by man for food and other necessaries. To him the smallest and most insignificant creature had a soul and was the equal of man, sharing the earth with him. He admired their skill and ingenuity and was eager to acquire some of it. To have the strength of the elephant, the speed of the eagle, the grace of a serpent, and the craftiness of the leopard—surely these were desirable attributes.

Swinging along without a hat and only a breech cloth and a short, striped almost sleeveless tunic that reached to his knees, his body glistening with the streams of perspiration that bathed it, Zo was intent on reaching Boloba before dark despite his late start. He knew that only by very fast walking could he reach the place before nightfall. Cele-

brated walkers made the distance easily in a
half day, but he had never gained that reputation. In the Devil Bush (boy's school) he had
become known as a great dancer, a good harp-
ist, a weaver of mats and builder of houses,
but he had gone on no very long walks. He
was more or less at home in the forest and
jungle. He knew its secrets, and could turn
them to his purpose: and he knew its dangers.
And the greatest of all dangers are those that
beset a lone pedestrian at night.

A strange, mysterious, awesome place, the
tropical forest, with a whole variety of
perfumes. Sometimes there rises an arresting odor suggestive of a flower garden
and one discovers a clump of exotic flowers
nearby. At other times the prevailing scent
is woodsy, fresh and green like its color, as
a garden smells after a shower. Then, at
times, one is reminded of an animal tent
in a circus. This is especially marked where
troops of monkeys are disporting themselves
in the topmost branches of forest giants,
when herds of elephants are not far off,
and when squirrels, snakes and porcupines
are about. But more repelling than any
other odor is that of moulding, rotting,
dead things—rising like a miasma in a swamp

and making one gasp for a breath of fresh,
clean air.

Again, the jungle is a great green prison,
impregnable by virtue of the amazing network and screen of vines and creepers that
bind tree to tree. Even with a sharp bush
knife and unflagging strength it is very difficult to cut one's way through once the trail
is abandoned. Progress is disheartingly slow
and dangers lurk in its dark recesses. No
wonder all but intrepid hunters keep to the
trail.

The trail is the only visible evidence of
humanity in the jungle. The traveler must
stay on it and, if wise, is very willing to do so.
It is the corridor that connects one center of
human life with another; the artery of communication between town and town. One
holds to it as a child to its mother, following
it religiously, faithfully. It means life to the
inexperienced; the jungle spells death. This
waving, pulsating mass of green on either side
of the pedestrian, touching him at times, is
almost bursting with life, breeds life in amazing, bewildering quantities and varieties, but
it is, in the main, life inimical to man; life
that preys upon him, his farms and his cattle,
annoys him at work and rest, fattens upon

him. It is not so much the larger animals
he has to fear, but the small ones, and the insects—rodents, gnats, beetles, ants and an
infinite, uncountable variety of others. These
dispute possession of the earth with man and
he has yet to prove himself the victor.

It was almost dark when Zo crossed a small
stream at the base of a low hill and toiled
up wearily to look upon Boloba, headquarters of District No. 1. Like Takama, the
town was surrounded by huge cottonwood
trees, but trees not quite so large or as lofty,
because Takama was the older place. There
were the usual huts, granaries and palaver
kitchen, but the number of buildings was
greater than in Takama.

The military compound, with its barracks
for a company of soldiers, its large guest
house for officials and other civilized folk,
several glorified whitewashed huts with verandahs, and smaller huts for servants, carriers,
porters, concubines and others, was itself a
little village off to one side of Boloba. A high
and neat fence surrounded it, only broken by
two gates both guarded by barefoot, black
sentries. Nevertheless, natives were freely
going in and out. The reason seemed to be

that those going in were carrying something while those leaving were empty-handed.

Zo sat down in the palaver kitchen, uncertain as to his next step. He now had a very lively respect for soldiers and so did not contemplate entering the gate. He might be stopped, questioned and perhaps seized. He was sure Pameta was in the compound. He finally concluded that the portion of the fence out of the range of the sentries' vision presented the most logical means of entrance.

Boloba was a Gola town and Zo went straight to the chief, who was glad to see someone from the neighboring Takama, and eager to hear the news about the happenings there. Zo told his story in detail, only neglecting to mention the ordeal of the whip. The chief lodged him with a couple in a very large hut where he was given a pan of hot food and had to relate his whole story over again to the man and his wife.

Africans are always eager to hear the news from outside their town. They can communicate certain bare facts by means of drums, but in the Dark Continent, as elsewhere, nothing is more welcome than a word-of-mouth report. The newcomer expects to be asked immediately he enters a town, "What is the news?" and it is expected that he will have some news to impart.

The couple was considerably shocked by Zo's account. To shoot down a great and widely respected chief and some of the elders of a town; to kidnap a bride, to then fine the town twenty-five pounds, that indeed was tyranny. At their request Zo described Pameta.

"Why, I saw her today," the man exclaimed, "when the Commissioner's party came back. I walked right by her hammock."

"How did she look? Was she hurt?" asked Zo, eagerly leaning forward, his face strained and tense.

"She just cried," answered the man. "Her feet were tied together. They took her to the Commissioner's place."

Zo's heart sank at this revelation. He had hoped that Pameta might be in a separate hut and that he would merely have to force entrance, lead her to an unwatched section of the fence, boost her over and flee to the depths of the forest. Now he would have to attempt entrance of the big man's house. This was certainly not a pleasing prospect. The man and his wife, young people like himself, kept asking him what he was going to do but he thought it best to keep his plans, such as they were, to himself.

He learned from them that Takama, because of its slightly out-of-the-way location had heretofore escaped the tyranny of Commissioner Jackson, which Boloba had borne from the first. Their girls had also been taken or inveigled to the barracks and their men had been forced to work around the compound, on the road, and act as carriers and porters at the whim of the District Commissioner and without pay. They were forced to supply the compound with huge quantities of food, including cattle, for which they received nothing. When, for any reason, their requisition was less than stipulated, their chief was whipped and the soldiers cuffed the people about.

What could they do against the soldiers' rifles? the man complained bitterly. They were just the District Commissioner's slaves. Between the food requisitions, the fines and the hut taxes—the latter payable only in British silver—it was about all they could do to get sufficient food for themselves. Now, as a crowning infamy, they were being forced to go out and work all day on the government road, which left no time to cut new farms out of the jungle. All who refused to go were fined.

This account somewhat dampened Zo's spirits. The government seemed so powerful and the people so powerless. How was one man to prevail against such a force when whole tribes and nations were impotent? And yet he was determined to try. So, stepping out into the darkness, he made for the compound. He crept stealthily along the fence until he came to the side away from the main gate. There was no one to see him grasp the rounded top of the fence with his powerful hands, and with tremendous effort, vault to the other side.

Lanterns shone in the small houses and carbide lights blazed in the big bungalow of Commissioner Jackson. Zo made for the latter, reached it safely, and went carefully around it, stooping to avoid the lights which would have exposed him. He came at last to a window where there was no light. Its wooden blinds were closed and barred. He listened intently. He was rewarded by the sound of a sob, then another and another. His heart leaped. It was she!

Inside the Commissioner's bungalow, Jack-

son and Captain Burns, commander of the
company of soldiers at the post, were awaiting
dinner. They worked together, these two,
and frequently dined together when both
were in Boloba. It was the Commissioner
who planned and Captain Burns who executed.
The Captain was a tall, spare, smooth-shaven
dark-brown fellow, with very square shoulders, a small waist, long bony hands and a
crafty countenance that warned one to beware
of him. He chuckled at the Commissioner's
cruel quips and sarcastic sallies, never failing
to lead his superior to believe that his wit and
wisdom were supreme.

The Commissioner was at home now after
a considerable tour of his district and he was
celebrating the occasion. He ordered Burns
to take off his khaki coat, open the collar of
his shirt and prepare to down some cocktails.

"Joe!" he yelled, "bring on the cocktails,
and put plenty of ice in them."

"Yassah, massah," replied Joe from the
cook house, a small screened room connected
with the bungalow by a narrow, screened
passage.

It was Jackson's delight to show off his Icy-
Ball refrigerator which operated not with
electricity but by a certain oil obtained from

a German store in Monrovia. Ice was a great rarity in the hinterland and to have it at will, day and night, placed one in a class alone. It was hard enough in these jungle settlements to get sufficient whiskey for cocktails, but to have little cubes of ice to put in the shaker was a princely luxury.

The Commissioner doted on princely luxuries and was quite eager to let people know he had them. In a year's time he had accumulated much to make his quarters attractive and comfortable. There were carbide or gasoline lights on tall stands in all of the rooms. The ceilings were of matched boards to keep out the rodents and insects that usually make a home of the attics of houses in Liberia. The floors were of oiled planks and unlike most Liberian houses, the place was screened. A large cabinet phonograph stood in a corner of the parlor and the Commissioner possessed records of songs still being sung in the cabarets of New York. Books there were none. A few aged newspapers and magazines handed on to him by missionaries were the extent of his library.

Mr. Jackson was not much concerned about reading. He had been to England and the Continent, so he did not consider it necessary for him to bother acquiring any more information. He preferred to utilize his ample spare time eating good food, drinking good liquor and living up to his rôle of the Solomon of Liberia. His scattered harem already numbered nearly twoscore girls and women but, as he said, he was always on the lookout for something fresh, and boasted of every conquest or, rather, kidnapping.

Joe, garbed in white from head to foot—Jackson's prescribed uniform for him—entered with a tray of cocktails in tall-stemmed amber glasses. Experience had taught Joe that he might have to dodge a boot or some other handy missile if he only brought two cocktails. The Commissioner lived up to the American tradition of drinking "until he felt it." Captain Burns was a worthy companion in this respect. They downed a couple of drinks each and Jackson's tongue began to loosen.

"Say!" he exclaimed, rearing back in the Canary Island wicker lounging chair and emphasizing his words by wagging an empty glass toward Burns, who was also resting quite easily, "I picked up the prettiest little thing you've seen in many a day. About fifteen,

I'd say. Right out of the bush and married just the day before I got her."

"Where'd you get her?" asked the Captain, leaning forward with the interest he always displayed when women were mentioned.

"Oh, I picked her up over at that next town where the gang rushed us last night and we had to give them a little taste of our pepper," Jackson informed him. "We took her away this morning and a neat job it was, too. That Joe is getting smarter every day. Why, they didn't even know the girl was gone. Good thing, too, because they might have started some more trouble."

"Yes," Burns agreed, taking another cocktail, "that Joe is sure smart, all right, but when do I see this beauty? You're not afraid to let me see her, are you?" This was a liberty of speech the mutual imbibing of cocktals permitted.

Jackson emptied another glass and laughed. He only laughed when he was highly amused, which was not often. "Why, your back's too weak," he scoffed. "You've got to be a good man to keep up with me."

"Oh, I'm not so slow," remarked Burns.

"Come on," said the Commissioner, "I'll

give you a look. That's the best you ever will
get." The two rose and walked over to the
bedroom. Jackson fished a key out of his
pocket and opened the door.

Convinced that Pameta was in the darkened room, Zo quietly went to work with his
long knife to effect an entrance. The blinds
were locked on the inside and it would
be necessary for him to unfasten their hinges
from the window frame. As the hinges were
screwed into very hard wood, he found the
task not to be as easy as he had anticipated. But
perseverance rewarded him, and in a half hour
or so he had completed the job. He laid the
blinds on the ground and crawled into the
bedroom. He was shaking with excitement.

"Pameta?" he whispered, rendered more
cautious by the voices in the next room. "Pameta, where are you?"

There was a stir on the bed at his right but
no answer. He tipped over to the bed and
felt a form. His hand traveled swiftly to the
feet and there, sure enough, were the cruel
cords binding the ankles. He severed them
in a trice, and then whispering in the girl's
ear, he cried, "Pameta! This is Zo. Come
quick, we must go."

Pameta would have cried out in joy but her husband placed his hand over her mouth. It seemed so wonderful that he had come for her when she had given up all hope. She passed her hands over her eyes in a gesture of surprise and bewilderment, rose quietly and with him leading her around chairs and slop jars, they made for the window and freedom.

A key turned in the lock and the door was thrown open. The native couple stood exposed to the amazed eyes of the District Commissioner and his guest. Zo leaped in front of Pameta and shouted to her to jump from the window, at the same time drawing his long knife to defend himself. But Burns, bigger and more accustomed to such frays, struck him on the jaw and the lad went backwards out of the window. The Captain blew his whistle and soldiers came running from all directions bearing lanterns and torches.

Somewhat dazed but alive to the danger, Zo sprang up and ran unsteadily toward the fence. Pameta was just ahead of him. Lights were everywhere now. They reached the fence safely. Zo was helping his wife to climb óver it when someone grabbed him by one leg and all three fell struggling to the ground. Soldiers with lanterns rushed up and captured Zo and Pameta. The man who had frustrated the escape was Joe.

Crestfallen at his failure, angry at himself, fearful of what awaited him and yet not regretting his effort to rescue his wife, Zo was marched back with Pameta to the bungalow and onto the verandah by an escort consisting of two soldiers, a sergeant and Joe.

Jackson came out followed by Captain Burns and, standing with hands on his hips, he glared at the Gola youth savagely. Zo boldly returned his glance. He expected the worst. He had done his best and failed. Now he was prepared to pay the penalty.

To a question put to him by the Commissioner through Joe, he replied, "I am Zo from Takama. I came for this girl because she is my wife. We were wed yesterday. You have no right to take her, she belongs to me. I paid eight pounds for her and I want her. You have taken her. You must return her to me."

"Well, what do you think of that?" asked Jackson, turning to the Captain. Then addressing the sergeant, he ordered, "Bring your whip, sergeant, and see if we can't teach this fellow something. The idea of breaking into my place! Why, I ought to put him in the kitchen!"

Even the impassive Joe shuddered at the mention of that form of punishment, perhaps the worst in Liberia. The victim is trussed up and placed on the crossbeams of a hut above a fire. Then, Liberian peppers, undoubtedly the hottest in the world, are thrown on the fire and the victim takes the consequences.

In about three minutes the noncommissioned officer returned with a long cord and the black whip he had used so effectively on Chief Bongomo the day before. Zo was bound hand and foot and thrown to the floor of the verandah. Baring his muscular right arm, the noncommissioned officer rained blow after blow upon the youth until the latter, though resolved to be stoical, cried out in pain.

Each puffing upon a fragrant cigar, the Commissioner and Burns viewed the performance with evident relish. It was just one of their normal amusements. Natives were beaten in their presence almost every day, and yet, both being sadists, they never failed to derive a certain enjoyment from it. Jackson just smiled a little cruelly, his small red eyes blinking with satisfaction, but the Captain, eager to applaud all that his chief approved, laughed once or twice. . . .

The two officials were but slightly less dark than the natives over whom they ruled but they felt no kinship with the aborigines for that reason. It was no more difficult for them to oppress and exploit fellow black men than it usually is for powerful whites to do the same thing to fellow white men. Color did not enter here—it was class that counted.

For a century the forefathers and contemporaries of Jackson and Burns had ruled these native folk. Each year the government had worked its way farther and farther into the hinterland by force and treaty until it extended its territory to the borders of the French and English colonies. Two million natives now obeyed and paid tribute to these black masters, supplying food and money in large quantities. Everywhere in this vast tropical territory, as large as the American state of Virginia, the word of these grandsons of Negro freedmen was law. Their forefathers had come here to this expanse of jungle to found a haven for the oppressed of the black race but their descendants were now guilty of the same cruelties from which they

had fled. The Americo-Liberians were to
rule; the natives to obey.

Burns was much more fanatical on the subject of class than Jackson. He never forgot
or allowed others to forget that he was a direct descendant of a pioneer who had come
over on the first ship sent by the American
Colonization Society; who had fought both
slavers and natives to preserve the republic,
and had finally served in many high offices.
Jackson was usually cruel when crossed or
angered in some way. Burns, on the contrary,
was cruel from calculation. It was one of his
greatest pastimes to devise new methods of
punishment. He had never been outside of
Liberia and his schooling at a mission station
had only carried him to the fifth grade. The
Holy Bible was the only book he had ever
read through. He would never concede that
anybody in the country was his intellectual superior and he would argue for hours on topics
of which he was almost totally ignorant. He
won arguments not by superior knowledge or
dialectics but by wearing out his opponent
with his stubbornness.

When Zo had been beaten sufficiently to
salve the outraged feelings of the District

Commissioner, he was taken away by the sergeant and a soldier and thrown into a dark hut. He soon discovered there were several other occupants, mainly Golas. They asked many questions but he was too wounded in body and soul to hold any conversation. In no position could he lie on the hard floor comfortably, for welts were everywhere on his back, thighs, legs and arms. While he was tossing about, the sergeant entered the hut bearing a lantern and followed by two soldiers, one carrying a rifle and the other bearing a small brown bag.

"Get up!" the sergeant commanded, kicking him with his heavy shoe. "Take off that jacket!"

Zo stiffly obeyed. At a nod from his superior, the soldier with the brown bag began rubbing salt into Zo's wounds. The terrible burning brought tears to his eyes and his lips quivered. After what seemed an eternity, the soldiers departed.

Left again to themselves, the other prisoners, like the unfortunate the world over, began to jest at Zo's expense.

"Bet he'll talk now," ventured one.

"Yes," said another, "an' I bet he talked when those soldiers laid that whip on him."

"What did you do, boy?" asked another.

But none of them could get a response out of Zo. He suffered in silence but set his jaw in determination to succeed in his quest even if Pameta were guarded by a hundred soldiers. He would not let them conquer him in this manner. Finally he fell asleep in spite of his smarting wounds. Weariness from the day's experiences had proved more powerful than pain.

Back again in her barred and locked room, Pameta lay across the bed staring ahead at the streak of yellow light that came under the door and through the keyhole. She felt perfectly hopeless, but her hatred of Jackson increased by the minute. They had forced her to witness the humiliation of her Zo and then laughed in her face. She could not forget that, ever. Somehow, some way she must hurt this Jackson as he had hurt so many others. How this would be accomplished she did not know, but it must be done. Of that she was positive.

Dinner was being served by the silent, immaculate Joe. There was a clean white cloth spread on the table, freshly polished silver knives, forks, condiment carriers, cream pitchers were in orderly array while well-laundered napkins were rolled in broad silver rings. The long-awaited dinner consisted of canned tomato soup, stewed turtle with eddoes and red peppers, roast mutton, greens cooked in palm oil, steaming rice, sliced bananas with powdered sugar and canned cream and, finally, coffee.

"Not many eating a meal like this in Monrovia," Jackson boasted between huge mouthfuls. "They can't afford it, Burns. Times are hard down there now. We're a whole lot better off up here."

The Captain agreed through a mouthful of mutton.

"I always believe in making a job pay," continued Jackson. "Smith didn't have anything when he quit this job, but you watch me when I quit. I won't care much whether I get another job or not."

Again the Captain agreed a little more audibly.

Usually Jackson and Burns lingered over their coffee and cigars but tonight the Commissioner dismissed the officer almost as soon as they had finished their coffee.

"Sorry," he apologized, as the Captain rose

to go, "but I've got some business to attend to."

"I know what that business is, too," the officer remarked dryly as he departed.

Burns had scarcely reached the bottom step from the verandah when the Commissioner rose, tossed away his half-smoked cigar and called Joe to pour him another drink. Thus fortified, he fished the bedroom key out of his pocket and for the second time that evening entered the chamber.

Pameta was not asleep. She was lying still, staring ahead, waiting for the Commissioner to put in his appearance. She had decided that if Zo could come all of the way from Takama to attempt her rescue, she could at least strike one blow for her freedom or at least to avenge the torture of her husband and the death of her father.

As the key turned in the lock, the girl slipped out of bed, seized one of the heavy jars on the floor, ran to the door and raised the missile above her head. As Jackson entered she closed her eyes, gritted her teeth and brought the jar down squarely upon his head with all of her strength. The man uttered a cry of astonishment and pain and staggered back into the other room.

"Joe! Joe!" he yelled, swaying in front of the bedroom door.

"Yassah, massah!" the servant cried, running in from the cook shack. He halted in surprise at the sight of the blood streaming from the Commissioner's head.

"Don't stand there like a damned fool!" Jackson moaned. "Lock that door and get me a cloth for my head."

He cursed at a great pace and threatening all sorts of punishment for Pameta but down in his heart he admired her more than ever. The others submitted themselves to him like so many docile cattle. This girl was different; she had spirit. He smiled, licking the blood from his lips.

CHAPTER FIVE

DAWN stole into Boloba with its customary
misty, tropical unreality; it came with the mil-
lion-voiced chorus of birds; dogs and goats disturbed the village with their usual daybreak
gambols; roosters shouted their prowess from
the eminences of gravestones and verandahs.
Women began stepping from the huts: slender
young girls with saucily pouting breasts and
bodies rejoicing in the first symmetry of
womanhood; plumper young women with
heavy, full breasts and babies wrapped securely astraddle their hips; strong-faced middle-aged women with graying hair, first
wrinkles showing, and breasts pendant, all
bearing buckets or jars upon their heads and
exchanging bits of gossip as they descended
the hill for the morning's supply of water.

Very shortly men clad in jackets of durable
but coarse striped goods and figured loin
cloths began to appear: strong men with
muscles rippling under their satiny black
skins; well-proportioned men with keen, un-
flinching eyes and strong white teeth which

they cleaned, as they walked, with a tough
piece of stick widely used in African tribes
for that purpose; men with long, slender limbs
and short, muscular torsos; men armed with
long, wide native knives, crude axes and mattocks. They were going to the jungle to clear
farms, or to work on the government road, or
to gather palm nuts for oil or palm leaves
for the manufacture of mats and hammocks.

Other men, the artisans, remained to weave
cloth, work in iron, manufacture leather or sit
for hours fashioning clay pots and water jars.
Two or three men, giants in stature and bearing long spears, made off along largely unused trails. Each was followed by a gangling
apprentice armed with bow and arrows. They
were going to hunt some of the forest animals and, with good fortune, to make a kill
or two. Meanwhile, small children innocent
of clothing but well streaked with white clay
were issuing forth to gambol in the lanes with
the goats and sharp-nosed, tan-colored little
Gola dogs.

Boloba, once the stronghold of a great and
warlike king, the tread of whose armies shook
the ground, was beginning its daily round of
work, talk, laughter and sorrow. Gone was
the old independence. Its waking hours were

now spent toiling for its rulers; toiling without recompense.

Over in the compound a rigid black bugler of the Frontier Force blew reveille, a rifle shot sounded and the lone-starred flag of the black republic soared to the top of the flag pole. Nearby Captain Burns' company stood at attention. Strong, well-selected fellows were these; often irresponsible; sometimes guilty of the most revolting cruelty at the behest of their haughty officers, but worst when in detachments under command of noncommissioned officers. They possessed the savagery instilled into the military class everywhere plus their native brand which, far from being eradicated by military discipline, became more strongly developed. Like professional soldiers the world over, they only needed the necessary orders and they were prepared to do anything, especially to loot villages.

Captain Burns seemed to be in good spirits. He had heard of Jackson's mishap of the night before and it opened new vistas; made him think of future possibilities. Suppose the ill-conditioned Commissioner was more seriously hurt than was believed? It was possible that anything might develop from that blow over the head.

The Captain had been jockeying for a district commissionership for the last three years. He had placed many pounds in proper places for the purpose of influencing the right people. He felt, moreover, that he was the logical successor to Jackson, since he knew District No. 1 better than anybody in Liberia. True, he was an officer of the Frontier Force, but there was nothing to prevent him from resigning if a better opportunity presented itself. He could hardly get over to the Commissioner's bungalow fast enough, so anxious was he to learn of the other's condition.

Jackson greeted him with disappointing and totally unexpected exuberance.

"I'll be all right shortly," the Commissioner boomed from the depths of his pillow. "It is just a scalp wound, although there's a damned painful bump there, too. Joe will soon get me back to normal. God damn it, Burns, it takes a whole lot to kill an old sinner like me."

"Yes," replied the Captain, striving to conceal the keen disappointment he felt, "you're lucky all right. It's a wonder she didn't fracture your skull. As it is you'll probably be up and around in a few days, but you'd better be careful of complications."

"There won't be any complications," declared Jackson dogmatically. "I'll leave the
whiskey alone and stop eating so much."

Joe came bearing the Commissioner's
breakfast on a tray. The servant eyed Captain Burns suspiciously. There was something about him that told Joe he was not the
Commissioner's friend. So he was forever
watching Burns, making careful inquiries
about him, checking up on his military and political activities. Joe had learned that employers value their help to the extent that the
latter prove indispensable. Hence, he was
always going out of his way to prove his worth
to his master.

"Burns!" ordered Jackson, clearing his
mouth of ham and eggs, "whatever you do,
get some of that rice and palm oil off to Monrovia today. We don't want Johnson on our
backs. There are enough people around the
Executive Mansion trying to get this job without antagonizing the President. Have all the
towns sent in their requisitions?"

"All but Takama and Jeh," the Captain replied, "and I guess there won't be any trouble
with Takama after that little party you staged
over there. As for Jeh, nothing has come
from there in over two months. I'm sending

Sergeant Bula over there with a couple of squads to touch them up a bit. Bula's got sense enough not to go too far. Good man, Bula. He's a real asset on the road work. He knows how to beat up the slackers without keeping them from work the next day."

"How much stuff have you got to go down?" asked Jackson, wiping his thick lips with a linen napkin.

"About two hundred and fifty kainjis of rice and thirty kerosene cans of oil," the Captain answered.

"What!" exploded the Commissioner, rising on one elbow, his little eyes snapping under his bandages. "Is that all we've got to go down? Why, I figured on at least four hundred kainjis and forty-five cans of oil."

"We used up the rest here," explained Burns hurriedly. "My boys eat pretty heavy, you know, and these women ain't far behind them."

"All right," snapped Jackson, frowning heavily, "send off what you can right now. I want the carriers well guarded. Not a single one must escape. Make the sergeant in charge understand that. I want every one of those men delivered to Sammy Williams."

"To Sammy Williams?" echoed Burns,

smiling knowingly. "Why, you must be going
in for big business. Forty boys! Why, you'll
be swimming in money."

"Well," the Commissioner remarked, washing down his last piece of toast with a swallow
of coffee, "I'm not in this game for my health."

Captain Burns departed to carry out the
Commissioner's orders. He called a bugler
and sent a message to the chief of Boloba demanding ten carriers at once. He yelled to
the sergeant of the guard and ordered him
to parade the thirty prisoners immediately.
He shouted to the first sergeant and Sergeant Bula to hurry to his office. He strode
along as he issued his orders and before he
reached his office in one end of the barracks
soldiers were running in all directions.

Zo with his back and legs still burning from
last night's whippings was paraded with the
other prisoners. It was a strange looking
group, clothed mainly in ragged and filthy
odds and ends, with quite a few of the men
scarcely clothed at all. Those who had possessed good cloths or jackets when brought to
the compound had been stripped by the soldiers and thrown the cast-off rags of others.

"You fight for your woman, eh?" asked a

man to Zo's left. In his tone there was more than a suggestion of mockery.

"Yes," answered Zo simply, "she is my wife."

Zo glanced at the man out of the corner of his eye, wondering how he had found out about the adventure of the night before. His neighbor was of medium height, very black, with a high, broad forehead and a finely shaped body. The corners of his mouth were extremely mobile, registering at will cynical amusement or disdain, but his eyes were his most curious feature. They never seemed to be fully opened, but when they were they reflected an alertness and intelligence that hardly went well with the strings and rags of clothing that hung upon his frame. Sometimes those eyes were dull and appeared lifeless; at other times they were as bright as stars.

Zo studied the man closely as he listened to him talk to a fellow on his other side, and his first reaction was one of dislike. Zo was a serious-minded lad despite his frequent laughter. He liked to joke but he did not believe in jesting about weighty matters and taking the tragedies of life so lightly. He believed that what he had been taught was right, and was willing to sacrifice much to see that right prevailed. He knew the raid on Takama had been grossly unjust and the kidnapping of Pameta even more so. Such occurrences were to be sealed in your heart and kept there securely, always fresh, always embittering the spirit until avenged.

"Listen, boy," said the fellow Zo had been studying, turning toward him, "do you know where we're going?"

"No, I don't," replied the younger man.

"Well, I'll tell you," continued the other, "we're going to Monrovia."

"Monrovia?" echoed Zo.

"Yes, Monrovia," the other man leered. "And they're going to put a big kainji of rice on that back of yours to help it heal up."

To Monrovia! Zo experienced a feeling of elation which was followed immediately by a consciousness of guilt because he had even for a moment been pleased that he was going away from Pameta. He was to be excused, however, because every native in the hinterland of Liberia has heard of Monrovia and wants to go there. To the back-country folk Monrovia is the largest of towns with enormous huts made of stone that rise two and three stories in the air, broad, straight streets

and great markets where everything ever heard
of can be bought. It is the one place where a
man mightier than the District Commissioner
sits and gives orders; an enormous place where
thousands and thousands of people live without the onerous restrictions imposed by tribal
laws and customs, a place where there are
plenty of shillings to be made by everybody
and anybody. Great iron canoes that could
hold everybody in a big native town, come puffing into the harbor from across the waters—
from distant, strange lands where the people's
skins are white. A wonderful place, indeed,
Monrovia!

Zo had heard Chief Bongomo once refer
nonchalantly but with poorly concealed pride
that he had been to Monrovia when he was
very young. Now it was possible that he also
might see the great place. Zo was in something of a dilemma: he was eager to rescue
Pameta, if possible, but he was also eager—
just couldn't help it—to see Monrovia. As
rescuing Pameta seemed rather difficult at the
present time, surrounded as he was by soldiers,
his mind turned to thoughts of the Liberian
capital.

"Are you sure we go to Monrovia?" he
asked the man beside him.

"Wait and see," advised the other knowingly. "I've been through this before and I know."

"How is that?" the Takama youth inquired.

"I mean they caught me once before for going into the bush and not working on the road, and they brought me here. Soon they called out all of us and made us carry kainjis to Monrovia," explained the older man.

"Then you've been to Monrovia?" asked Zo, eyeing the fellow with admiration mingled with incredulity.

"Why, of course," replied the other disdainfully. "That's nothing. I worked in Monrovia for a long time."

"Is it as wonderful as they all say?" Zo asked eagerly.

"No place is as wonderful as they say," the man answered. "I've always been disappointed in places."

"Say," said Zo, a note of respect in his voice, "what's your name—mine's Zo."

"Mine's Soki," said the other smiling. The two shook hands and as their palms would have fallen apart, they snapped their middle fingers three times in accordance with the custom prevailing in much of West Africa. The two middle fingers are pressed tightly against each other and partially hooked. Suddenly they are pulled away and snapped against the heels of their respective thumbs.

"What did they do to you, Soki, when you had carried the kainji to Monrovia?" asked Zo.

"Ha!" scoffed the other. "Do you think I was fool enough to go into Monrovia with them? No, I ran away the first day. Wait, you will see. It is quite simple."

"But the soldiers"—— objected Zo.

"Bah!" was Soki's reply. He spat on the ground and then slowly winked one of his half-closed eyes.

Zo took heart. So one *could* escape. If one man had managed to escape, could not others do likewise? Zo was at the age where he believed that he could equal any other man in accomplishment. He had, indeed, that rare combination of qualities so necessary to achievement: a level head, common sense and a supreme confidence in his ability.

Joe was treading softly about the Commissioner's bungalow ordering his little flunkies around, getting the chores done. He was humming a Mendi song and appeared much

pleased with himself. A few minutes before
he had gone to Pameta's room, given her a
pitcher of water for her morning ablutions
and then brought her breakfast. While she
was eating, he had talked of her predicament,
sympathized with her, played upon her emo-
tions until she had fallen upon his shoulders
in tears. She needed a friend so badly in this
place and here was one. Joe made it a point
to attempt the seduction of his master's chief
women and this was but the opening gun of
his new campaign. He had not been rebuffed
and consequently he was in high spirits.

"Joe!" called the Commissioner from his
bed.

"Yassah, massah!" replied the well-trained
Bassa man, rushing to the bedroom.

"Joe," asked Jackson when the other appeared, "do you know how many kainjis of
rice came here this month?"

"Yassah. Boy at storehouse he say 'bout
four hundred and fifty kainjis."

"How much palm oil?"

"Fifty kerosene cans, sah."

"Did any rice and oil go for Monrovia while
we gone, eh?"

"Yassah. First sergeant he palaver to me
las' night. He say too much soldiers have to

go for Monrovia. He say lottsa boy go down
with kainjis last week."

"Who send the boys for Monrovia, eh?"

"Cap'n Burns, sah."

"Well, that's all Joe."

Joe left the room immediately. Valuable
man, Joe, the District Commissioner mused
as he lay propped up in his bed. He would go
and find out things without being told. Quite
a remarkable quality in a native. . . . So Burns
was just the sort of chap he thought he was.
. . . Trying to get some side money at his
expense, eh? Well, he'd show him who
was in charge of District No. 1. . . . Wonder who he'd sent that rice and oil to?
The dirty skunk! . . . Well, there'd be a
change, all right, and there was no time like
the present."

"Joe!" he yelled again.

"Yassah, massah!" answered Joe, appearing
impassive in the doorway.

"Call Sergeant Junga," Jackson ordered,
referring to the noncommissioned officer who
had accompanied him on his recent tour.

Very shortly the sergeant appeared, stiff as
a ramrod, in the doorway, saluted the Commissioner, and got a somewhat sloppy return.

"Joe! Get pen and paper," ordered the

Commissioner. His servant returned almost immediately with the writing material.

Jackson wrote a few lines on a sheet of paper and folded it. Joe handed him a long, official Manila envelope and a smaller plain white envelope. The note was placed in the smaller envelope which was sealed inside the larger one. Joe disappeared and returned with wax and a lighted candle. He took the envelope, waxed it and then Jackson imbedded his signet ring into the warm substance. A leather wallet with a flat lock was produced, the letter placed inside and the wallet locked.

"Sergeant Junga," snapped the Commissioner, glancing sharply at the noncommissioned officer, "do you still want to be sergeant?"

"Yassah," replied the sergeant, now somewhat nervous.

"Well, then," continued Jackson, "nobody must know you have that letter and no one must touch that wallet. Understand?"

"Yassah," replied the sergeant, taking the proffered wallet and stuffing it in his shirt.

"You take that detachment to Monrovia this morning, eh?"

"Yassah."

"All right, that's all. Tell Captain Burns to report here."

Well! Now he'd show the smart Captain Burns something. Getting just a little too clever, he was. Jackson lay back on his pillow, a sneering smile on his face. Better get Burns out of the way until he could hear from Johnson and have him transferred. . . . Let's see, where could the fellow be sent? Ah! Jeh, of course.

The worst trail in Liberia led to the isolated town of Jeh from which no requisition of food had been received. It was at least sixty miles by trail from Boloba to Jeh and the journey led through a great primeval forest infested with wild beasts. There were treacherous swamps through which a strong man could fight his way only with great difficulty against the sucking black mud. Of course Sergeant Bula could do the job up there satisfactorily enough, but why not make the mission more important than it really was and send the Captain along?

Captain Burns was stunned when he heard the order. He cordially hated these expeditions to remote places off the beaten path. He could not use his hammock over such rough, almost nonexistent trails as the one that led

to Jeh, and it was worth one's life to cross
some of those swamps. The Captain had
never been to Jeh but the assessor of hut taxes
who had made the trip several times had
warned him against it. A mistake on the trail
might lead one into the dread marshes of the
Mano River, that uninhabited section which
easily bribed Liberian boundary officials had
accepted from England in exchange for the
fertile, thickly populated territory above the
Pendembu railhead in Sierra Leone. But orders were orders, so the haughty Captain put
on the best face possible.

"There are a lot of Mendi people from Sierra Leone around that vicinity," Jackson explained blandly, "so I don't think it is wise to
trust a corrective expedition to a sergeant. He
might injure or kill a British subject and then
there would be hell to pay. We can't afford
to have any international trouble right now,
you know. So it's best for you to go along.
The assessor hasn't been up that way in a long
time, so you can collect the hut taxes, too.
You'd better start as soon as you get those
boys off to Monrovia. Sergeant Junga will be
in command, will he not?"

"Yes, I'm taking Sergeant Bula with me,"
Burns replied with evident chagrin.

"Well, that's all, then," said Jackson. "Better get things going."

Captain Burns went out boiling with rage. He was being practically exiled for two weeks. Why? Had Jackson found out about the rice and palm oil or was he really sincere about wanting him to lead the detachment to Jeh? There was something funny about the whole business. The lanky officer stamped angrily across the parade ground to make ready his equipment for the journey.

The ten men from Boloba, taken from work in the jungle, marched into the compound and were grouped indiscriminately with the prisoners by the indifferent soldiers. Forty men were now lined up waiting patiently for orders. Forty men with very few exceptions who knew not where they were going. Forty men who had no choice in the matter. Forty men who had committed no real crime except being born under a despotic government. Forty men who did not expect any pay for their labor and were not going to get any.

Sergeant Junga now appeared, swelled with the importance of his mission, and shouted orders here and there like a field marshal. The forty men were marched to the store house where the requisitions of rice and palm oil from the forty villages of District No. 1 were kept.

To each kainji of rice was fastened a gallon can of palm oil. The entire load weighed about sixty pounds. As each man slung his kainji on his back and thrust his arms through the shoulder straps, he was shoved again into line. When the men were loaded, Sergeant Junga marched them back to their former position and reported to Captain Burns that all was ready. The Captain nodded and the forty carriers, led by one soldier and guarded by nineteen others, passed out of the gate, through Boloba, and into the jungle.

The tropical forest is always cool compared to the open spaces. Even on the hottest days when the jungle resembles a steam bath, fugitive breezes cause some leaves to ripple and branches here and there to sway. Silence prevails during the heat of the day, save for the songs of a few birds and the chatter of occasional troops of monkeys. Human voices carry clear and far through the maze of green that hems in the trail.

The loads seemed light at first and the men stepped with a spring, talking and singing, but as they drew farther away from Boloba and the day advanced, their burdens became heavier and the pace slowed. The fibre shoulder straps cut into the flesh, streams of perspiration ran off their glistening limbs and the sharp odor of toiling bodies arose to mingle with the musky, woodsy smell the jungle exuded this morning.

The trail, well kept close to the village, became increasingly carpeted with entwined roots, stones, and bare rocks that cruelly impeded the progress of the column. Up and down hill they struggled, often crossing rapid little streams where sometimes they were permitted to throw themselves down like animals and suck up the cool water.

Zo was walking behind Soki at the latter's suggestion. The load was becoming unbearable to Zo. With each step it rubbed against the welts on his back and made them raw again. The idea of escape grew increasingly attractive as his pain sharpened. Once he looked questioningly at Soki but the latter shook his head and frowned. The time to make a dash had not yet come.

On and on the men walked, sometimes stumbling over roots and rocks, at other times struggling against the embrace of thorny bushes. Fatigue grew. The tangled green

walls of the jungle seemed to press in closer
upon them. Up and down hill the column
crawled, ever slower and slower. Persistent
insects of innumerable varieties sailed around
their heads. The dangerous driver ants swarm-
ing on the trail in millions often forced the
heavily laden men to run forty and fifty yards
to escape. Then, in safety, all would stop and
one by one pull off the carnivorous insects. To
walk slowly or stop amid a swarm of driver
ants, from which even leopards and elephants
ran in desperation, would be suicidal, for they
destroy everything in their path.

Would they never reach the next town?
Each carrier, each soldier asked himself that
question again and again. At a brief halt late
in the afternoon, Sergeant Junga urged them
to hurry lest they be caught in the forest at
nightfall. Slowly the sun sank and the jungle
darkened. The column, marching in single
file and extended over a quarter mile of trail,
wound in and out, making all possible haste
to its goal.

They came to a steep declivity. The column began to descend, each man feeling here
and there for a secure foothold as any misstep
might mean a broken neck. Soki stepped more
quickly than before.

"Watch me!" he cautioned in a low voice. "And be quick!"

Half way down the hill there was a turn in the trail with a huge tree at the angle. This tree was so large that its exposed roots, like giant claws grasping the earth, rose four or five feet above the ground in narrow ridges before joining the trunk. Each carrier had to crawl laboriously over each root, going half way around the tree before getting on the trail again. When Soki reached this point, instead of going just half way around the forest giant, he went about three-quarters of the way around and then squatted behind a big root. Zo quickly followed him, his heart pounding with excitement. The man some distance behind them was so absorbed in watching his own progress that he did not notice their unusual movement, and because of the extension of the column, the soldier behind him was unable to see what was happening.

Zo and Soki waited a full half hour before stirring from their hiding place, in order to make sure that the last member of the party had passed. Then silently Soki led the way back trail for close to fifteen minutes of fast walking, turning into a side trail across which the leader of the column had placed a green branch to indicate that the main trail was being followed. After a quarter of an hour of rather difficult walking along this less used trail, they arrived at a half town.

It was only a collection of eight or ten huts and sheds in the midst of a large farm clearing. Charred stumps rising here and there resembled scarecrows. There were about ten or fifteen people in the place.

Soki frankly told of his and Zo's escape, knowing the inhabitants would be sympathetic. It was supper time and the two men were invited to have a dish of the steaming rice, fish and palm oil. They wolfed the food down greedily. Then a kindly old woman rubbed some ointment on Zo's back and legs.

Relieved of their burdens and filled with food, the two crawled into one corner of a hut and prepared to get some sleep. It was dark now and they felt secure at least until tomorrow. Soki had observed that staying in the town was not exactly the last word in safety, since some of the soldiers were Golas and knew the country, but Zo refused to go any farther and chance a night in the jungle, unarmed as they were. Tomorrow Zo planned to return to Boloba and try again to free Pameta. He had almost succeeded at the first try. Perhaps he'd have better luck next time. They had just dozed off when one of the villagers shook them vigorously and yelled "Get up and run! The soldiers are coming!"

They stumbled to the door of the hut and saw at the entrance to the clearing a party of soldiers bearing long, lighted torches and hurrying toward the settlement.

"This way!" cried Soki, running swiftly for the bush. Zo followed close behind him. They stumbled and fell two or three times and the soldiers heard them. At once the pursuit began, the soldiers screaming to the fugitives to halt, the blazing torches streaming out behind them like banners from Hades.

The two men had at least a hundred yards advantage of the soldiers and carried no heavy rifles. There was a chance for escape. If they could have luck enough to stumble upon the continuation of the side trail by which they had entered the town, they might easily out-run their pursuers. Hoping against hope they plunged recklessly into the velvety darkness of the jungle.

If the jungle is unfriendly by day and jealously guards its secrets with an almost impenetrable tangles of vines, bushes and trees, it is an out and out enemy of man

at night. Helpless is man in this direction-
less maze. Without light or food he cannot hope to get far. He may fight against
his fate; he may slave heroically with a
bush knife, but the more he struggles the
worse it is for him. The terrible night jungle
holds him fast.

The torches of the pursuing soldiers grew
inexorably closer as Soki and Zo frantically
wormed their way through the tangled underbrush. They tore at vines and branches until
their hands were bleeding. The soldiers drew
nearer. They yelled to the fugitives to halt
and return. Two bullets emphasized the command. Soki and Zo fought on through the
jungle. It was maddeningly slow work. Now
the soldiers were following them into the underbrush.

Suddenly the two came to an open space and
for a moment their hearts leaped with hope.
It was a short-lived one, for what had appeared an open field was in reality a swamp!
Somewhere they knew there was a native log
walk across it, but where? They could see
nothing, not even each other. They paused a
moment in indecision. The lights of the pursuing soldiers grew closer. They must either
cross or be captured.

Soki skirted along the edge of the swamp until he thought he felt something resembling a log underfoot. "This way!" he cried. He stepped hurriedly, boldly forward and began to cross the morass as fast as the darkness and the irregularly spaced logs would permit. Close behind him came Zo. The soldiers were nearing the edge of the swamp. Scratched, torn, battered and bloody from their battle through the jungle, the two men felt the first thrill of escape as they neared the other side. Once safely across they could easily outdistance the soldiers, now that they had miraculously found the trail.

Soki proceeded gingerly but leaped back with a cry of terror as the log upon which he had stepped slithered off into the mud. His backward step found no support and he sank into the black ooze. Zo had hold of his hand immediately, trying frantically to pull him from the morass. Silently, desperately the two fought against the sucking mud. Soki sank lower and lower. Almost in tears, Zo tugged fruitlessly to extricate his friend. On solid ground he might have succeeded but here the logs of the pathway moved this way and that in the black slime.

"Come back!" yelled one of the soldiers, "or we kill you right there."

"Run! Run, you fool!" whispered Soki, now almost up to his throat in the mud. "Run, I tell you! Get out of here! You can't help me; save yourself." Soki was resigned to his fate. As was his wont, he was prepared to take his predicament philosophically. He was, like most Africans, a fatalist. What was to be was to be. If it had not been intended for him to die in this manner, he would have escaped.

"I won't go," Zo declared, as he doggedly tugged at the other's arm. Zo felt sure he could make good his escape but a sense of duty kept him at Soki's side. He could not desert a friend that way. Convinced finally of his inability to pull Soki out, he yelled for help to the soldiers on the other bank.

With their aid Soki was finally rescued. The two men were then marched back to the half town to get their discarded kainjis. In an hour they were in the town where the column was staying for the night.

Sergeant Junga met them, whip in hand, gloating over his shrewdness in knowing where he could send soldiers to find them. He had been over the route before and knew the country well. Under ordinary circumstances he would not have pursued the fugitives, but the District Commissioner had warned him that not a man must escape.

He spared Zo because of the condition of his back but Soki was lashed unmercifully. Then the two were shoved into a hut with eight others.

"Well," remarked Soki, "I guess we'll go to Monrovia after all."

CHAPTER SIX

VICE PRESIDENT SAMUEL WILLIAMS of Liberia stood in the semidarkness of a ramshackle warehouse on the water front of Monrovia and rubbed his palms together with satisfaction. There was money in sight again and the Honorable Mr. Williams felt almost gay. Before him were the forty porters Sergeant Junga had brought from Boloba, huddled together, talking quietly, wondering what was to be done with them. In one corner of the warehouse their loads of rice and palm oil were neatly piled up ready for distribution to the "right" people.

Mr. Williams, or Sammy Williams as he was most frequently called by his intimates, was a big two hundred and fifty-pound man well over six feet in height. He was generally in good humor and never lost an opportunity to expose his tombstone teeth in a capacious smile. He loved a good joke and told many himself. His laughter was loud and infectious. He dispelled gloom wherever it reposed and was known far and wide as a good fellow.

The Vice President was more than a jester and comedian, however. He had his serious side. On certain Sundays he could be found in the Presbyterian church, pacing the altar, beating the lectern with his massive fists and quoting Holy Writ to the accompaniment of streams of perspiration and saliva. Mr. Williams was in high favor as a preacher with the almost fanatically Christian Americo-Liberians. They declared that he knew "how to stir" them.

The chief interest of Sammy Williams was making as much money as possible. There was nothing he loved so well, and to the accumulation of it he bent most of his energy and talent. He had early discovered that politics in Liberia was the surest and least laborious road to wealth, so he had become a politician. Now he was a power in the Conservative Party and his word was almost law. He made and broke lesser politicians, and it was said that Sidney Cooper Johnson was now President because of Sammy Williams' support and backing. Quite naturally, Mr. Williams received many favors of distinctly monetary value.

Much of Sammy Williams' versatility was due to a considerable sojourn in the United States of America, whence he had been sent by

his parents many years ago to attend one of
the larger universities. Not long after his arrival, Sammy began seeing a little too much of
high society and his money dwindled alarm-
ingly. Always handy with a pen, he had
forged a check. The American police being
more efficient in detection than the Liberian
gendarmerie, Sammy was sent to Sing Sing
where he learned much from his associates that
was useful when he entered Liberian politics later on. He never hid the fact that he
had been incarcerated in the States. Only a
few days before an incoming missionary had
stated in answer to Sammy's question that he
was a graduate of Dartmouth. "Fine!"
Sammy exploded, "I'm a graduate of Penn."
The Vice President always had to have his little joke.

He looked over the huddle of men again,
made another mental calculation, smiled and
walked out of the building. At the door he
warned the barefoot sentry of the dire calami-
ties that would befall him if a single one of
the natives escaped. The soldier saluted and
the Vice President strolled down the dusty
thoroughfare, nodding this way and that to
white merchants, Americo-Liberians and native peddlers. Everybody liked Sammy be-

cause he was so democratic. He would drink
wine from a native's gourd or champagne from
a merchant's long-stemmed glass with equal
gusto. He was equally at home in a certain
shack in Kru town or at a social function in
the Executive Mansion.

Hurrying up the hill from the water front,
he arrived puffing and perspiring a few minutes later at the residence of John Collins, the
Spanish Consul. Mr. Collins, a sharp-eyed,
white-haired Liberian of small stature, looked
up as the Vice President barged into his office.

"Well, what can I do for the distinguished
Vice President today," he queried, a slight
trace of mockery in his voice, as Williams fell
into a complaining chair near his desk.

"A big, cool drink, John, for God's sake,"
said Williams, tossing his helmet aside and
mopping his sepia brow with a bandana handkerchief. "It's hot as hell out there."

"Boy!" shouted the consul. "Two bottles
of beer."

A little black fellow came in with the frosted
bottles and filled glasses for the two men. Mr.
Williams tossed down his beer greedily and
filled his glass again. Mr. Collins drank more
slowly.

"Get your papers ready, John," said Williams. "I've got forty laborers to go and they're all husky fellows."

"Well, you know I'm always ready to do business," Collins replied. "The boat won't be here for a couple of days. By the way, where'd you get so many?"

"Jackson recruited them up in his district. He's right on the job, that fellow. This is the third bunch he's sent down since he's been up there," Williams explained.

"I suppose all of these boys are volunteers, eager to work on the plantations," Collins observed, gazing steadily at Williams with a smirk on his face.

"Oh, of course," said Williams, smiling broadly. "I wouldn't think of sending anyone against his will."

He reached in his coat pocket and fished out a soiled piece of paper and handed it to the consul.

"That's the list of names," said Williams.

"Now we're all set," Collins remarked, "and I'll settle our differences as soon as possible. It does seem now that we're getting to the place where we can depend on a regular supply of labor."

"Exactly!" was the Vice President's comment.

A few minutes later Mr. Williams emerged
from the Spanish consul's office and sauntered
slowly down the sun-drenched street bowing
and beaming as he encountered friends and
acquaintances. As he passed a two-story stone
building a small boy ran out to him and said,
"Mr. Saunders says he'd like to speak with
you a minute, Mr. Williams."

Mr. Williams' joviality fled and a frown
ruffled his forehead. He wanted nothing to
do with Tom Saunders and yet it was well not
to ignore him. With a suppressed curse he
turned and followed the youngster into the
building.

Mr. Williams was not the only Americo-
Liberian politician whom Tom Saunders an-
noyed. As a matter of fact, Mr. Saunders
was a very sharp thorn in the side of the
entire Conservative Party. A naturalized
citizen hailing originally from America and
filled with Yankee ideas of business and efficiency, he had for thirty years fought hard
against the destructive, reactionary forces in
the little republic. He saw more clearly than
the other citizens that the policies and practices of the ruling class would eventually end
in the ruination of Liberia.

It was Tom Saunders who had introduced

to Liberia the first telephone system, the first
electric-light system and the first ice plant,
and it was Tom Saunders who had organized
the Liberal Party to oppose and challenge the
policies of the Conservatives. When the year
for presidential elections rolled around, he
was always heading the ticket of the Liberal
Party but always he lost. The Conservatives
managed to win majorities through the ju-
dicious circulation of fraudulent deeds to
property, the looting of ballot boxes, the
wholesale distribution of gin to voters, and
the illegal coöperation of police and public
officials. The party leaders had not studied
American political practices in vain.

Tom Saunders had been called the gadfly
of Liberia. He was always on the go, up
and down the coast and into the hinterland,
uncovering evidence of fraud, graft and numerous illegal practices of which the public
officials were guilty. This news he published
under biting black headlines in his weekly newspaper, "The Liberian Liberal." Around him
he had gathered a devoted and loyal group of
the younger Liberians and those who were
eager to put a stop to the evils that were un-
dermining and destroying the state. They
constituted a small but energetic minority and

their activities caused the Conservatives no little concern. They had again and again exposed the slave traffic in which almost all of the government officials were involved, until the outside world was beginning to take cognizance of it and foreign offices of great powers were asking their representatives in Liberia to report on it.

It was small wonder, then, that the Vice President was loath to talk with Tom Saunders. Yet on the surface Mr. Williams always pretended they were great friends. He had found that to be the better way.

"Good morning, Brother Saunders!" he boomed as he entered the office of the business man. "I hope God has blessed you abundantly since we last met."

"No more than usual," said Saunders, waving the Vice President to a chair. "Won't you sit down?"

Saunders, a slenderly built black man of distinguished appearance, pressed a button on the side of his glass-topped desk and leaned back in his swivel chair. A servant all in white appeared.

"What will you have, Williams?" asked Saunders.

"I believe some cold lemonade would go well right now," Williams beamed.

The servant departed and the two men looked at each other. Williams was a little puzzled; Saunders was smiling slightly.

"Well," said Williams, expansively, "how's business these days?"

"It seems to be pretty good down on the water front," said Saunders, eyeing Williams significantly.

"Yes," Williams observed, with justifiable suspicion, "it does seem to be good down there."

The servant entered with the refreshments and filled two large glasses. Williams, with a grimace, took a polite sip from his glass and then set it down. Saunders smiled meditatively.

"Williams," said Saunders at last, "I just wanted to tell you that I know all about the arrival of those forty boys down in that warehouse and I warn you and all of your friends that unless this traffic is stopped I'm going to carry the fight outside of the country. You people don't seem to realize that you are defeating your own ends by carrying on this business."

"You're very much mistaken, Tom," replied Williams in a hard voice that belied his smile. "All those boys have signed up of their own free will to go to Fernando Po. Times are hard up country and they're anxious to go where they can get some real money."

"Yes, and some sleeping sickness and elephantiasis, too," added Saunders, sarcastically.

"Now, now, Tom," said Williams soothingly, "you're always seeing the worst side. If these fellows didn't want to go, you know very well we wouldn't be sending them. We also have the interests of the natives at heart."

"You can't take me in with such nonsense, Williams. Don't you know that I know Commissioner Jackson rounded up those fellows and sent them down here against their will? Why, they don't even know where they're going! If they are so eager to go to Fernando Po, why did Jackson have to send along twenty soldiers to guard them?"

"Well, Tom," said Williams, rising to go, "you and I always have a fight whenever we meet. We just see things different, that's all. You're wasting a whole lot of energy trying to uncover evils that don't exist."

"All right," said Saunders, also rising, "I just thought I'd warn you that this is the last straw. I've fought within the country for thirty years to clean up these evils you describe as nonexistent. Now I'm going outside and see what can be done."

"What do you mean to do?" asked Williams, halting in the doorway, now somewhat concerned.

"You'll find that out if you ship out those boys," Saunders warned.

"Good day, Brother Saunders," boomed the Vice President, walking out into the sunshine. He was glad to get away before he lost his poise.

More uneasy than he had pretended over Saunders' threat, he went immediately to the Executive Mansion. The sentry stopped pacing, faced to the front and snappily saluted; the detachment of the guard on the verandah rose hastily, formed ranks and saluted; several chiefs from the back country sitting on the other side of the verandah also rose and bowed low. The Vice President saluted, bowed and beamed as he entered the building. When he had passed, the sergeant of the guard explained to the chiefs who the great man was.

Sammy Williams brushed by Colonel Fitzsimmons, the President's aide-de-camp, and rushed into the latter's private office. Presi-

dent Johnson looked up from his papers,
wearing an expression of annoyance which he
banished when he saw who his caller was.

"Hello, Sammy!"

"Hello, Johnson!"

"What can I do for you?" asked the President.

"I was just talking to Tom Saunders. He
knows all about those forty boys Jackson just
sent down and said he would go outside the
country for help to put a stop to it. Do you
think there's anything to that?"

"Don't worry," said the President. "Tom
Saunders can't hurt us, Sammy. We belong
to the League of Nations, don't we? And the
United States will never be sufficiently interested to intervene. He may arouse some talk
abroad, but that will soon blow over. Just go
right ahead and send out as much labor as you
can get. The business is legal and you are a
licensed labor agent."

"Yes, I know all that, Johnson," said Williams, "but I'm not so sure that carrying bad
reports out of the country won't hurt us. The
French and English are just waiting for
another excuse to take advantage of us. You
know very well that Tom Saunders will do
as he says."

"Well, well," the President observed, "I repeat there's nothing to get excited about. Don't forget that I was Secretary of State for many years and know how to handle such matters. . . . Now, tell me, how much rice did Jackson send down?"

"Forty kainjis of rice and forty gallons of palm oil," Williams replied, now somewhat reassured.

"That's fine! Now we shall have good news to tell the cabinet when it meets," said the President.

"But what about Henderson?" Williams objected. "Are you going to keep him in the cabinet after the attitude he's shown? He's always refused to accept his part of the requisitions on the ground that they are illegally obtained, and only yesterday I heard that he was going to try to stop the exportation of labor from Monrovia, claiming that it is illegal because this is a restricted district. What are you going to do with a fellow like that?"

"The Attorney General is a young man," replied His Excellency, "full of foreign ideas, and not altogether practical. With my assistance he'll learn much. Don't worry about him nor about Tom Saunders. Remember, Sammy, threats aren't acts. It's what people can actually do that may hurt us, and neither of those fellows can really do anything."

"I can't see why you keep a fellow like that in the cabinet," Williams persisted. "He hears all of our plans and knows just what we're doing. Why not put him out and select some good party man?"

"Never fear, Sammy," said the President, blandly, "I'm sure I can handle Henderson nicely. He's not very well fixed, is he?"

"Not that I know of," Williams admitted.

"He has no business except the law, has he?" continued the President.

"No," Williams agreed.

"And he can be disbarred for malpractice, can't he," inquired the Chief Executive, rubbing his hands together, his eyes twinkling.

"Yes, that's possible," said the Vice President.

"Well, then," concluded President Johnson, "I think we have the situation in hand. If Mr. Henderson goes along with us, he will continue to add that desirable respectability to our cabinet which so impresses many of our voters, but if Mr. Henderson chooses to take an opposite course, his public career will probably end ignominiously. I do not think it will be difficult to impress upon him that he is only valu-

able to us in the degree that he ignores the
letter of the law where our interests are
concerned."

"You're pretty sharp, Johnson," said Williams, beaming as he rose to go.

"Thanks, Sammy," His Excellency replied
suavely. "Perhaps that's why I'm President."

The warehouse was close and dark. The
only openings through which fresh air might
come were small windows over the front and
back doors. The toilet facilities were extremely primitive and the odor in the place
was sickening. Added to this was the acrid
smell arising from the sweating bodies of forty
unwashed natives lying in their foul rags.
Overhead a galvanized iron roof intensified the
heat of the broiling March sun.

The men had been marched into Monrovia
early that morning from the military compound just outside the city and hustled into
their present abode. The Boloba men had
loudly complained against not being permitted
to return home, but Sergeant Junga quieted
them by promising to take them back in a day
or so.

Zo was greatly disappointed. He had expected to see something of the big city, but

instead the column was brought in by a round-about way to the warehouse. What was to be done with them now? Where were they going? He turned to Soki for answer.

"Don't know," replied Soki. "Who knows what Liberians will do to natives?"

"But they ought to tell us," insisted Zo, earnestly. "We are men the same as they are. We have some rights. We should be treated better."

"You've got a lot to learn," Soki remarked, smiling at his youthful companion.

"Well, you can see yourself that it isn't right," Zo continued. "Don't the Liberians take our food and our money? Aren't we taking care of them, as you might say? Then for their own benefit they should treat us better."

Soki merely snorted disgustedly and turned over on his side. He was willing to take things as they came when he could do nothing about it. There was no use wasting your breath over the inevitable. Like Soki, the other men sat around stoically awaiting whatever was in store for them, but not a few indulged in idle speculation as to their immediate future.

The day under the hot tin roof passed slowly. Late in the afternoon the sun relented

somewhat and several cooling drafts off the
sea came through the two small windows. At
sundown they were fed sparingly and the
doors thrown open a little while to air out the
place. Through the night, between short naps,
they could hear the guards being changed, the
lap of the water at the back of the warehouse,
and the drums over in Kru Town, where the
usual moonlight dances were in progress.

For two more days their imprisonment continued. The monotony was broken once by a
visit from the Vice President, who came to see
if the men were still in good health. This was
an important matter, since the Spanish planters only paid for able-bodied laborers.

When he entered, several of the men, including Zo, surrounded him and asked what
was to be done with them. Fortunately, Mr.
Williams could speak no language except
English, although he surmised the burden of
their queries. So he waved them aside good-
naturedly and went beaming on his way.

At daybreak on the morning of the third
day the back door of the warehouse was
thrown open and the men ordered out. They
stumbled along awkwardly as the outer bright-
ness temporarily blinded them. Waiting soldiers helped them into three long Kru surf

boats. They were cursed and hurried along, sometimes pushed and shoved. The Spanish consul, who stood nearby, had ordered that the embarkation must be speedily concluded. No use giving the white foreigners a topic for conversation.

The three boats were soon loaded. With a quiet signal from Mr. Collins, the stout Kru oarsmen bent to their tasks and the boats moved out into the channel between the sandbar and the shore. The human cargo was hardly visible. The natives had been forced into the bottoms of the big boats, under the seats of the oarsmen.

The surf boats ran down the channel alongside the shore for about two miles until they came opposite a narrow opening in the bar where the water eddied and swirled dangerously. To the accompaniment of considerable shouting, the boats were skillfully shot through into the open sea. The helmsmen shouted fresh orders, while great waves tossed the craft about like eggshells.

About a mile from the sandbar the oarsmen stopped rowing, and the boats wallowed in the troughs of the waves. A wait of fifteen minutes followed and then a streamer of smoke indicated the approach of the *Santa Clara,*

en route from Rio de Oro to Fernando Po and
adjacent Spanish settlements.   She steamed
close to the trio of surf boats, her anchor rum-
bled into the depths of the sea and the board-
ing ladder was lowered.   The surf boats drew
closer, until the leading one touched the ladder.   Consul Collins, spry for his age, ran up
on deck and shook hands with the captain.

The soldiers, plying their rifle butts and
bayonet points, hustled the forty men aboard
the dingy steamer and then below decks.
Somewhat reluctantly, the natives obeyed.
They had never been to sea before and most
of them were seeing it for the first time.   All
of their lives they had spent in the jungle;
now they were surrounded by water, and what
chance was there for escape?

Two of the three boats immediately departed on the long trip back to shore.   The
remaining one waited for Mr. Collins and
what little cargo there might be for Monrovia.
It was still there when the Liberian customs
and mail boat rowed alongside, loaded with
important-looking black officials.   They had
seen enough to make them smile cynically and
chuckle among themselves but, like minor officials everywhere, in public they would hold
their peace.

CHAPTER SEVEN

THE *Santa Clara* was old and weather-
beaten. Little time seemed to be spent in
painting and cleaning her. Where the forty
men were confined was in the fore part of the
ship, under the main deck. The room was
hardly large enough for all of its occupants,
and there was much crowding. Two portholes
alone afforded them light and air. The accumulated odors of many previous bodies rose
to mix with those of the Gola men. In one
corner of the room was a pile of smelly sacks
and blankets upon which a sailor indicated
they might lie.

As the little ship got under way, the men
scrambled for positions at the portholes to get
one last glimpse of their native land, the
strong pushing aside the weak, so that the
latter had to be content with whatever reports
were given them. Zo was one of the lucky few
who secured a place.

There was Cape Mesurado jutting out
boldly into the sea, with a little white light-
house atop of it. Sprawled out behind and

reaching down to the water front were the white buildings and red roofs of the Liberian capital. From a distance Monrovia is without doubt one of the most attractive towns on the West African coast: it is only when one goes ashore that the illusion vanishes, quickly and cruelly.

The men's quarters were very hot. Even breathing was difficult when the door was closed and only the portholes could be depended upon for air. The small steamer rolled like a shell even in the smooth tropical sea and it was not long before the closeness of the room was polluted by seasickness.

Two or three of the bolder spirits joined Zo in kicking on the door for some relief from the stench. It was not very long before a Spanish sailor came, threw open the heavy iron door, and with many oaths laid about him with a black whip. The men crouched in the corner, endeavoring as best they could to avoid the biting strokes. At last the man stopped, went out and slammed the door shut behind him.

There was silence while the men looked hopelessly at each other. They would not dare kick on the door again because all were afraid of the whip. Every man knew how it felt because every one of them had experienced its torture. But what were they to do? The room was becoming unbearable and more of the men were getting ill. They knew no Spanish and only Soki could speak a few words of broken English. The sailor who was in charge of them knew only his own language.

They were just cattle being shipped off to some place they knew not where—victims of the thinly disguised slave traffic that annually took others like them from their homes to the distant plantations. Like cattle they lay on the iron floor, filthy and perspiring.

The following morning they were permitted to exercise on the lower deck while their room was being washed out with a hose. Fresh air never seemed so good before. Always they had thought little of its value, but now they were fully able to appreciate it.

It was while they were on the deck that an officer passed and Soki took a chance and spoke to him in English. "Massah," he pleaded, "please let boys be outside. We work." The officer turned like a flash and struck Soki on the mouth for his presumption. From the look on the officer's face one would have imagined that Soki had insulted him.

The other men stood around silently as the blood oozed from Soki's lips.

Each day toward evening they were given rice, palm oil and some water. Day after day grew hotter as they neared the equator, but always the door of their room was kept fastened except when the place was being hosed out. No more efforts were made to get the Spanish to let them work around the ship. Soki's experience had compelled them to relinquish that idea. He swore he would not try it again and the others could not converse with the Spanish even if they had wished.

Soki kept to one corner near Zo and said little. There was really nothing to say. There they were cooped up, and to escape was an impossibility. Why talk about it? No use to cry and fret; that would be childish. Better to sit quiet and think. What was to be was to be. Life was like that and had always been like that.

At first Zo fumed about the injustice of being taken off this way, but after a while he too saved his breath. For hours they would lie silent, each man to his own thoughts. Those who complained the oftenest were the ten men from Boloba who had been requisitioned to carry kainjis of rice to Monrovia. They were

exceedingly vocal at times about the decep-
tion practiced upon them, but even they soon
realized that protest could have no effect here.

One day, at last, after what was beginning
to seem an eternity, a shout went up from two
of the men peering out of the portholes. The
others rushed to see what was the cause of
the excitement. Off at a distance the watchers
had seen land. Two great mountains separated by an expanse of sea were to be observed. One was obviously an island, and
toward that they were veering.

One after the other the men took their places
at the portholes to see the approaching land.
Blessed land! No matter what or where it
was, any land was beautiful now. The men
laughed, chatted and slapped each other on the
back. Where all had been silent and brooding
before, there was now something like gaiety.
Even the bitterness which each native had kept
locked in his heart was gone for the time being.

The *Santa Clara* came closer to the island
mountain. The porthole observers could now
see more distinctly to what manner of place
they were bound. The island had at first
seemed a single mountain clothed with vege-

tation from base to summit. It was now seen
to be several high mountains, each covered
with forests and all joined together. Down
the intervening valleys ribbons of water
poured over the cliffs into the sea. Finally
they saw many little white buildings and what
appeared to be cultivated fields.

The *Santa Clara* cruised into a small harbor apparently gouged out of the side of the
mountain, and dropped anchor. Wherever
they might be, the men were at least gratified
to know that they had reached their destina-
tion: very soon now they would be let out into
the fresh air and sunshine; very soon they
would be out among the warehouses and the
residences and the groves of huge trees that
could be seen through the portholes.

The iron door was opened and a sailor motioned to them to come outside. They filed
out gratefully, lining up on the deck. It was
a beautiful place to which they had been trans-
ported. In the clear air the mountains seemed
like a green canvas upon which were painted
falling streams, white houses and public buildings. Below, the sea was deep blue; above, the
sky was cloudless. The heat was terrific. On
shore could be seen a few people in white

clothing walking slowly about carrying um-
brellas.

When they were finally taken ashore, many
of the men felt like kissing the good earth,
such a wonderful treat was it to again be on
firm ground. But there was no time for that.
Mulatto officials, nicknamed Portos from their
Negro and Portuguese descent, herded the
newcomers under an open shed, where they
were counted and examined.

A black man dressed in cool white clothing,
wearing a white helmet, white shoes and carrying an ivory-headed umbrella approached
the group. He looked over the men, spoke a
word or two to the officials, and then addressed
the men in Kpwessi, a language understood all
over Liberia.

"I am the Liberian consul," he said. "You
have been engaged to work here for two years
and you will be paid good money, much more
than you could ever earn in Liberia. Do your
work well and you will get along all right. I
am here to protect your interests and to see
that you are sent home when your contract
has expired."

The effect on the men of hearing a familiar
language spoken was almost electric. They
broke ranks and surrounded him, excitedly

gesticulating, demanding why they had been
sent from home and denying that they had
come of their own free will. The Spanish
officials beat them back into line. Mr. Simmons, the Liberian consul, strolled leisurely
off down the street.

There were numerous questions they wanted
to ask him. One or two even shouted questions after him only to be buffeted for their
trouble. Mr. Simmons was their only link to
the homeland. They did not know that the
consul was an exceedingly slender reed upon
which to lean. He was primarily interested in
the men as a money-making proposition. Out
of the six dollars they were supposed to get
for their labor each month, Mr. Simmons was
alloted three dollars for protecting their interests. He and the Spanish were on excellent
terms. If he could at the end of a man's
two-year term persuade him to remain for
two more years, he was given twelve of the
twenty-five dollars each man received upon
discharge.

So Fernando Po was a lucrative post for
Mr. Simmons. He was not overburdened
with work and money was coming in regularly. Of course some of this money found
its way back to Monrovia and into the pockets

of certain high officials, but Mr. Simmons
expected to pay for the post he held. He
sometimes privately deplored the fact that
very few of the laborers came of their own
volition; but his conscience never urged him
to protest against a practice which so liberally
augmented his meagre salary.

Zo's hopes had risen when Mr. Simmons
spoke to them; but when the immaculately
dressed little gentleman ignored their questions and went about his business, Soki, who
stood next to him, smiled cynically and said:

"He won't listen to you or to any of us.
He cares nothing about us. I could easily see
that. He is just another Liberian."

"But he promised to protect us," said Zo,
"and see that we got back home."

"That's just talk," Soki scoffed. "You
watch what I say, if we ever leave here it will
surprise me. We are here to work and they'll
probably work us to death. I don't expect
to see my people again."

"Perhaps we can get away," suggested Zo,
hopefully.

"Get away " echoed Soki. "How? Do you
think we can swim to that land over there?"

"Just the same," Zo persisted, "there will
some day come a chance."

"Well, you have plenty of time to wait for it," remarked his comrade. "You have the right spirit, Zo, and I hope you keep it. I can see you'll need it here."

Their conversation was interrupted by the half-caste officials who now divided them into four groups of ten each and marched them off in different directions. By staying close together and doing a bit of manoeuvring the two friends managed to get in the same group. They were thankful for that.

With their guards behind them they trudged along a dusty road while the sun beat down upon their bare heads and ragged bodies. After two or three hours they arrived at a big plantation with row upon row of trees and bushes stretching in all directions. There were many neat, whitewashed sheds and warehouses. Off to one side stood the residence of the planter in the center of a circle of huge shade trees.

The tired men were lined up again. This time a swarthy white man with two women walked out leisurely to inspect them. The man looked them over carefully as he circled the group, nodding his approval and making jovial comments on them to the ladies.

The inspection over, they were herded into

a long, low warehouse with the usual corrugated iron roof. As soon as they were all inside, the heavy door was closed behind.

"We are always being locked up," Soki observed.

The place was in semidarkness, only lit by a foot deep opening under the eaves which ran all around the house. Here at least they were going to have proper ventilation. When their eyes became accustomed to the darkness, they saw that their abode was filled with narrow beds constructed of cocoa staves and banana leaves. There was hardly enough room in the place to get about. There were now no other occupants of the building. Tired from standing in the heat at the seaport and from the long walk to the plantation, the men threw themselves down on the nearest beds and most of them were soon fast asleep.

"Maybe we could get away to the mountains," Zo suggested to the drowsy Soki. "The bush is very thick up there."

"Wait," said Soki, "until we know the place better. We shall soon learn."

"I saw some little boats at the dock," Zo continued, "perhaps we can steal one of them sometime and cross to the other side."

"Yes," Soki agreed, "it is all possible and

you'll have plenty of time to try it. But right now I'm going to sleep."

The warehouse was an oven under the tin roof, with a strong odor of unwashed bodies. Zo wondered what it would be like when filled to capacity.

The sun was sinking rapidly and the cool of the evening had set in when the big door was thrown open and a great crowd of men entered. The ten newcomers rose to meet them and discovered that all were from Liberia. There was much exchanging of news and information. Here were representatives of almost every tribe in Liberia. At home they had despised and been taught to look down on each other; here they were welded by force of circumstances into a solidarity induced by common misery. Golas, Vais, G'Bandes, Buzis, Kpwessis, Guios, Bassas and Greboes, they sat together in a foreign land and talked of home.

They still sat talking long after they had consumed their daily ration of one pound of rice, salt fish, coffee and palm oil. The veterans told about Fernando Po and the routine of work and the newcomers related how they were brought against their will from the hinterland. It turned out that all of the men had been recruited in about the same way. They too had seen their chiefs fined, beaten, humiliated and sometimes shot down. They too had been forced to work on the roads and carry heavy burdens through the steaming jungles.

"Isn't it possible to get away from here?" Zo asked of a big Bassa man named Georgie.

"It is possible," he replied, "but few have done so."

"Why don't they?" Zo asked.

"Look here," said Georgie, "I've been here now for a long time. If there was a chance to escape do you think I would stay? Do you think anybody would stay? No! We would all be gone if we could get away. Do you think anyone can swim that twenty miles to the other side and not make chop for the sharks?"

"But isn't it possible to steal a boat?" persisted Zo.

"Oh, I know it looks easy now," said the Bassa man, "but it's different when you get out there. I once knew a fellow here named Bobo. Do any of you fellows remember Bobo! . . . Well, it doesn't matter. Anyhow, Bobo stole a little boat and started to paddle for the mainland. Like most of us he knew

very little about such things, and these waters
are dangerous."

"What happened to him?" asked Zo.

"The current was so swift it carried him
away," Georgie replied. "We never heard of
him again and the last time we saw him he
was being carried out to sea. A Kru man
might reach the shore over there, but the Krus
are trained to handle boats. A boat is no place
for a bush boy."

"Is it very hard to get away to the seashore
without the guards seeing you?" Zo inquired
persistently.

"They are always on the alert," said
Georgie. "That is their business. They are
half white and half black, but they serve the
white man always."

"What about going to the mountains?"

"Hah, the mountains," echoed Georgie.
"Yes, you can go to the mountains like many
others have done, but you will be glad to come
back from the mountains. Death is there also.
You have no knife, no spear, no arrows, yet
there are animals in those forests. Also the
Bubis."

"Who are the Bubis?"

"They are cruel bush people who will torture you and make you work for them. They

serve no man, white or black, wear no cloth and kill for pleasure. Many men have run away from the plantations and gone to the mountains, but few return."

"Well," said Zo, "I don't care. I would rather take my chances with them than to stay here. Have you not said that many men die with disease? How is it better to be enslaved by the Spaniards than by the Bubis?"

"All right," Georgie exclaimed, "anytime you get ready to go we'll help you, but I warn you that to go into those mountains is no good. How can you expect to succeed with nothing where the white man with his guns has failed?"

Although the men were tired, they talked in low tones until well past the usual time for going to sleep. Then slowly silence settled over the crowded place.

At the first streak of dawn, the door was thrown open and a mulatto overseer ordered the men outside in English. With little preliminaries they were lined up and sent off in details under other overseers. Zo and Soki managed, as usual, to stay together. Though the older man seldom spoke, his presence was comforting. He was mature and practical, and his cynicism was a good foil for Zo's optimism and impetuosity.

With three other men they were put to work carrying wood to dry the cocoa in the big kitchen. In these sheds a fire was placed over the washed beans for that purpose. Each piece of wood was six or seven feet long and quite heavy. The wood had to be carried a considerable distance and only one piece could be taken at a time. The task was carrying twenty-five pieces of this firewood, and by eleven o'clock their overseer indicated that the job was finished and marched them back to the warehouse.

In the afternoon they were set to work cutting weeds and bushes from around the cocoa trees with bush knives. As they bent over and slashed away under the blazing sun, the perspiration ran down into their eyes, sometimes blinding them temporarily. Zo began to wonder how one could steal one of the bush knives. He would need one when he made his dash for freedom. When he returned from work that evening he discovered why the knives were not stolen. Each man's knife was taken from him and locked in a big box in the tool house, which was itself locked.

Each day was much like the preceding one: up at daybreak, working from six to eleven and again from one to six; the same mo-

notonous diet, and then heavy slumber to prepare for the next day's toil. Some days they
picked and broke open the cocoa pods, the
task being the filling of six kerosene cans full.
At other times they were issued picks and
shovels and sent to work on the motor roads.
Often when a steamer came they were taken
to port to help load and unload it. Again
they might be put to work digging fifty four-
foot holes each for planting coffee.

There was no amusement, no entertainment,
no diversion. They went out at dawn and returned at sunset. They never seemed to get
fully rested. Most of the men became thin
and gaunt, easy victims of any passing malady.

Only occasional trips to the hospital broke
the monotonous routine of labor. About once
a week some man was taken sick, frequently
with malarial fever. Sometimes he would be
returned, but often he succumbed because of
no reserve vitality to resist the onslaughts of
the fever. The men only received news from
the outside world when a man returned from
the hospital and when more laborers came
from Liberia. After a time they began to
wish for more Liberian natives to arrive or for
more comrades to go to the hospital.

Their biggest event was the monthly payday, when they were given six pesos for their

thirty days of toil. The money did not last long, but getting it was a break in the monotony. The planters furnished all facilities to regain the men's money. Workers with money were less docile and tractable than those without it.

On their first payday, the new men were surprised to see the swarm of peddlers who were permitted to haunt the sleeping quarters, selling shirts, shorts, colored handkerchiefs, cheap bracelets and candy. Many of those who had grown tired of their filthy rags bought bright, new, clean clothing sold at three and four times its worth.

Women came also, selling their wares at prices no less exorbitant. They were not clean, prepossessing girls such as the men had known at home, but at least they were women. Under their circumstances almost any woman seemed beautiful and desirable. When one has slaved under the hot sun for an entire month and tossed on one's couch in an agony of desire, thinking of one's wife or wives back home, even the most flat-chested and pimply prostitute is a relief. To hold one of these social pariahs in one's arms for only a few brief minutes seems heavenly. Between these many attractions the six pesos soon vanished.

This monthly procedure was incredibly sor-

did. The peddlers were everywhere begging
the "boys" to buy in a language they could not
understand. All too few women were permitted on the plantation for the satisfaction
of the sex-starved men. For this state of
affairs, Zo afterward learned, the overseers
were to blame. They supplied the women, and
the fewer there were the more money each
would make. Zo was tortured like the rest,
but he could not somehow bring himself to join
the queues of men awaiting their turns. His
turn, he declared, would never come if he had
to make love in such a shameful way.

He saved as much as possible of his six pesos
and hid it under his bed. He was sure he'd
need money when he ran away.

"You are a fool!" said Soki, who would not
deny the flesh regardless of the manner of
satisfying it. "You have but a short time to
live, my friend, and any woman is better than
none. You will never see that wife of yours
again. Don't you know that if you have
money around here some of these overseers
will find where you are hiding it and take it
for themselves?"

But Zo was too determined on his course
to be swayed by such arguments. The others
could make animals of themselves and stay

there perhaps to die, but he was already weary of the unremittent toil and frequent beatings to which they were subjected. His soul rebelled against this servitude. So he kept his mouth shut and increased his little horde of coins.

Although Fernando Po is a Spanish colony, English is generally spoken by its inhabitants along the coast. As he knew no language except his native Gola and a little Kpwessi, Zo decided to pick up as much English as he could. Jack, his Porto overseer, would be as good teacher as any.

Every time Jack spoke, Zo listened. In this way he learned a new word now and then. He would repeat familiar words over and over again to himself at night and during his work, until they were memorized. Soki already knew a little English and that helped immensely. Between them they assembled a workable vocabulary. It was easy to do this in their position where there were no other demands on their minds. All day long they had an overseer to think for them, which relieved them of the trouble. As long as they worked their arms and backs, their masters cared little about their minds.

About six months after their arrival, Zo met

Blackie. The latter, a Grebo lad, was working with him and many others loading a steamer with bags of cocoa beans. During their rest period, the two struck up an acquaintance and the inevitable talk about home began. This led shortly to discussion of escape. Zo had some few coins now and he knew a little English. He was ready to go at the first opportunity.

"Tell me," asked Zo, "is there really a chance of getting away from here?"

"Yes, it is possible," the other replied, his face setting grimly, "but it is very hard to do. I once escaped, and that's why I'm still here slaving away. I'm doing extra time because I had to spend a whole year in prison for my trouble. I am now making up that year. But if I see another real chance to go, I'll go quick enough."

"Tell me of your escape?" asked Zo, drawing closer. Here at last was a man who had actually tried to do what he dreamed of doing.

Blackie was paying dearly for his adventure and derived a certain satisfaction from talking about it.

"I was in the venereal ward at the hospital," he began. "They don't watch you very closely there and it looked like a good place to make a getaway. It is always full, you know, especially soon after payday, and men are being brought in or sent back to work all of the time. The night before I was to be sent back, I slipped out, stole a pair of trousers and a shirt, and got away.

"I was making for the mountains, and knowing I would need something with which to trade with the Bubis, I went by my plantation and made for the tool house. There was a strong lock on the door and I had nothing to get it open with. I could have used a stone, but I was afraid of making too much noise. After tugging for an hour trying to open the door, I had to give it up.

"Well, it was very dark, with no moon and very few stars out, but I knew where to find the trail. I had been along it many times, gathering firewood. By daybreak I was well in the big forests. It was so good to be free again, to be your own boss. Except for a few noises in the bush, I heard nothing, but I tell you it's frightening business being up there alone.

"Toward midday I began to want to eat. I managed to find some cassava, and that went very well. Then came the rain. I knew I could not stay in the forest unarmed and with-

out shelter so I began looking for a Bubi
town. They are very hard to find because the
people hide them deep in the bush. I decided
to walk up the bed of a stream, hoping it would
lead me to a town. The current was very
swift and I didn't make very much speed.

"When it began to get dark and I was about
to give up the job and make a place to sleep
for the night, I reached a little town of about
ten or twelve huts. I walked into it and was
immediately surrounded by a crowd of men
and boys. They could not speak my language
and I couldn't speak theirs. I made signs to
show that I was hungry and tried to explain
in the same way that I was not a spy sent
among them, but an escaped laborer. This is
very hard to do and I do not wonder they did
not understand. They palavered a long time
among themselves and you can imagine how
I felt, not knowing what would happen the
next minute." Zo nodded excitedly and
Blackie went on:

"Well, you know the Bubis are very suspicious. If they doubt you at all they'll not
trust you. They hate the white men and the
Portos, and they despise us for being the slaves
of the white men. They won't work for the
white man and he can't make them work for

him. I made the mistake of coming up there dressed as a Porto. Anyway, they finally gave me a little rice and let me sleep in one of the sheds. I felt lucky that they didn't kill me, although," he added, "they didn't seem a bad people—just very cautious.

"I had at least expected to be held there to work for them, but early the next morning they gave me a little cooked rice and fish in a banana leaf and two husky fellows led me back by the same trail almost to the first Spanish settlement. They stood in the trail to see that I didn't turn back."

"What did you do then?" asked Zo, completely engrossed in this story.

"Well, you can imagine I didn't plan to go back to the plantation. I hid in the bush until late at night and then going around the plantation made for the seashore to look for a small boat. If I couldn't escape to the mountains, at least I might paddle over to the Cameroons.

"I was lucky enough to find quite a large boat with oars in it, but it was chained to a small wharf. I had nothing with which to break the chain, but finally I found a sharp stone and went to work. Perhaps I made too much noise." Blackie paused, frowning meditatively, then he shrugged and said: "At any rate, just when I thought I was making good headway, two Portos grabbed me from behind, and here I am. Maybe I would have drowned out there in the sea or been carried off by the current, but at least I wouldn't be working like a slave here."

Blackie sighed wearily and looked at his toes. Out of deference for his feelings, Zo said nothing. What, indeed, was there to say to a man who had actually escaped to the mountains and almost got away by sea? But was it not possible for him to succeed where another had failed? At least he could try.

CHAPTER EIGHT

THE prisoner always has one great advantage
over his guards: he knows when he is going to
escape, and they do not. In the eyes of Jack,
his Porto overseer, Zo was a model laborer.
Not only did he do well whatever he was directed to do, but he had picked up sufficient
English to be able to understand the orders
given him. Zo seemed so tractable that no
one thought of him planning to run away. The
overseer relaxed his vigilance where Zo was
concerned, and if there was a job for just one
man to do Zo was sent unwatched to do it.

The possibility of escape seemed much
nearer when one day he was chosen to work
on one of the motor trucks as a helper. The
work was little easier than what he'd been
doing, but the chief value of the job was that
it allowed him to be in town almost every day.
His English was useful since Juan, the Porto
chauffeur, knew all of the ins and outs of Port
Clarence, San Carlos and Conception, the
three ports of Fernando Po, and also of
Basile, its tiny capital. He also knew where

cleaner women could be obtained than those
who swarmed to the plantation once a month.
Zo sought hard to become good friends with
Juan.

The chauffeur was a merry blade, almost
always half full of wine and forever talking
of comely girls with many winks of the eye
and mysterious smiles. As he talked, Zo's
woman hunger would rise. He longed for
contact with these girls of whom the chauffeur
spoke. He was afraid to ask where they could
be found: it was better to wait.

Juan was a loquacious fellow and loved to
talk of his two or three trips to the mainland.
Zo always encouraged the man to talk, for
was he not planning to go that way some day?
As the truck bowled along the smooth road-
way, the reckless Juan, driving with one hand
and gesticulating with the other, would paint
glowing pictures of the good times to be had
in Duala, Old Calabar, Lagos and Accra. A
few dollars would take one across the way to
Duala, while only a few more would take one
to the incomparable Lagos and Accra. If the
traveler wasn't particular where he slept, it
was possible to go on most any ship.

This information led Zo to an orgy of
speculation. Was it not probable, he argued,

that the others had gone about escaping from Fernando Po in the wrong way? Why risk one's life in a little boat when there were big steamers leaving all of the time?

He discussed the matter with Soki every night. While the latter was ready to attempt a getaway in a small boat, he saw no chance of getting aboard a steamer.

"Where will you get clothes?" he objected. "And where will you get the papers? You know you must have papers or they won't let you aboard, even if you get by the Portos. These people are not fools. They know how to keep you here."

"It is not hard to hide on one of the steamers," answered Zo. "You know that as well as I do. Then, when the boat is well away, we could come from our hiding places and offer to pay our fare. It will be easy, I tell you."

"But if you are caught," Soki warned, "remember it means one or two years longer here. Only one more year here and you'll be free."

"One more year?" said Zo bitterly. "Why, we may all be dead in another year. Every week one of our friends goes to the hospital and we see him no more. Do you want to wait for that? Then think of our comrades who sit and sleep all of the time and finally die.

Shall we go back to Monrovia in that condition, as many others have gone? No, Soki, it is better that we get away as soon as possible."

"Well," said the other man, half agreeing, "I'll think about it. But I still believe it's going to be very risky. I am not anxious to stay here any more than you are, but I want to know that at least I have an even chance of getting away."

"This is an even chance," Zo insisted, "and remember I have some money."

Juan very early learned that Zo had a little money and frequently hinted to him to buy a small bottle of wine. The chauffeur loved his wine, and Zo thought it was good policy to spend a few centavos occasionally in that way, thus cementing their friendship. Since he wanted certain favors, he felt called upon to grant certain favors.

Moreover, he had come to like Juan quite a bit. Before the trouble at Takama, Zo had been a gay lad, much given to laughter and good times. Juan was the jovial type of person he liked, and he imagined that if he were free the two might enjoy themselves in the cafés and less public places of the little ports. Even so there were brief periods during their frequent visits to these towns when Zo almost forgot his position.

At last, one day when they had finished their work sooner than usual, Juan took Zo to see Marie. She lived in a charming little house and was entirely different from any woman Zo·had ever seen. And of course he had not seen many. She was light yellow in color, had cascades of curly black hair that fell to her waist, was over medium height, well rounded and extremely voluptuous. Her every movement aroused the senses, whether she reclined gracefully on a couch, was leaning against a door frame or swinging lightly down one of the dusty streets. When she was animated, her large black eyes sparkled brightly, like jewels in a Hindu temple.

Juan drank and drank, with Zo doing the buying, until he finally dropped off to sleep. Zo had been too long without a woman to succumb to wine when at last he was alone with one who was not only clean and comely, but strikingly different. Desire blazed in his veins. For the time being he forgot his wrongs, his common sense, everything but the woman before him.

There is a certain affinity between individuals of opposite colors. The fascination of the unknown is so alluring that mutual stimulation is inevitable. Zo was black and Marie was almost white, there was plenty of wine in the house, and the unsophisticated Gola lad suggested that he had some money left to buy more. Marie laughed encouragingly, showing her sharp little white teeth and nodding her mass of ebony curls.

Inexperienced with any women except his own and totally ignorant of the routine with which sex must be approached among civilized people, Zo felt awkward, and was slow to avail himself of opportunities offered. He was rather uncertain how his overtures might be received, and not at all aware of the true relations between Juan and Marie.

The girl was without moral inhibitions. A female of easy virtue, she had been on her own since adolescence and had not done at all badly. She owned her little cottage, purchased with the assistance of many overseers and petty officials, while her reputation as a charming hostess was even known to certain wealthy planters. Her particular weakness was for strong black men, especially when they shyly admitted they had money.

"Marie sorry you mus' work so hard," she

said, placing her plump yellow hand on his shoulder.

"I no work hard now," Zo replied in his meagre English, drawing away a little.

"But you are so strong!" she exclaimed, feeling of his arms. "Such muscle! I bet you squeeze a poor girl like me to death. Come, put your han' aroun' me and let us see."

Zo did as he was told but, for all his desire, did so rather gingerly. She threw her plump, warm arm about his neck and drew him to her. His wide nostrils caught the odor of her cheap, exotic perfume and his head swam. Marie rose hastily and poured more wine. Juan slept on.

As usual with unsophisticated young men, Zo began to paint rosy pictures of future visits at Marie's. He found her hospitality to be even greater than he had anticipated and he was delighted. It did not occur to him at the time that Marie's favors might prove a little too costly. Wine and sex have a way of making such considerations seem unimportant and inconsequential.

When Juan sobered up late that afternoon, the other two understood each other very well and Zo was minus a month's precious pay.

But he did not care. For the first time since
the day of his marriage celebration, he was
lighthearted and carefree. When he and Juan
drove away from the little house, Zo carefully
noted its location. En route to the plantation
he was smiling but silent, and unmindful of
the continuous flow of talk from the loose-
tongued chauffeur. He could not speak to
Juan of the experience which loomed so great
in his eyes, for he could not yet be sure what
were the exact relations between the chauffeur
and Marie. Nor did it seem quite right to ask,
under the circumstances.

That night, when the tired men fell into
their mean beds after the usual monotonous
meal, Zo could remain quiet no longer, but in
undertone, with poorly concealed enthusiasm
poured out the rich experience of the day to
Soki.

"Fool!" hissed Soki. "Now you will spend
your money and .forget all of your fine plans
for escape to the mainland. Always some
woman is spoiling men's plans!"

"But don't you see that she will be a help
to me?" Zo pleaded.

"How?" asked the other, sneeringly. "By
taking all of your money?"

"I cannot buy the paper and clothes I need to go aboard the steamer, can I?" Zo queried, defensively. "Well, she can."

"It looks bad to me," his comrade grumbled. "No good ever comes from mixing women up with things like this. It has always been so; it will be so in this case."

As a matter of fact, Zo's plan to get the assistance of Marie in his proposed effort to escape was an afterthought designed to deceive Soki, but he had spoken too enthusiastically to fool his friend. Soki knew that neither escape or anything else except pleasures of the flesh had been in Zo's mind that afternoon. Zo knew this too.

When the truck again had to go to town two days later, Juan casually suggested that they stop for a while at Marie's after finishing their errand. Zo was delighted at the thought, and showed it by a display of his white teeth. In the hope that they might again visit the pretty little house in the lane, he had brought along five or six of his hard-earned pesos to purchase wine and other things. He had excused this proposed expenditure which he could ill afford on the ground that it was a part of his elaborate plan of escape. He had hoarded his money for many months, depriving himself of the very sorry but much needed pleasure that all of the men more or less enjoyed for a few brief minutes one day a month. The demands of a healthy body could no longer be denied in the face of such an attractive opportunity.

The events of the afternoon differed not at all from those of the first visit. After several glasses of wine, the chauffeur went obligingly to sleep. Marie was quite as hospitable as before. Engrossed in this transient affair, Zo did not see Juan occasionally open one eye and then slowly close it again. On the way back to the plantation Zo was bubbling over with enthusiasm as on the previous afternoon.

Although he knew Soki would reprimand him for spending another month's pay, Zo could not keep from relating the incidents of the afternoon in very graphic detail to Soki. It is practically impossible for any human being, male or female, to keep a sex secret. Men, particularly, seem miserable if they cannot boast of what they call their conquests. To this universal rule African men are no exception.

"I said the other night that you were a fool," Soki remarked wearily, "but you are young and that is to be expected. It takes experience to make a man wise. When you have grown older and seen more of life, you will know that all women are alike and that all of them are a great trouble."

"You are wrong, Soki," Zo objected strenuously. "Marie has promised to get the clothes and ticket for me the next time I come to town and bring the money. She is very anxious to help me get away."

"What!" shouted Soki, half rising from his bunk. "Did you tell her of your plan? Why, you're even a bigger fool than I thought you were!"

"Well, how could I keep from telling her if I wanted her help?" asked Zo, again on the defensive. "You admit we cannot go to the mountains, while it is too dangerous by sea, so what else is there to do except try my plan?"

"All right," was Soki's reply, "but remember what I told you about women."

In most matters Zo had great respect for Soki's judgment, but in this instance he felt sure that his friend was wrong. He was confident that Marie would do as she promised, and he did not believe that Juan would be too inquisitive.

On the next trip to town Zo could hardly unload the coffee beans from the truck fast enough and reload it with merchandise for the plantation. When they were about ready to drive back, Zo hinted to Juan that a little wine might go down very well. He was afraid Juan might not otherwise stop at Marie's that afternoon. He was very anxious that they should, because he had heard that an American passenger freighter was expected in port in two days. Normally he would have waited for Juan to suggest visiting Marie, but today he was too eager to wait. The jovial Porto readily agreed, and the big truck was swung into a side street and thence to the little house in the lane.

Zo was more excited than he had been since leaving Monrovia. Today he was carrying out the first step of his plan. His pocket was bulging with a handkerchief full of pesos. He had in all the equivalent of eighteen dollars. With this Marie was to purchase passage to Duala, a cheap khaki coat and a pair of trousers, an old hat and a pair of old shoes from one of the greasy Syrian merchants.

"Oooh!" cried Marie, when they entered, "I am so glad you have come back to my house. I am ver' pleased to see you."

She appeared as delighted to see them as if
they had been away for several months. That
was Marie's way.

"Let's have a bottle of that wine, Marie,"
Juan ordered, flopping down on a couch.

"Yes, some wine," Zo echoed, attempting to
effect the nonchalance of the gay and careless
chauffeur.

He really felt expansive and lordly himself, today. There was little chance that his
project would be dogged by failure. In a
short time now he would be away from all of
this. In a week, perhaps, he would be walking
the streets of Duala.

While Marie was getting the big straw-
covered demijohn of wine and pouring its
blood-red contents into three large glasses, Zo
was sitting back on the cushions of the couch,
dreaming of the future freedom. There he
was in Duala. He was well dressed and had
five or six of the Spanish coins in his pocket.
A rich white man saw and called him. He
asked Zo if he wanted a job. Zo said he did.
The man gave him a job as clerk in his big
general store. Zo worked there for many
months and saved his money. Then one day
he went to his employer and declared he was
anxious to go back to Liberia and get his wife,

Pameta, and bring her back with him. The rich white man nodded his approval and gave him some money to help pay his passage on the next steamer. Then after a pleasant voyage, he landed at Monrovia, went to the President of Liberia, complaining against District Commissioner Jackson. The latter was forced to give up the girl and together Zo and Pameta returned to Duala, where they lived in a pretty little house in a garden at the end of a lane and had many fine children.

"Here's to the women!" Juan toasted, interrupting Zo's daydream.

Zo started, smiled sheepishly and reached for his glass. Marie sat close beside him, he could feel the warmth of her body, and his heart leaped with anticipation.

Juan seemed to be able to keep his head better today than on the two previous occasions, though he drank oftener than the other two. Time passed, another bottle of wine was bought by Zo, and Juan drank most of it. He still showed no inclination to slumber. Zo began to grow nervous. He could not give Marie the money while Juan was awake and looking on, because he did not even now know exactly what were the relations between the swarthy chauffeur and the girl, nor did he

want the former to know that he had accumulated such an unprecedented sum of money
for a plantation laborer. Between women and
the hucksters, the overwhelming majority of
the boys were rid of their six pesos shortly
after they received them on their monthly
payday.

It was not until Zo had paid for the third
bottle of wine and it was half consumed that
Juan rose lazily, put on his khaki-colored sun
helmet, and obligingly announced, "I go down
the street for one minute, maybe little longer.
Zo, you wait here for me. Don't go outside.
Policeman get you and then there be plenty
trouble."

Juan had scarcely departed and Zo had
hardly emitted a sigh of relief before Marie's
plump arm circled the lad's neck and her lips
found his. It was a strange new sensation
to Zo—this kissing, but he liked it immensely.
Marie enjoyed his inexperience and taught
him this Occidental art of love with gusto.

Time was short. Juan would soon be back.
So, reaching into his pocket, Zo pulled out the
money-laden handkerchief and handed its contents gratefully to Marie. She had said she
would help him and he believed it more now
than before. One had to trust someone, he

argued to himself . . . and, well, Marie was so nice.

Juan soon came hustling back, announcing that they must return to the plantation at once.   The truck bumped out of the lane and onto the high road.   All of the way back Juan talked volubly of everything under the sun except Marie, while he steered with one hand and gesticulated with the other. The fact that he seldom mentioned the girl led Zo to believe that he was not intimate with her, and somehow this thought made the Gola lad feel a little happy. He caught himself thinking of her warm arms, her almost-white skin, her big, sparkling black eyes and wavy black hair.   Then he recalled with a feeling of guilt that Pameta was his wife.

He said nothing that night to Soki of the afternoon's experience because he knew what Soki's reply would be. No, he would wait until he had obtained the clothes and ticket before boasting of the progress of his plan. So he talked of many other things.   And Soki, being wise, did not mention the subject which he knew was uppermost in his friend's mind.

The next morning at sunrise the men filed

out of the warehouse as usual to go to their
daily tasks. Zo lined up with them as a matter of form. The stout mulatto overseer came
down the line, assigning the men to various
gangs. When he came to Zo, he picked him
out for the road gang.

"Pardon, massah," Zo objected, "but I work
on truck."

"Shut up!" growled the Porto. "You go
where I send you or you get the whip."

He passed on, shooting a wicked side glance
at the surprised Gola lad. The other men
laughed at his change of fortune. Misery
loves company. Those who are down rejoice
when another is thrust to their level. Although
Zo's work on the truck had been arduous, he
had aroused the jealousy of the others by
being able to ride to town every day or so.

All that day Zo worked mechanically, much
bewildered by the turn of events, quite dazed
by disappointment. A score of questions
kept flashing around in his head. Why had
he been taken off the truck? What had they
discovered? Why hadn't Juan asked to be
given him back? How now would he get his
clothes and ticket from Marie? How would
he get to the steamer that left tomorrow?

When the gang was being marched back to
the warehouse by Jack, Zo's former overseer,
the lad desperately asked why he had been
taken off the truck.

"Juan, he say you no good," explained the
Porto, "so Carlos he give him another man.
He say you run off to woman alla time. Now
you take rest on road." The man laughed
aloud at his jest.

The truth dawned upon Zo with blinding
suddenness. He felt furious, then desperate,
then discouraged, in turn. He had only six
pesos left. With all of his deprivation, he had
little more than the others who had taken their
six pesos each month and invested it in the
cult of Venus.

After eating, he told his sad story to Soki
and Big Georgie, the Bassa man. The latter
shouted with laughter when he heard the tale,
until the tears ran down his rusty black
cheeks. It was some time before he was able
to explain his great levity.

"That is an old trick," he said. "Two or
three boys have been fooled that way since
I've been here. You see, that girl Marie is
one of his women. . . . They will drink much
wine with your pesos, Zo."

Georgie got up off Soki's bed and started

around the warehouse to tell what he had heard. Eager for news, the men gathered around him, laughing in a chorus at the story. Zo was furious at what he considered Georgie's unethical conduct. He had expected the Bassa man to keep the news to himself, not realizing that he was asking altogether too much. He turned to Soki for sympathy, but his friend, disgusted by the gullibility he had displayed, turned on his side, grumbling, "I said you were a fool."

The hours, days and weeks rolled on monotonously as before and the rainy season came again. The overseers watched Zo more closely, and several times they searched his bunk for money, but found none. Zo was through being thrifty. He spent his six pesos with the rest on the one day in the month when they could forget for a few minutes that they were slaves.

"You might as well wait now until your time is up," Soki had advised soon after the unfortunate incident with Marie and Juan, when Zo had again broached the subject of escape. "A few moons now and you'll be back in Liberia. Why take a chance and get caught?"

Zo agreed this was the counsel of reason. Even though he had failed in his plan, he derived some slight comfort from the belief that he had dared more than any of his fellow laborers. He had at least tried to get away.

A new group of laborers came to Fernando Po from Liberia. Most of them were Kpwessis. There was the usual exchange of news and advice. Zo and Soki joined the others who surrounded the group that evening to hear what was going on back home. A big, wide-eyed fellow with very mobile face acted as spokesman for the others.

"Before, when you men came," he said, "the Liberian bosses stole the boys to send here or they fooled them into coming. Now there is no longer any pretense, and the country people are in terror. Soldiers come and ask for so many men and the chiefs have to give them whether they want to or not.

"We were sitting around the palaver kitchen in my village one afternoon when the soldiers came. The officer got out of his hammock and called for the chief. When the chief had come, the officer said, 'I want twenty men from this town for Fernando Po.' Just like that. The chief called our people together and the officer picked out twenty of the strongest young men. Their wives wailed, but it did no good. It was a very sad time, I tell you.

"When we were lined up, the chief was told to give us food to eat on the trail to Monrovia. So we each had to carry a kainji of rice and when we got to Monrovia the rice was taken from us. On the trail the villages had to feed us.

"Many of the people are going into the bush and building new towns where the Liberians can't find them. Those who do not run away have to pay taxes on the huts left vacant or the soldiers are sent to punish them. Such is the condition." The recital ended, and the others shook their heads sadly.

More than a third of the newcomers showed the marks of the lash on their backs and legs, many yet entirely unhealed. The sight of these scars and the memory of the past aroused by the tale of the Kpwessi man depressed his hearers and a deep silence hung over the stuffy warehouse. What were they to do about it? Once, long ago, before the coming of their supposedly civilized rulers, they had been a happy and carefree people. Today they were only slaves to be worked and whipped, who welcomed death when it came.

The recent arrivals were soon adjusted to the routine of the plantation and things settled down to their usual tempo. Day followed day in customary succession. Coffee bushes and cocoa trees were planted and harvested, firewood in huge quantities was cut, roads were built and repaired, ships were loaded and unloaded. Rain or shine, the work went on. Those who were slow, awkward or balky, received several lashes administered with a big black whip by the corpulent mulatto head overseer. Those who fought back against the system were jailed for periods of a few months or a year. Relentlessly the system ground out gold for its beneficiaries. Coffee and cocoa flowed to the markets of the world to grace civilized breakfast tables. The fate of those who toiled in the burning sun or driving rain was a very minor consideration to the Spanish planters, while the civilized world had never even heard of Fernando Po.

The monotony and insufficient quantity of the food, coupled with the fact that it was not altogether nourishing, lessened their resistance to disease. Of fresh vegetables they had none, and the same was true of fruit. Their sole beverage aside from water was coffee, often without sugar, and never with milk or cream. There was consequently a fairly large representation from the farm in the hospital. They went away, many of them, never to return, and none was paid for the days spent in the sickroom.

One morning, shortly before Big Georgie's time was to expire, he failed to get up with the others at dawn. Big Carlos, the head overseer, trembling with rage, went to the man's bunk to see what was the matter. Big Carlos was held responsible for the progress of the work on the plantation and he became infuriated when any worker was unable to report in the mornings.

"Geet up!" he shouted, kicking the form wrapped tightly in a blanket. "Geet up from there!"

"Georgie no can come, massah," said the Bassa man, his teeth clicking like castanets and his whole body shaking. "I sick."

Carlos snatched the blanket off the man and saw for himself that Georgie had the fever. He cursed the laborer and stamped irritably out of the warehouse. The men stood around, awaiting their assignment to gangs; wondering what was the matter with Georgie, the jester of the company. In a minute the head overseer returned with a bottle of quinine tablets and went inside to Georgie's bunk.

The low coastal plain circling the island of Fernando Po is overhung, night and morning, with a miasmic mist. Mosquitoes swarm there, and the shadow of death lies over the place. Up higher, along the face of the mountains, it is cooler and more healthful, but the plantations are not on the mountains.

When some of the men returned for the midday rest, Georgie was wet with perspiration, his heart was beating fast and he could scarcely raise his aching head from the crude pillow. He looked hopelessly at the ring of workers about his bunk, and his usually heavy voice was now just a mechanical whisper. They gave him a bit of rice, which was all they had to eat, and when he had finished they gave him more quinine, as the head overseer had directed.

At night, when the gangs returned, it was raining heavily and the temperature was low. All were eager to find out about Big Georgie. When they rushed into their quarters the Bassa man was gone. The place seemed different without him, for he had helped somewhat to ease the hardship of their service with

his infectious good humor. Now he had followed the others to the hospital from which
so many never returned.

Fever and disease were taking a heavy toll.
Rain fell in torrents, and when it ceased for
short periods, mosquitoes and tsetse flies bred
in countless stagnant pools and swarmed over
the lowlands. Zo congratulated himself that
so far he had escaped. He felt almost immune, now that he had gone so long without
any illness worse than indigestion. Soki, too,
had escaped, but he expressed the fear that,
with others going so rapidly, he could not be
sure of seeing Liberia again.

They were both working on the road gang
one afternoon when Zo suddenly noticed with
alarm that he was not perspiring. Never had
that happened before. Not to perspire in the
tropics is as strange as perspiring in the frigid
zone. He felt tired, but he worked harder,
thinking to bring forth the sweat. He was
rewarded for his effort with gooseflesh covering his entire body. He knew now that it was
fever.

Upon his return from work, he reported to
Big Carlos and was given two large quinine
pills. After eating he took them and, wrapping up in his blanket, perspired profusely for

several hours. That night it rained hard and at dawn it was very cool. The chill came, and shook him violently. Big Carlos gave him two more pills. Again the sweat dampened the blankets, but an hour afterward the chill returned, shaking him vigorously, straining his muscles and causing pains in his chest. Then chill and fever followed each other regularly.

At noon, when the Spanish doctor came and looked at him, Zo could not lift his aching head from the pillow; indeed, he could scarcely think, for the pains darted through and through his brain. The doctor ordered him put in a truck and taken to the hospital, and two orderlies lifted him up roughly and carried him out.

It was the finest place he had ever slept in, that hospital, but it was far from being the sort of place it should have been. Sitting high on the side of a mountain, surrounded by shade trees and clipped lawns, the cement building was devoid of all equipment except the most essential, and that was not modern. The sick men were all in one big ward, over which calloused Porto orderlies ruled with an iron hand. It was only superficially clean, and the one physician handled all cases, whatever they might be.

But to Zo, coming from that plantation warehouse, the hospital seemed palatial. He was given pajamas and placed in an iron bed which had springs and a mattress. He did not know how many countless sufferers from all maladies had slept on that mattress, which had never been fumigated, or between the sheets, which had not been changed. However, the windows were screened and one could look out of them over the great plantations, to the blue sea and the mainland in the distance.

The ride to the hospital had shaken Zo up some and he had a feeling of nausea at the pit of his stomach. This soon changed to a chill that shook him like a leaf in the breeze, and then he fell into a deep sleep, awakening to find himself wet with perspiration and suffering from a terrific headache.

As a general thing the adult West Coast Africans are immune from malaria, having usually contracted it in childhood, but these undernourished laborers, with their weakened resistance, took longer than the usual three or four days to recover, if they recovered at all.

Not far from Zo was the bed of Big Georgie, and the next morning, after the convalescent patients had cleaned the ward under the direction of the orderlies, he dragged himself

over to the bed of the Bassa man to see how
he was getting along.

Georgie looked up at him almost unknow-
ing, then nodded his head slowly in recognition.
His appearance was startling. The eyes were
congested or ferrety, the nostrils and lips very
red, the tongue scarlet. Zo placed his hand
on the man's forehead and found it almost
like fire.

"So sick! So sick!" Georgie kept whispering
mechanically.

"You'll be all right pretty soon, Georgie,"
Zo lied, for he had a feeling that the warehouse
jester had seen the last of his companions in
slavery.

"Get back to your bed!" yelled an orderly,
entering the ward, and Zo dragged himself
to his place. He felt that he also might never
see home again.

That evening just before supper he again
stole to Georgie's bed. The man's skin was
almost ice cold and of a yellowish tint, perhaps more green than yellow. Georgie could
not speak. He was vomiting effortlessly, like
an infant, and the fluid was black against the
whiteness of the basin he held in his unsteady
hands. He looked at Zo appealingly, hopelessly. Zo turned and went back to his bed

unable to stand the sight any longer. Late that night he saw them carrying the limp form of Georgie out of the ward. In the morning he asked the orderly of what disease his jovial friend had died and the man replied, "Yellow fever."

Only a short while before Big Georgie was the life of the warehouse; a few days more and he would have been on his way back to his native forests to boast to country folk of his experiences on the dread island; back to his hut, his wives and his children. Now he was dead.

In the ward were three or four men suffering from a disease which Zo learned from the orderly was called elephantiasis. One of the men whose bed was across from him had an enormously swollen lower leg. The flesh was hard and firm to the touch while the skin was roughened with a network of dilated lymphatics. Here and there on the surface vesicles had formed, some of which were always breaking and discharging a chylelike fluid.

Another of these men had a scrotum swollen to huge size and hard as a gourd. The skin was coarse and wartlike and covered with revolting ulcers. When the man lifted his sheet one day and displayed himself to Zo, the latter shuddered at the sight.

The other two men with enormously swollen feet and lower legs were in the final stages of the disease. All day they remained silent as though sleeping, occasionally drooling watery liquid from the corners of their mouths.

"They won't be here long," the orderly confided to Zo.

Zo felt it would be a blessing for such horribly afflicted ones to die. There were times when even he courted death, that solver of all earthly problems; the Great Emancipator that frees the body of all disease and the spirit of all desire.

Many of the laborers paid dearly for their one day of pleasure a month. Almost all of the women who were permitted to come to the plantations on payday were dangerously infected with venereal disease. As a consequence, there was always a stream of men going to the hospital for treatment. They occupied one end of the ward. The Porto orderlies were less kind to them than to the other patients, often making them wait hours for a drink of water.

Some of these unfortunates had their faces and arms covered with scaly, pimply or pustular skin eruptions. Others had horrible ulcerations on their lips and tongues. In one case, in a far corner, the disease had gone to the victim's brain and he gabbled and drooled like an idiot.

On the other side of Zo, propped resignedly on a pillow, was a man suffering from the yaws. Being so close at hand, Zo was able to see the inroads the contagious tropical disease had made. At intervals, all over the visible parts of the man's body, there were eruptions the size of a sixpence or a shilling. Sometimes these pustules broke and exuded a thick, smelly fluid that dried whitish on top of the sore and formed as a yellowish-brown crust around the base. The hairs protruding from the yaws were whitish. In some places between the larger eruptions appeared small pimples with whitish tops.

Zo had never seen so much revolting disease. In Takama the people had been unusually healthy; here it seemed that everyone was destined to catch something. It was most depressing. He began to long to get back to the plantation. There one did not at least see the terrible misery of the victims of an iniquitous system. There one could breathe the clean fresh air instead of the obnoxious odors of the sickroom. There one felt optimistic about completing one's service; here one grew pessimistic and hopeless.

The hospital had at least one redeeming feature: it was an excellent place to exchange news and gossip. There were laborers from many different plantations and they talked for hours about their overseers, their food and their work. Those who were under unusually cruel overseers actually boasted of the fact, relating with a certain gusto the number of times a week men were whipped and showing with pride the scars of their own beatings, like veterans of the war displaying their wounds.

At last Zo's fever abated, the chills ceased and the nauseous feeling left the pit of his stomach. The terrific headache stopped and no longer was he unable to raise his head from the pillow upon waking. He still felt a bit weak, but the doctor decreed that he should be returned to his plantation.

The plantation seemed almost like home after the hospital. There were many old friends and the best friend of all, Soki. They gathered about him that night and listened to the latest news. All of them had friends and acquaintances on other plantations and were anxious to know how they were getting along.

Finally Zo and Soki were alone, side by side.

"I missed you very much," said Soki, placing his hand on his friend's shoulder. "It didn't seem the same around here."

"And I missed you, too," said Zo. "It is a terrible place—that hospital. It makes you feel you will never see home again."

"Well, it won't be long before we'll see home now," declared Soki. "The next boat will take us away from Fernando Po."

"And how glad I'll be to get away, too," Zo replied. "How long the time has been! . . . What do you plan to do when you get back to Liberia, Soki?"

"I'll stop right in Monrovia," said Soki, "and get work with some of the white people. They always pay you your money without palaver."

"Won't you go back to your village at all?" asked Zo.

"No," the other replied, "Monrovia is the best place. They treat you better there. No raids. No taxes. No beatings. Plenty of money. The people there dance every night the moon shines. Ah, yes, it is much better to live in Monrovia than in the back country."

"But suppose you can get no work?" Zo persisted. "Then what will you do? In the village there is always plenty for everyone; in Monrovia would you not starve if you found no work?"

"Oh, but you haven't had a chance to really see Monrovia and live there," said Soki. "A smart man can always make money there. And you have better things to eat, too; fine things from across the water in cans already cooked. You can also get better clothes than in the village. Then think of the women—women from every tribe, and you don't have to buy them either! Ah, Monrovia is the best place, I tell you."

"Yes," Zo contended, "but the women in Monrovia, are they not sick like these here? Will you not have to go to the doctor after being with them? In the villages the women are clean and healthy. I think the village is the best place to be happy."

"And have the soldiers come there and take your women, your food and your wine," added Soki, "and you are unable to do anything about it. You go back to the village, but I intend to stay in town."

While Zo argued in favor of the village, he was intrigued by the picture of Monrovia

drawn by Soki. He had all of the country
boy's desire to experience the pleasures offered
by the city, even a straggling, unkempt little
town like Monrovia with its rocky, trash-ridden
streets and lanes. He decided to himself that
even though he was going up country to hunt
for Pameta, he would tarry in Monrovia long
enough to see something of life there.

And so, the final day of service arrived; the
day for which they had been patiently waiting
for two years. Tomorrow the little steamer
would nose into port and the remnants of another batch of laborers would start back to
their native land.

The work seemed easier that day than ever
before. They chatted light-heartedly as they
carried firewood to the cocoa kitchens. As the
end of the day neared, the men somewhat
slackened their pace, loitering along, talking
about home. Soki was especially voluble as
he described the high times he would have
when at last they were paid off in Monrovia.
He felt he was as good as home already. The
sun was slowly setting, a great burnished plate
about to dip into the watery horizon.

Suddenly he was pushed violently from behind and fell sprawling to the ground. He
scrambled to his feet and turned to face Big

Carlos, the head overseer. A stream of vile language flowed from that worthy's lips.

"Whatsa matter you no do you work?" shouted the Porto. "You drag along drag along alla da time. What you t'ink dis is, eh? Come on, come on, pick up de stick and hurry up, you swine!"

Soki had for two years endured such treatment from Big Carlos and others, always maintaining an excellent reserve, always keeping his temper, always remembering that the quickest way to get free was to take everything and say nothing. He knew as did the others that it was part of the plan of their masters to jail as many laborers as possible and thus keep them for longer periods, during which time the men received not even the usual six pesos a month.

But today, for some unaccountable reason, Soki could not contain himself. Perhaps it was because this was his last day—almost the last hour of the last day. The accumulated and suppressed rage and resentment of two years rushed to his head and with his black face contorted with anger, he turned upon the fat overseer with bared teeth and both fists raised. From a little way off the others in the gang watched the scene apprehensively, fearfully.

Big Carlos jumped back in surprise at this show of temper. His hand went to his pistol holster and the heavy automatic flashed in the fading sunlight. Soki, a horrified expression supplanting his look of rage, shrank back. The head overseer, chuckling now with satisfaction, returned the pistol to his holster and turning on his heel walked away, saying a word to the gang overseer in passing. He could have killed Soki with no fear of punishment for the crime, but he had other plans.

The gang glumly finished its work and was marched back to the warehouse. Each man felt that the last had not been heard of the unfortunate incident. Soki cursed himself for having been so foolish on his last day. Anything might happen now. He knew Big Carlos and was accordingly disturbed.

"Oh, what a fool I was!" he exclaimed to Zo. "But I couldn't help myself. For two years I have been kicked and pushed around by these people and held back my temper. This afternoon I went wild."

"It is too bad," Zo remarked sympathetically. "I wonder what Big Carlos will do. He is a hard, cruel man, you know. I fear him more than the others."

"Well," said Soki in a tone of resignation, "we'll know very soon."

Morning came with the mighty chorus of birds to greet the rising sun. Zo, Soki and three others—all that remained of the original ten—were taken to the ship on a truckload of bags of coffee and cocoa beans. Zo noted that Juan of unpleasant memory was driving, but he felt little animosity toward the Porto this morning. He was willing to let the dead past bury its dead.

Long before they arrived they could see the small steamer that was to carry them back to Liberia. The sight increased their joy. Very soon, now, they would be aboard her, looking back at Fernando Po for the first time.

"We are almost away, my friend," said Zo to Soki. "It looks as if Big Carlos decided to do nothing. After all, you did not strike him."

"I'll feel better when I get aboard the boat," Soki declared.

Under the same long open shed where they had first been examined upon arrival, all those who were returning to Liberia were assembled. Zo counted nineteen in all. There had been forty in the beginning. The remainder were in the hospital, in prison or dead. Only one of the original Boloba villagers was present. His hand was swollen enormously from elephantiasis, his head hung down between his shoulders and his eyes were half closed.

Off to one side stood two mulatto policemen. It seemed that they were awaiting someone. Sure enough, after an hour under the shed, Mr. Simmons, the Liberian consul, immaculate in white suit, shoes and helmet, came sauntering up with his clerk bearing a large book.

The consul was unusually courteous this morning. He told the men in Kpwessi of the many changes he was bringing about in housing and feeding of plantation laborers and that in the future work would not be so difficult. Then, very persuasively, he sought to interest them in signing up for another period of service. Times were very hard in Liberia, he said, and it was most difficult to get food there now, but in Fernando Po there was plenty for all. Those on their second period of service would be treated much better than those on their first, he insisted. They would not have to live in the warehouses but would be permitted to live in their own hut with a woman. All of the best jobs, he went on, would be given to second termers.

The men listened stolidly. The policemen lazed to one side. Mr. Simmons rambled on. The sun rose higher. The consul got no response to his appeal. The men had long memories and were not to be taken in by such talk. The urge to get away from this island prison was too strong in them to be dissuaded by a representative of a class for whom they felt nothing but hatred. So they completely ignored Mr. Simmons and began talking among themselves. Finally he departed with his clerk down the narrow, dusty street.

He had scarcely turned the corner when an automobile bearing Señor Alicante, the owner of the plantation where Zo and Soki had slaved, drove up. In the car with him was Big Carlos. The two jumped out and approached the departing group.

Señor Alicante motioned to one of the policemen who came hastily to his side. The three now approached the group. Both Zo and Soki felt apprehensive. What was going to be done now?

"Take that man!" ordered Big Carlos, pointing to Soki. "Take him to the prison. He attacked me yesterday."

Señor Alicante nodded his approval and the policeman pulled Soki from the group and marched him away. Zo and the others were stunned into silence. The Spaniard and his overseer got into the automobile and drove away. It had all happened so suddenly that even now they could hardly realize that Soki was gone.

"What will they do to him?" Zo asked the remaining policeman.

"It is a serious offense, assaulting an overseer," said the officer. "He will surely get a year."

"But he didn't strike Big Carlos," said Zo.

"Do you want to stay and testify?" asked the policeman in a syrupy tone, thrusting his face nearer. "Do any of you want to stay and help out your friend at his trial?"

Even Zo was not prepared to do that. No one answered the policeman. All of them instinctively sensed a trick to keep them on the island. Their time was up and they wanted to go. Even their regard for Soki could not persuade them to speak in his behalf at this hour.

A swarthy official now came and, calling their names off a list, lined them up and marched them aboard the ship. Not until the vessel had left the harbor and turned northward did they actually feel free. Their two years in Fernando Po had been a nightmare and as the distance between them, and their erstwhile green prison increased they felt safer and grew gayer. Only Zo was sad. He had lost his best friend.

CHAPTER NINE

PAMETA stood on the third floor balcony of
David Jackson's big new town house gazing
absently into the sun-scorched street below.
She was a much more mature girl than the
Pameta who had been kidnapped from Takama over two years before. The lines of char-
acter were stronger in her face and in the
depths of her eyes there was greater determination.

Forced now for these two years to live as
the favorite supplementary wife of the District Commissioner, something within her, a
sort of magnificent stubbornness, had prevented her from submitting resignedly and
without a struggle to the murderer of her
father. Her people, she knew, thought her
dead, and she never expected to see Zo, her
husband, again. Both Jackson and his man
Joe had told her of his exportation to Fernando Po, but although she thus felt alone in
the world, she would not gracefully accept the
situation as it was. With time her hatred of

Jackson had grown instead of abating and she made no effort to conceal her feelings.

This attitude had merely made the Commissioner want her more. As most of his native women listlessly accepted his attentions, it was something of a treat to have at least one concubine that fought him off on every occasion. He had sought to seduce her with pretty headkerchiefs, bracelets and attractive dresses only to be thrown into a fury by her continued indifference. In Sadistic moods, he had sometimes whipped her or twisted her slender wrists until she was forced to submit. But she never did so willingly. She remained the same Pameta so far as he was concerned, persistently insisting that she be returned to her home and people.

Twice during her captivity Pameta had run away, only to be pursued, captured and ignominiously dragged back to her sneering master. Now she was in Monrovia enjoying a greater freedom of movement than she had previously. She was pleased with the life of the city. People were always passing back and forth. Occasionally she had a word with one of her fellow tribesmen. From the top balcony of the mansion one could look far out to sea or across the level coastal plain to the distant hills.

Sometimes she was permitted to go to the market down on the water front, mingle with the crowd of nondescript natives and pretend for a few minutes that she was free. She found Monrovia much more to her liking than the forced isolation of Boloba where, because of the closeness of Takama, she was watched more jealously. She had found little to divert her in the long journeys made with Jackson, swinging back and forth in the big hammock that had been Gonda's.

Poor Gonda! Once so strong, pretty and coquettish, she was gone now and, perhaps, forgotten by her former master. A year before she had shown alarming symptoms of a loathsome social disease. It had grown rapidly worse and, lodging in her brain, had made her a hopeless idiot. Jackson, who had enjoyed her body, and was perhaps responsible for her condition, had turned her over to a native witch doctor. The latter's potions had proved too powerful and Gonda now occupied some nameless grave in the hinterland.

Pameta often wondered if she would suffer the same fate. She no longer gloried in her former good health. Her skin was pimply with here and there a small sore and her joints frequently ached with rheumatism, especially

during the rainy season. Often severe pains in
the small of her back made her take to her bed,
much to the disgust and annoyance of Florence Jackson, the Commissioner's wife, for
whom she acted as personal maid. Sometimes
when she was feeling worse than ever, Pameta thought that death would be a convenient
way out for her. Certainly life held nothing
for her but shame.

David Jackson's new concrete-block residence was a very ugly balconied structure that
had cost him much more than it was worth,
but it was the envy of the Monrovian aristocracy. It stood on a rocky, weed-grown street
near the ocean, and from its cupola on a fair
day one could see Cape Mount, nearly fifty
miles up the coast.

According to the standards of Monrovia,
Jackson's home was most luxuriously furnished. From foreign consuls to Kru boat-
men, the six thousand inhabitants of the city
were great impressed. The house was equip-
ped with a private electric-light system; that
there was an imported fountain surrounded by
palms in the main parlor, while two Icy-Ball
refrigerators in the cook house assured visitors
of iced drinks even though Tom Saunders' ice

plant should break down. Everybody worth while in the capital's exclusive set had paid the Jacksons a visit just to inspect the new house. Only Tom Saunders stayed away. He swore that there was human blood on every concrete block. His weekly newspaper said so with bold-face type. The Liberians of the Liberal Party agreed with him, but the government officials only smiled.

A dozen or more native servants picked up at random by Mr. Jackson kept the big house clean and attended to the wants of the Commissioner and his wife. They ranged in age from little children to full grown men and women, but they all had one thing in common: they were not paid for their labor. Nor did they expect any wages. Were they not the personal servants of a great man? And did they not have plenty of food? If they got no wages, they were at least not unique among the servants of Americo-Liberians. The Commissioner himself would have been quite surprised had anyone raised the point that his help were unpaid. Such had been the custom for scores of years, so why should he be expected to change it?

The men servants and the children slept in

cell-like cubicles under the house where no
light and little air penetrated, but the women
servants, including Pameta, had quarters on
the top floor under the gently sloping roof,
conveniently close to the suite of the Commissioner.

It was a well-ordered household but one in
which much hatred and enmity stalked. The
women servants especially quarreled over the
veriest trifles, snapping viciously at each other
on every occasion. Each little favor or present
received by one from the master was the subject of disparaging comment from the others.
Tales were carried back and forth to the mistress, to the master and between each other.
Because she was shown greater consideration
than the others, Pameta was cordially hated.
Her every move was watched and misinter-
preted, and so communicated to Jackson or
his wife. There was a certain distinction that
went with being a great man's favorite which
the other women desired. Pameta would have
gladly yielded her place to either of them but
it was not within her power to do so.

In this household Pameta felt terribly alone.
No one of the servants, except the two little
children, pretended to be her friend. She had
been forced by long experience to suspect

Joe's every act of friendship. She had only been in the mansion for a month and already she was wondering how she would be able to stand the strain much longer.

Mrs. Jackson, like most of the aristocratic Liberian ladies, liked to pretend that her husband kept no concubines in their home, although she knew better. This affected ignorance was the safest attitude for a Liberian lady to assume. Keeping concubines was a traditional custom of the prominent men of the republic, and in the absence of feminism there was really nothing the women could do about it. It was better, they reasoned, to pretend to ignore the practice. Nevertheless, Florence Jackson hated the institution, hated her position as head of a harem, and hated each and every one of the women though she knew they were not responsible for being there.

A Bachelor of Arts from an American Negro college in the United States, she had, upon graduation, pictured for herself a married life enveloped in an aura of romance and marked by a deep and mutual love. Returning to her Liberian homeland, she had been forced by fallen family fortunes to wed David Jackson because of his wealth and position.

She knew very well Jackson had sought her hand in marriage because of the added prominence an alliance with her distinguished if impecunious family would lend. Jackson was laying the groundwork for the presidency, she knew, and the marriage was but a part of his strategy.

She had married him upon the insistance of her parents, who saw in him a most desirable son-in-law. Even though she cared little for her husband, whose uncouthness and cruelty often shocked her, she did not relish the idea of sharing him with four other women. The situation she considered humiliating. She had on two or three occasions denounced the arrangement only to be told that she "had too much American in her."

She often smiled cynically at the living irony that is Liberia. Her forefathers, freed Negroes from Maryland, had come to Liberia filled with Christian ideals, trained to Anglo-Saxon customs and suffused with the true spirit of pioneers. They had planned to establish in Africa a replica of America. Instead of conquering Africa, she realized that they, and especially their descendants, had been conquered by Africa. One by one they had adopted the worst habits and customs of the aborigines they exploited and despised.

Florence Jackson was not unaware of the certain social advantages of concubinage as practiced by the natives. It was by no means an unmixed evil. Under the system in the back country there was no prostitution, and the average concubine enjoyed more leisure and freedom than many of the working-class women in Europe and America. They did not have children so frequently as their white sisters and they were unmolested by their masters during menstruation and pregnancy. The older and more prominent the man became, the more concubines he had and the less was the sexual demand upon them. Marriage under such circumstances was more of an institution than a career, but in the shadow of this institution there was always romance. Lovers lurk in the background where polygamous though jealous men dominate the social life. It was so in Liberia as elsewhere.

But despite her understanding and appreciation of the merits of concubinage, Florence Jackson in her six months of married life was unable to reconcile herself completely to being nothing more than chief wife. She was an in-

curable romanticist, and there was no romance
in such an existence. She often grew bitter
about it all, and rather than risk another quar-
rel with her husband she took out her spite
on the servants. She ruled her household like
a martinet. On the slightest provocation she
would go into paroxyms of rage, slapping and
cuffing whoever happened to be in the immediate vicinity. The women feared her and she
hated them.

She was in a very ill-humor this day. One
of the women had appeared wearing a new silk
cloth on her head and the sight of it had
aroused the anger of the mistress. All such
articles, she knew, came from Jackson. Unable to do anything about it except to curse
the girl on some shallow pretense, she had been
mistreating the other servants all day.

Now she called to her a ragged youngster
of ten, one of the household's two little pawns.
Childlike, he had tarried on the way back from
an errand and Florence Jackson grimly determined that she would teach him a lesson.
Whimpering but obedient the little fellow
went to her sitting-room to receive his chastise-
ment.

When the child was within reach she

grasped him by the collar of his tunic and, producing a leather belt, whipped him about the buttocks and legs until his screams rang pitifully through the house. Each outcry seemed to sooth her nerves as nothing else could have done and she plied the belt with a sort of savage satisfaction until he fell gasping at her feet.

"Now get up and go downstairs," she commanded in a hard, metallic voice. Her pretty nut-brown face was as hard as flint and her ample bosom heaved up and down from the exertion.

The boy raised himself slowly from the floor, gazed at her a fleeting moment with big, accusing, tear-reddened eyes and limped out of the room. With an expression of relentless cruelty on her countenance, the mistress of the house walked out to the balcony and flopped down in a wicker chair. She began rocking back and forth, fanning herself vigorously. For some reason she was unable to explain, she always seemed to feel better after whipping one of the pawns or cuffing an adult servant. It relieved a certain strain within her. Whenever she felt remorse over her reversion to barbarism, she comforted herself with the knowledge that her servants were perhaps treated better than those of other Liberian families.

The two little pawns were made to work quite as steadily about the house as the grown servants. Jackson had promised their parents to send them to school so they might "learn book," but he thought no more about it after the promise was made. Other Liberian families sent their little pawns to school but usually to carry the books of their pampered children. It was no uncommon sight in Monrovia to see a well-dressed Americo-Liberian child going to school followed by a ragged youngster of perhaps his age carrying his books. Both might be of exactly the same color but nevertheless a great gulf separated them. As there were social classes far removed from each other in white countries, so there were in this black republic.

Pameta was the only real friend of the little pawns in the household. After one of their frequent whippings at the hands of Mrs. Jackson, they would come weeping to Pameta and she would comfort them. This scarcely pleased the mistress, and the other women knew it, so on every such occasion they would run to Mrs. Jackson and tell her.

This time the weeping little boy encountered Pameta on the first floor and ran to her open arms. She hugged him close and stroked his head while he sobbed in great gasps. One of the other women passing by saw them and immediately started upstairs. Pameta knew she had gone to tell Mrs. Jackson and followed her.

"Missy," the woman reported, going to her mistress on the balcony, "Pameta she pet little boy you whip."

"All right, Kama," the lady answered, closing her eyes and nervously biting her lip.

From within the doorway Pameta listened to the tattling. As the woman passed her to go downstairs again, the enraged Pameta reached out and grabbed her, snatched off her headkerchief and began pulling her hair and scratching her face. The other woman screamed at the sudden attack but fought back vigorously.

"Stop it! Stop it!" yelled Mrs. Jackson coming in from the balcony, pulling the two women apart. "How dare you start a disturbance in this house?"

"Pameta she do it," complained the tattler.

"Oh, so you started this, did you?" the mistress queried, turning her baleful glance on the offending Pameta. Then with a quick blow of her open hand she slapped the girl's face resoundingly.

Doubly angered, Pameta started for her mistress with a look in her eyes that boded the lady no good. Uttering a little squeal of rage she sank her hands into her mistress's throat. The other woman, horrified at such effrontery, pulled the girl back while Mrs. Jackson gasped with rage and humiliation.

"Oh, I'll get you!" the mistress threatened. "You just wait."

She returned to the balcony in fury, conjuring up visions of the worst punishment imaginable. It was outrageous that she, a lady, should be attacked by one of her servants, her own maid, her husband's chief concubine. She felt certain Jackson would do nothing about it. He would blame her for having struck Pameta, something he had warned her not to do, knowing the girl's temper.

But there were other ways of getting even; ways that were secret and mysterious. The cultured Mrs. Jackson smiled grimly at the comforting thought.

A month previously David Jackson had joined his wife in Monrovia because he was expecting to be given a better position. He had certainly earned promotion and President Johnson had promised it at the first opportunity. Never before had a District Commissioner sent such a large amount of food and taxes into Monrovia. Never before had the Fernando Po traffic been so lucrative to all concerned. Jackson had kept a steady stream of "boys" coming down to the coast for exportation. Almost every prominent man in the Conservative Party had directly benefited in some way from Jackson's efficient administration of District No. 1. The Commissioner had often admitted to close friends in strictest confidence that he had experienced occasional difficulties in carrying out his work, but never anything to demand the attention of the central government. True, he had been compelled to whip a chief here or raid a village there, but in the main, he would add cheerfully, there had been little disturbance of native life.

The noted District Commissioner did not consider such small matters as kidnapping girls, selling the nation's wards into servitude, and levying exorbitant taxes and food requisitions on impoverished villages as any disturbance of native life. In the first place, like most of his colleagues, he knew very little of native

life and cared less. His primary interests
were accumulating money and gaining promotion, and in the pursuit of these ideals he discarded as an unnecessary encumbrance any
scruples remaining from his mission-school
training. To David Jackson the natives were
but rungs on the ladder to riches and power,
a view shared by the majority of Americo-
Liberians.

He was reclining in an easy chair on his sec-
ond-floor balcony when a servant announced
the Vice President of Liberia. Sammy Williams, looking more prosperous than ever,
barged through the doorway and exposing his
even rows of white tombstone teeth he wrung
the hand of the District Commissioner.

"Well, well, David," he boomed, dropping
into a complaining wicker chair, I've got good
news for you."

"Wait," said Jackson, "we might as well
have a bit of Scotch and soda first."

"I don't care if I do, David," said the other.

After he had emptied his glass, the Vice
President leaned forward in a confidential
manner and placed his big hand on Jackson's
knee.

"You're going to get that promotion," he
announced.

"What are they giving me?" asked Jackson.

"You know what you've been asking me for, and what you've asked Johnson for, don't you?" countered the other.

"The Public Works job?" asked the delighted Commissioner. "Do you really think I can get that, Sammy?"

"I don't think about things, my boy," boomed the Vice President. "I know what I'm talking about. All I've got to do is to say the word and you're appointed. I just came from Johnson's office."

"Well, for God's sake, put it through," begged Jackson with the earnestness of office-seekers the world over."

"Sure, that's as good as settled now," replied Williams.

"What do I have to do on that job?" asked the Commissioner.

"Build motor roads connecting Districts One, Two and Three with Monrovia, so we can get out more piassava, kola nuts, rice and palm oil. That will be your job, and Johnson told me to impress upon you the importance of this work. Imports have exceeded exports for about eight years now, haven't they? And we've got to change that before we go bankrupt. The only way we can prevent it is to sell more of our hinterland products. Understand?"

"What's the appropriation?" asked Jackson. "How much money will I have to do this work with? It's a mighty big job, you know."

"There isn't any appropriation, David," said Williams. "The government has neither money or tools. You'll just have to do the best you can. We'll be right behind you in everything. If you make good there's a possible chance for you to succeed Johnson. He will hardly be renominated, and the boys know too much about me to put me in the Executive Mansion. I guess they're afraid I'd steal something," he added, gazing righteously at his friend, his eyes dancing with mirth.

"I guess you know I'll have to get labor up country, don't you?" said Jackson.

"Go right ahead," replied the Vice President. "We'll give you all the soldiers you need."

"And I suppose you know," continued Jackson, "that there is necessarily going to be hell to pay up there. You can't go too far with those people, you know, or they'll move over the border."

"You're not getting soft, are you?" sneered Williams, pouring out another drink. "What we want is roads, and we don't care how you get them. See?"

"Well, I just thought I'd warn you," said Jackson. "Now, when do I start?"

"Just as soon as you get your appointment," Williams declared.

"All right," the Commissioner stated, "I'll leave in a couple of days. Thanks so much, Sammy, for helping me."

"Not at all, David, not at all," boomed the Vice President, rising a little unsteadily. "Just don't forget me when you have a few 'boys' to spare. You know we can't stop doing business because of a little road building."

A servant brought Williams his khaki-colored sun helmet. The Vice President trudged downstairs, and walked out to his gleaming limousine. The uniformed black chauffeur started the car, and it lurched away over the uneven surface of the street.

Commissioner Jackson poured himself a heavy drink and, sipping it slowly, fell back in his easy chair. Things were indeed coming his way. First, District Commissioner; now Director of Public Works. Who could tell where he might end? His little piglike eyes

glowed at the thought that some day he might
be President.

The Right Reverend Henry Briggs, Bishop
of Liberia, immaculately clad in gleaming
white, stepped from his automobile and walked
into the office of Tom Saunders, head of the
Liberal Party. The good Bishop liked Tom
Saunders very much, but he always visited him
after nightfall. He had his reasons for doing
this, chief among them being that he did not
wish to antagonize the present government.

"Good evening, Bishop!" said Saunders,
rising from behind his flat-top desk and extending his hand. "It's been some time since
I've seen you. Where have you been?"

"Good evening, Brother Saunders!" said
the Bishop, wringing his hand. "I've been
away, down as far as Cape Palmas, you know,
and I'll tell you I've been shocked by what
I've seen."

"How's that?" asked Saunders.

"Oh, this boy traffic. It's terrible, Saunders," the clergyman declared. "It is bad
enough when laymen are involved, but I've
found that several of our ministers are impli-
cated, some of them teachers in our college.
All of the way back I've been wondering what

can be done about it. Perhaps you have some ideas."

"What's to be done?" echoed Saunders, his slender jaw tightening belligerently, "why, throw them out of the church. That's what ought to be done. And then they ought to be indicted along with everybody involved. As Bishop of the church, it seems to me, you ought to take the initiative in matters of this kind, Briggs. If the church is going to condone such evils, it might as well close up shop."

"But we've got to move carefully, Saunders," said the Bishop. "There are some prominent officials involved and I'm not sure that bringing charges would help the cause of the church right now. I suppose you are familiar with the talk that has been going the rounds of government circles about barring the missionaries from the country and establishing a Liberian church. Well, it is within the power of Johnson and his underlings to do that very thing and, personally, I believe such a step would prove disastrous to Liberia."

"First you ask me what's to be done," Saunders accused, "and then when I tell you what to do, you balk. Frankly, Bishop, I cannot see that either you or the other missionaries have taken the right attitude toward the atrocities inflicted on the natives. Instead of asking what Christ would do under similar circumstances and guiding yourself accordingly, you bend the knee to expediency. What does it matter if a few missionaries lose their jobs if we can focus the attention of the world on the crimes committed against black men by black men?"

"Wait, wait now, Saunders," soothed the clergyman. "You're just a little too radical, while the church must be, in general, conservative. We must work within the framework of the government, but not antagonize the government when there is so much for us to do here that is proving beneficial to the aborigines. You mustn't forget that."

"Why, I've just got through advising you to work within the framework of government when I tell you to have the guilty clergymen indicted along with .the politicians who are covering up and profiting from their guilt. I can see nothing radical about that. If the missionaries are not going to stand up for what is right, I can't see what good they are. The greatest service you can do the natives now is to tell the world how they are being tortured, enslaved and murdered." Saunders' eyes flashed.

"Yes, yes," the Bishop agreed, "but I still maintain that the church has other interests which must not be jeopardized. Our chief mission is to bring the message of Jesus Christ to the heathen."

"And if the church remains silent and inactive in the face of the evils being daily perpetrated against the heathens, as you call them, there will soon be no heathens to convert. Do you realize, Bishop, that hundreds of men have been sent into virtual slavery this year; that their homes have been broken up and family life destroyed? Do you know that scores of towns have been overtaxed and dozens of chiefs humiliated by public whippings? Do you know that soldiers go about the country doing as they please, destroying huts and violating women? This sort of thing must stop, and I, for one, intend to stop it if I die in the attempt. It seems to me that a powerful organization like your church could at least do as much as I am doing. You could at least let the world know what is going on. Instead, you go on visits to the States and you never say a word about the atrocities you have witnessed. It remained for me, a nonchurchgoer, to go to the United States last year and tell the people over there the truth."

"You have been severely criticized for that, too," said the white clergyman. "President Johnson accuses you of playing into the hands of the white imperialists, and thus endangering the independence of Liberia."

"What do I care what Johnson says?" sneered Saunders. "He is the most guilty one of the lot. I have proof that he has been getting ten dollars for every boy exported. Commissioner Jackson has been getting twenty-five, and Vice President Williams rakes off fifteen. I would rather see Liberia lose her independence than to see her native life destroyed by grafting crooks. Then, too, any talk about playing into the hands of the white imperialists comes with poor grace from Sidney Johnson. It was he who arranged for the Red Rock Rubber Company to get their ninety-nine year lease; it was he who arranged for the two million and a half dollar foreign loan that is choking the country, and it was he who endeavored to get the English subsidiary of the United Fruit Company to come in and establish banana plantations. I would like to know what good it does a country like this to be independent when the masses of the people are enslaved?"

Saunders was tense and perspiring as he

talked. He banged the glass top of his desk often, and mopped his brow the rest of the time. Now he leaned back in his swivel chair, and pressed a button. A servant came, and he ordered lemonade for two.

"Tom," declared the Bishop, "I agree so thoroughly with most of what you say that I hate to disagree on some points. But, after all, you are a politician, while the church is dealing in religion. We necessarily have to approach these evils differently."

"Well, you'll never solve them by preaching. You people have done that for seventy-five years, only to see the products of your instruction enslaving and debauching and murdering their wards. It's a mighty funny religion you people have. How you can see boys come back here from Fernando Po, reeking with foul diseases, and not tell the world about it is beyond me."

"We have taken the matter of the Fernando Po traffic up with the President," the Bishop retorted, "and he has promised to do something about it."

"Humph!" Saunders snorted in disgust. "That's like going to the King of Cats, requesting that the slaughter of rats cease. What you ought to do is to throw out the

guilty clergymen in your church as a warning
to other evildoers. Certainly you have jurisdiction over your own ministers."

"I'll think that over, Saunders," said the
Bishop. "You know, we really want to do
something, but we can't afford to go as far
as you would wish just yet."

"Well, I suppose a little gesture is better
than none at all," Saunders said wearily, as
the Bishop rose to go, "but I certainly long
to see the day when the Christian church will
try to practice Christianity."

Bishop Briggs' car had hardly vanished
around the corner when another visitor was
announced: Rufus Henderson, Attorney General of Liberia. He also was a nocturnal,
though frequent, visitor. A fine, upstanding
black fellow of distinguished family, he had
had the advantage of an American education,
and was rated as one of the great legal authorities in a republic where law was the only
pursuit of the upper classes. He entered
Saunders' office cautiously and sat down, nervously turning his helmet in his hands. The
two men greeted each other familiarly.

"Well, Rufe," said Saunders to the younger
man, "what's up now?"

"They're going to appoint David Jackson Director of Public Works," he replied, "and you know what that means."

"Yes, I know what it means. It means that we are due to see worse crimes committed against the natives than ever before. As Attorney General I should think you'd know what to do about it, Rufe," said Saunders, accusingly. "The entire cabinet, including yourself, could be indicted for complicity in this boy traffic. You have known what was going on ever since you accepted your portfolio. Why don't you prefer charges against the whole crew?"

"I'd love to do it, Saunders," the other replied, "but it would be worth my job and perhaps my life. You know I have nothing, no money and no property to speak of. They would crush me, and I've got a wife and children to look after."

"Oh, hell!" Saunders exploded, "come over with us and I'll see that you're taken care of. Where you belong is in the Liberal Party. Hundreds of the younger men who have, like yourself, had the benefit of education, are joining us. Young Liberia is aroused, and as a young man your place is with Young Liberia. What have you to fear? They won't

dare do anything to you, and with your knowledge of the rascalities of the Conservative
Party you can be of real help to Liberia.
Right now, I must frankly say that I consider
you a hindrance. The trouble with you is that
the Conservative Party has you scared. If
they were anything but a pack of lazy cowards,
do you think I could have fought them for
thirty years without getting a scratch?"

"I have always admired your courage,
Saunders," the Attorney General answered,
"but I'm differently situated than you are.
You have money and a business: I have
neither."

"Why, God damn it!" Saunders exploded,
"haven't I offered you a job? You can be
my attorney and personal representative, can't
you? I'll pay you as much as you get from
the government, and won't ask you to do anything that's not right."

"I'd like to take you up on that, Saunders,"
said the other man, somewhat heartened. "I
have sat by for three years now, with my
mouth closed, because I didn't want to starve.
It has been a battle, Saunders; a battle between making a living and serving the real
interests of the people. Now I see that I must
make some decision. The appointment of

David Jackson as Director of Public Works is a little too much for me to swallow. Either his kind must go or the republic will soon cease to be. Frankly, I came here tonight with the hope that when I told you of this latest appointment you might make some such offer as you have."

"Well," snapped Saunders, "are you ready to quit? If so, you're hired here and now, and you can trust me not to let you down."

"Thanks, Tom," said Henderson gratefully, a great load off his shoulders, "I don't know how I can thank you."

"Don't thank me," replied Saunders, "just pull your chair up to the desk and write out your resignation as Attorney General, stating your reasons. I'll carry the whole thing in the Liberal next week. . . . This is a great thing you have done, Rufe. It will encourage hundreds of young men who are now hesitating to line themselves up with us. The Liberal Party is the salvation of Liberia, my boy. If we don't clean up from within, somebody's going to clean up from without. I've just come from abroad and I know what I'm talking about."

The two men shook hands, and Henderson went out into the darkness. Saunders gazed at the written resignation on his desk, sealed it in an envelope, and pressed a button on the side of his desk.

"Jack," he said to the servant who answered the call, "take this over to President Johnson's house and tell him I'm sending it with my compliments."

Tom Saunders leaned back in his swivel chair and chuckled. A good evening's work had been accomplished. The Liberal Party had scored heavily tonight, and he was always greatly pleased when he could thrust a fresh thorn in the side of the government. Now, he mused, if he could only bring about an international investigation of his numerous charges, his cup would be filled to overflowing. For that purpose he had journeyed to Europe and America, and he was daily expecting a cablegram informing him that his efforts had been rewarded. Once his charges were substantiated he expected a supervised election, and that would mean victory for the Liberal Party and a new deal for Liberia.

Three days later a long column of soldiers, porters, hammock carriers and overseers wended its way north from Kakata. David Jackson, Director of Public Works, lolled im-

portantly in his hammock, a dead cigar in the
corner of his mouth and a bottle of whiskey
by his side. The Director was feeling gay
today. He was beginning on a new job and,
like a new broom, he intended to sweep clean.
He had only to build the desired roads and
he saw the presidency looming ahead.

A few paces behind him rode Pameta and
one other woman from his town house. Pameta was very ill. Her back and joints ached,
and more of the sores were breaking out on
her body. She did not know what was the
cause of her malady and there was no one to
tell her.

The day was hot and humid. The encircling
jungle was like a steam bath. No breeze
stirred. At times the odor from the perspiring carriers grew so sickening that Pameta
almost fainted. Even the Director stopped
the column several times in an effort to draw
a clean breath of air.

The column was headed for a town named
Webbo, which was to be the immediate headquarters of the road-building work. A pla-
toon of soldiers under a lieutenant had preceded them and was notifying the town chiefs
of the quotas of men they must furnish on
pain of heavy fine.

As the column passed through each village, Jackson called the chief, and, through Joe, told him bluntly what was expected of him and his people. Each chief knew the great man did not speak idly. His evil reputation had preceded him, and they were prepared for the worst.

Next to Scotch whiskey, the Director of Public Works liked the good palm wine, fresh from the tree. At each town he demanded a gourd of the liquor and drank heartily before passing it on to his young overseers. When he finally arrived at Webbo, he was speaking incoherently and had to be helped from his hammock by the ever-present Joe. The villagers stood around watching everything intently, but they wisely kept their thoughts to themselves.

The next morning all of the available male labor from nearby towns assembled at Webbo. Each laborer had a little package of food wrapped in a banana leaf, and each carried some crude native tool, such as a knife, mattock, or rough spade of wood. They came in gangs, each town's contingent keeping together, with drummers and other musicians to play while the work went on.

The work started at once in both directions,

and proceeded rather slowly. The government was furnishing no tools, and the crude instruments brought by the natives made the labor even harder. The overseers were younger members of the Conservative Party, or the scions of great families for whom President Johnson had been unable to find jobs. They acted also as surveyors, although none of them had ever seen a first-class road or knew anything about surveying. They ignored contours, and laid out the road in a tangent over hill and dale.

A part of the requisitioned natives stayed in Webbo to build barracks for the Director, his overseers and the soldiers. Natives were placed in charge of this work, and as a consequence the framework rose rapidly. In a very few days it was completed, and the task of plastering the structure with mud from the ant hills was turned over to the women.

This afforded the soldiers great fun. As the women crawled up the native ladders, the soldiers would stick them from behind with rifles or small branches. The women would complain loudly and the soldiers would shout with laughter. Jackson, who sat in the door of his hut, enjoyed the play quite as much as his men.

He always felt more at home in the field than in town. There one had to exercise caution in what one did because of the presence of the white foreigners, but out here he was king and could do as he pleased.

The work had been going on for ten days when a delegation of town chiefs came to Webbo to complain of the effect the daily requisitioning of labor was having. One big chief who could speak some English laid the case before Jackson.

"Big massah," he began, as the others circled around behind him. "De gove'ment take mans too much. Alla mans come here an' nobody lef' to cut farm. We no can get food without mans to farm. Please, massah, do not take too much mans. Farms grow bush too quick. Let us send some mans and keep some. We all like gove'ment, but we mus' have rice, cassava and palm oil. I have speak."

"I hear what you say," said Jackson, in a steely voice. He was enraged that anybody should question the wisdom of his arrangements. Who were these chiefs, to criticize the Director of Public Works? Had not the government delegated him to build roads regardless of everything?

"If soup is too hot for you," warned the

Director, "blow on it until it gets cool. Understand? You do as you're told or I'll fine all of you. Now get out of here, and don't come back!"

The spokesman translated the Director's remarks. The chiefs looked bewildered and incredulous. After all, what they had asked seemed very reasonable to them. They silently withdrew, and when out of earshot of the government official chattered heatedly among themselves as they went down the road to their respective towns.

Jackson returned to his easy chair, his little red eyes snapping with amusement. He was very well satisfied with the way he had handled the chiefs, and congratulated himself on his leniency. Could he not have fined or whipped them for their effrontery? Of course. And who could have stopped him?

CHAPTER TEN

Zo came from the office of the Spanish consul in Monrovia with beaming face and bulging pocket. Five pounds, along with the few dollars he already possessed, made him richer than he had ever dreamed. He felt happy, carefree and a trifle bewildered, undecided as to what he should do first. He looked hesitantly up and down the sunny, weed-grown street, hardly knowing which way to turn. For so long had he been a slave that it was difficult to accustom himself to the rôle of a free man. At last he decided to go toward the water front where, in all probability, he might meet some of his countrymen. He planned to return to Boloba to inquire about Pameta, but first he wanted to see something of this city of which Soki had spoken so enthusiastically. Down the steep hill he sauntered, eyes and ears open to catch every sound and observe every sight.

The street along the water front of Monrovia is a straggling artery of trade, lined on both sides by stores, customs houses and warehouses. More money changes hands here than anywhere in the black republic, and here the white man is lord. Black Liberian officials may subsist by practicing law and holding office, but the alien white man makes a better living by controlling the trade of the country. With one or two exceptions the shops along the water front of Monrovia are his. From Holland, Germany, France, England, the United States, Syria, Greece and India, the merchants have come bringing canned goods, hardware, liquors and bright clothes of striking pattern for the native trade. Black clerks standing behind high counters wait upon the nondescript crowd, selling everything from kerosene to tin trunks amid a pandemonium that would drive those unused to it into an insane asylum. Farther back in the stores stand the white cashiers, accepting the money. Outside, a milling crowd of natives from a dozen different nations wanders aimlessly up and down the street, looking, chattering and spending.

Liberian stores are conspicuously absent from the water front. The aristocracy does not take well to trade and commerce. Frequently a Liberian will have a farm operated by unpaid "boys," from which he ekes out a

meagre existence, but in general they prefer
the more genteel professions of politics, law,
teaching and preaching, in neither of which
are the hands soiled or the finer sensibilities
disturbed by unwanted contact with the "inferior" natives.

No Liberian youths are to be found behind
the counters of the white merchants on the
Monrovian water front. The clerks are black,
but they are Negroes from Lagos, Accra,
Takoradi, Freetown, Conokry, Bathhurst and
Dakar, whom the storekeepers find more honest and industrious and less concerned with
politics and litigation.

Zo trudged from one end of the street to
the other, looking and listening, suppressing
numerous temptations to spend his money.
With difficulty he pulled himself away from
heaps of cheap bracelets and necklaces and
piles of shirts, shorts and brilliant handkerchiefs. From one store to the other he went,
his money burning a hole in his pocket: but
he made no purchases.

At the public market, a long, wide, open
shed leading from the street down to the water,
he wended his way among the little stands
where scores of women of many tribes were
trying to sell fruit, vegetables and peanuts.

The market was a place of a thousand arresting odors. Along one side ran an open cement-lined ditch half filled with green, stagnant water over which the ragged, scabby natives stepped nonchalantly. The direct rays of the midday sun struck the corrugated iron roof, turning the shed into an oven. Yet many of the women sat there impassively, often not making a sale all day. Zo bought a handful of peanuts, and munched them as he wandered among the folk.

He saw plenty of Golas, but no one from Boloba or Takama. One lad, resplendent in a khaki uniform with brass buttons and insignia, told Zo that he was a messenger at the American legation, and offered to get him a job there in the laundry. Zo declined. He was not planning to stay in Monrovia more than a day or two. Nevertheless, he agreed to go with the messenger and see what the legation was like.

The two men marched to the far end of the street, climbed the hill and came shortly to a large white balconied residence surrounded by a grove of trees. They went around in back to see the laundry man, who was also a Gola. When Zo told them that he was just from Fernando Po, they deferred to him as though

he were a conquering hero. Servants came
from all parts of the house to hear about the
dread island. They hung on every word that
dropped from his lips, seeming to envy him
in spite of the hardships he so graphically
described.

When suppertime came they gave him some
of their food, and arranged for him to sleep
under the house while he was in town. Zo
would probably have been kept talking until
midnight had not the moon in all of its tropical
brilliance risen and turned night into day. On
such nights Africa dances, and the laundryman suggested that they go down to Kru
town and stop also at the Bassa settlement
to see the dancing.

They had hardly started down rocky Carew
Street, from the legation, when they heard the
tap of drums calling the dancers from their
huts and shacks; calling them out under the
moon to sing, shuffle and stamp their feet to
intricate African rhythms.

There is something about the sound of
native drums that instantly attracts and holds
the attention. It has a hypnotic effect, drawing you to the dance to watch the quick movements of supple limbs and perhaps compelling
you to participate. Natives offer no re-

sistance, but go willingly and joyfully.
Americo-Liberians and white people go as if
on a slumming party, but they go, concealing
their emotional stirrings with deprecating
smiles.

And to what better place can one go on a
moonlight night in the tropics? There, on
earth hardened by countless feet, great crowds
move rhythmically to the syncopated tumult
of the drums and the tuneful blasts of the
horns while, overhead, the cool evening breeze
stirs the palm fronds.

Zo had not been to a dance since the fatal
afternoon following his marriage. The thud-
ding of the drums brought memories of Pameta and Takama. How well she had danced,
that day! And where was she now? He
longed for the sight of her, remembering her
clean, smooth body, her laughing mouth and
sparkling eyes. Would he ever see her
again?

The two men wended their way through the
crowd to its inner margin. The musicians
were working industriously now, and individual dancers were leaping in the air and
executing intricate footwork, to the delighted
plaudits of the spectators. One by one these
solo dancers made their contribution to the

evening's entertainment, and then disappeared in the crowd to watch other dancers.

It was impossible for Zo not to be drawn to the moon-bathed circle. Had he not been known as the best dancer in Takama? He dashed suddenly to the center of the ring, leaped high into the air, his legs moving to simulate running. Again on the ground, he stopped stock-still, crouching with his knees bent. Then, catlike, he circled the dancing place, sniffing like the leopard. The drums, which had temporarily yielded to the horns, now beat louder and faster, and Zo, a whirlwind of arms and legs, thrilled the crowd with his magnificent caperings until it screamed its approval.

It was past midnight when Zo and the laundryman, gay and perspiring, left the dance. There was a certain house in Kru town, according to the latter, where liquor might be purchased and comely girls obtained. They started through the lanes of the settlement, looking for this place of pleasure. Zo was prepared to spend six or eight shillings to see what attractions Monrovia offered.

The two men were walking along, talking rather loudly, when a uniformed figure appeared out of the shadows and halted them.

It was a policeman, a barefooted policeman, upholding the majesty of Liberian law. They were, he charged, disturbing the peace.

He marched them up the steep hill to the jail, the laundryman ahead, Zo behind him, and the officer bringing up the rear. As they turned the corner at the top of the hill, the laundryman dashed off and disappeared like a flash into the blackness of the night. Zo would have followed, but the policeman grabbed him and drew a club.

To Zo the Monrovia jail seemed the last word in filthiness. Nothing aboard the Spanish ship or in Fernando Po equaled it. The odor inside the place was revolting, a mixture of body smells, caked offal, and decaying things. He was pushed into a cell where a number of unfortunates lay sleeping on the bare floor. He had perforce to join them, since there was neither bench, box nor chair in the place.

He could not sleep. Indeed, he could scarcely breathe. He was unable to understand what law he had violated by merely walking down the street, talking to a friend. How much would they fine him? He became alarmed at the thought that his freedom might cost him one or two of his precious pounds.

The sun was quite high next morning when, with several other men, many of whom had returned on the same boat with him from Fernando Po, Zo was marched out of the jail to the police court. En route, he learned from his acquaintances that they also had been arrested for disturbing the peace, and their money taken from them by the police sergeant.

The rickety one-room police court resembled less a public building than the caricature of a public building. It was a wooden structure with sagging porch and roof, and perched on crooked pillars. Inside, an important-looking black man was sitting on the bench, ready to mete out justice or its Liberian equivalent, glancing at the assemblage over a pair of gold-rimmed spectacles, plump and self-satisfied.

Zo's captor told what sounded like a straightforward story. He was on his post, he began, when he heard a great disturbance. He investigated, and found the accused and another man in a fight. He arrested both, but the other man escaped. The Judge looked over his glasses at Zo while the court attorney eloquently advised a heavy fine. When the latter had finished his harangue, the Judge

called him to the bench and conversed softly
with him.

"Did the sergeant search him?" asked the
judge.

"Yes, he had seven pounds," the attorney
replied.

"Seven pounds!" the Judge exclaimed,
evincing added interest in the case. "Where
did he get seven pounds?"

"Oh, he's one of the boys who came back
from Fernando Po yesterday, and Collins
paid him off," the attorney informed him.
"We managed to run down several of them
last night."

The attorney returned to his place, and the
Judge importantly turned the pages of a large
volume before him. Finally he looked up,
adjusted his glasses, cleared his throat, and
gave sentence.

"I fine the accused ten pounds for disturbing the peace in the early hours of the morning," he said solemnly.

"But, your honor," the attorney objected,
"this young man only has seven pounds. I
urge clemency. After all, he is new here, and
next time he will know better."

The Judge pondered this appeal for what
he considered an adequate length of time,

while the nondescript crowd of prisoners and policemen waited with bated breath for his decision. The jurist at last rubbed his chin thoughtfully, and then in a benevolent tone declared: "As this is the first offense of the young man, the court reduces the fine to seven pounds."

The police sergeant turned over to the court clerk the handkerchief containing Zo's money, while the attorney called the next case. Zo stood, rather dazed, looking first at the Judge and then at the court clerk counting out the fruit of two years' toil. He was on the point of protesting when the court attendant plucked him by his shirt sleeve, advised him to leave at once before the Judge changed his mind, that he should consider himself fortunate to have escaped so easily.

Zo waited outside on the porch long enough to see several of the lads from Fernando Po fined sums equal to what they had possessed when arrested. Then he turned away, heartsick, and trudged down the street, penniless.

Tired and hungry, Zo strode into Webbo the evening of the third day from Monrovia. Though he had no money, he knew he could get food and a place to sleep in every village.

The natives were always eager to hear about lands far distant across the seas, to which people traveled in huge, iron canoes that belched smoke and moved very fast through the water. The Webbo folk were no exception, and Zo was fed well.

Ever since leaving Kakata he had heard complaints from the people against the work they were being forced to do without compensation. The complaints were louder in Webbo than any place he had touched. Not only must the town supply its quota of laborers, but it must also furnish food and build barracks for overseers, soldiers and the Director of Public Works. To escape this situation, many of the people had run away into the bush, where the soldiers could not find them. There they were establishing new towns. This was their only form of retaliation.

Zo listened to them patiently and politely, but he had seen and experienced so much cruelty and injustice that he had become a little calloused. After all, he was merely passing through on the way to his country, and in any event he could not help them. They were paying the penalty for having been born in Liberia.

Before the sun rose, next morning, he was

up and making for the trail that led into the
Gola country. Carrying only a stout stick,
he hurried down the well-beaten path, humming a Mendi song and hoping to reach the
St. Paul river before nightfall. He had gone
perhaps two or three miles along the green
corridor when he came upon a small settlement of about fifteen huts, astride of the trail.

He was half-way through the settlement
when a soldier, armed with a long rifle with
fixed bayonet, stepped from behind a hut and
ordered him to halt. Zo was at first inclined
to run, but he realized that the soldier would
shoot him down. He had not forgotten the
massacre at Takama, and had a lively respect
for firearms.

A corporal came up and, taking Zo in
charge, thrust him into a nearby hut guarded
by an armed sentry. The sun was out now
and the cool interior of the hut was more comfortable than the street outside. When his
eyes had become accustomed to the darkness,
he discovered that he was not alone. There
were at least a half dozen other natives sharing the hut with him. Addressing them in
Kpwessi, he learned that, like him, they had
all been seized as they sought to pass through
the soldiers' camp the day before.

In a short time the door was opened, and the seven men were ordered outside and lined up by the soldiers. Each was issued a native bush knife or a mattock, and the group was marched back along the trail to Webbo, followed closely by two armed soldiers.

Zo felt greatly depressed. Ill fortune seemed to dog his footsteps. Just when he had thought himself free, he was a slave again.

Just outside of the town they came upon scores of men working on the new road with their crude tools. With their knives and mattocks, the newcomers joined the others in cutting brush and chopping grass and weeds from the sections laid out by the two overseers. These young Liberian gentlemen, helmeted and dressed in khaki shirts and shorts, with golf stockings and tennis shoes, sat in the shade of a big tree nearby, coming occasionally to the side of the road to issue fresh orders. The actual work of handling the laborers was left to noncommissioned officers.

A tall fellow Zo had met the night before in Webbo, came down the road from the town, swinging a mattock. When he reached the gang, he sought to sneak in among the other laborers, but the eye of a nearby corporal was too sharp. He yelled to the tardy one to come to him, and then escorted him over to the big tree where the overseers were lounging.

"Dis boy he come just now," the corporal explained.

"What's the matter with you?" asked one of the Liberians, the corporal acting as interpreter.

"Massah, I very sick last night," the native replied.

"All right," said the overseer, "we give you medicine to make you well, eh? Corporal, take him away and tell the sergeant to fix him."

Before the two reached him, the sergeant produced a big black whip, and waited grimly. Willing soldier hands trussed up the villager and threw him to the ground. The sergeant rolled up his sleeve and began whipping him. The lash rose and fell, cutting into the man's skin· and raising cruel welts on his back and legs. The other workers kept busily at their tasks, sometimes stealthily glancing around when a louder outcry came from the victim.

"That happens every day," said a Kpwessi man working beside Zo. "Everybody that comes late is beaten. It is not fair. We must cut farm, keep up the trails, pay taxes, and now we have to build the road. If we are

always working on the road, when are we to
find time to do anything else? You see now
why we work so fast: we want to get rid of
these people as quickly as possible. They eat
up our food, take our women for wives, and
pay us nothing."

The beating of the drums somehow made
the work easier, as did the singing that accompanied it. The knives and mattocks rose
and fell rhythmically, while the sweat glistened
on the nearly nude bodies of the laborers. At
midday work ceased while the overseers had
their lunch served to them under the big tree.
The men were allowed to rest while their
bosses ate. Unaccustomed as most of them
were to road work, they needed rest. Because
of his long experience at the same sort of thing
in Fernando Po, Zo found the work to be not
very difficult, but he knew it would have been
easier if the swarms of natives had been supplied with picks, shovels and wheelbarrows.
As it was, they were using sorry makeshifts,
and carrying off the dirt in native baskets.

Work ended around six o'clock in the evening. When the men from Webbo lined up to
march back to their town under their head-
man, Zo sidled in among them. He reasoned
that the overseers did not know one native

from the other, and as a consequence this
would enable him to escape.   He planned to
get away from the village as soon as possible
and take a narrow, secret trail, of which he
had heard that day, to a hidden settlement far
in the bush.   From there, he had been told,
one could easily get to the Gola country across
the river.

As the Webbo men marched away, the two
guards lined up the kidnapped workers, and
were about to start off with them, when it was
discovered that there were only six instead of
seven.   They yelled to the crowd of Webbo
men to return.   As the gang started to march
back, Zo fell to the rear and, when no one was
looking, slid safely into the jungle.   He fought
his way about fifty yards into the tangle of
underbrush and vines, then waited until the
soldiers and villagers had passed on.   A few
minutes afterward, he followed them cautiously into town.

The secret trail being some distance the
other side of Webbo, he strode quickly through
the village and along the newly finished
stretch of road.   He had gone but a very short
distance when he noticed for the first time a
new settlement of big huts, in the midst of
which rose a tall flagpole.   There was no flag

flying from it now, but he knew that one had been there during the day. There would surely be soldiers here, he reasoned, and, fearing to be caught again and forced to labor on the road, he retraced his steps to Webbo to await the concealing shadows of dusk.

David Jackson sat on the verandah of his new quarters, enjoying a good cigar after his usual heavy dinner. Nearby Joe was clearing off the table.

"Joe!" called the Director.

"Yassah, massah," the servant replied.

"Go tell Pameta to come here!" the big man commanded.

"Pameta she sick too much," Joe informed him.

"I don't care if she is," Jackson snapped, "tell her to come here. I'm tired of her foolishness and I'm going to put a stop to it. She's more trouble than my wife."

Joe ran to do his master's bidding.

Jackson grumbled about the obstinacy of Pameta. It looked as though two years as his woman ought to break her will, and yet he had to force her every time he wanted her. Last night she had refused to come to him, pleading illness. Why, he had hardly even

seen her since their arrival at Webbo. He
was getting tired of it. For a long time it
had been intriguing to have a native woman
who did not accept caresses passively, but now
he had enough of that. She must submit willingly to him or he would know the reason why.
Yes, there would have to be a change. His
little eyes grew cold and hard, and his lip
curled cruelly.

"She too sick to come, she say," reported
Joe, returning from his mission.

"Well, by God!" shouted Jackson, greatly
affronted, "I'll go down there myself and see
what this means."

He rose, poured himself a stiff drink of
whiskey at the sideboard, then stamped angrily
out of the room.

Pameta's hut was located close to the road,
the largest in the women's end of the compound. Its two doors were wide open. The
girl was lying, face to the wall, on the sleeping-platform. When Jackson arrived, he
strode right into the place, walked over, and
snatched her up from the bed.

"When I call you, God damn you, you
come! Do you hear?" he shouted. "I'm tired
of this damn foolishness. You're no better

than these other women. . . . Come on, get
up and go to my place."

"Massah, Pameta no can go; Pameta too
sick to go," she gasped.

"Well, by God!" he blurted, grasping her
around the waist, "then you don't have to go
up there. We'll just stay right down here."

"No, no," she cried, recoiling from him,
"Pameta too sick."

"Oh, hell," he retorted, pushing her onto
the sleeping-platform, "I've heard that too
often."

The girl collapsed on the bed, and he stood
up over her, gloating. At last she was going
to submit without a struggle. He chuckled in
drunken satisfaction at her passive acceptance
of his attentions.

He finally rose, and the young girl lay
motionless, gasping, still faintly protesting
against the outrage of her pain-wracked body.
As he stood swaying above her, he conceived
the idea of forcing her to return with him to
his cottage, whether she wanted to or not.
Was he not master?

"Come on," he commanded, grasping her
by the shoulder and pulling her outside the
hut, "you're going with me, going up to my

place. 'S too prim'tive down here for me. Come on!"

Pameta looked wan and drawn, as she stumbled into the fading daylight. Her head was held high no longer, and at each step she coughed or spat. He followed her out, and then for the first time he noticed something he had not observed before. There were large dark spots on her arms, neck and legs. Jackson recoiled in loathing and alarm at the sight. He thought instantly of Gonda and the other women who had developed the same fatal skin eruptions. Guilt and anger were in conflict within him.

"Please, massah, you help me?" begged Pameta, in her broken English, as she leaned against the wall of the hut, "I so sick inside; maybe I die. Please, massah, give Pameta good medicine stop hurt quick. . . . Massah, you make Pameta sick like this. . . . Please, please help Pameta."

Jackson, somewhat sobered, licked his dry lips and gazed fixedly at the girl, horror written all over his evil brown face. He was limp with fear at the thought that he had possessed her in such a condition. Now she stretched out her spotted arms to him in an appealing gesture, and came nearer. Speak-

ing incoherently, begging for help with a
heart-stirring eloquence, one of her out-
stretched hands fell upon his shoulder.

Horrified, he pushed her violently away
from him. She staggered back and fell on
the edge of the new road. Jackson almost
ran to his cottage, hastened inside, and poured
down drink after drink of whiskey in an attempt to wash away the memory of his recent
experience.

Coughing and vomiting, Pameta lay where
she had fallen, too weak to rise. She felt that
death was near, and she welcomed it. She
knew she could not go on as she had; could
not live with the fierce pains assailing her and
the hacking coughs wracking her body. As
she lay there beside the road built to
bring prosperity to Liberia, she thought of
her happy childhood in Takama, disporting
through its lanes, and dreaming of marriage
under the shade of the giant cottonwood trees.
She saw again Chief Bongomo, her illustrious
father, and the good Badé, her mother. She
remembered her marriage night with Zo, and
the feasting and dancing that followed the
proof of her virginity. It was all past now;
only a pleasant dream to look back upon as
she lay dying.

It was now dusk and, eager to be off before darkness rendered the finding of the secret trail too difficult, Zo started swiftly down the new road. There were no soldiers about, and this fact reassured him. He was almost light-hearted once more, and he chuckled as he thought how cleverly he had escaped from the soldiers on the road work. Very soon now he would be where the entire Frontier Force could not find him.

He had almost passed the military compound when he heard a moan and, glancing about, he saw in the rapidly vanishing light the prostrate figure of a native woman alongside the road. He was loath to stop in such a dangerous place, but was impelled to do so by some inner urge. He knelt beside the woman, raised her head, and then almost dropped it in astonishment as he recognized Pameta. Yes, it was Pameta, but what a different Pameta from the lively young virgin he had held in his arms over two years ago in Takama. She looked at least ten years older. And those terrible spots! How many times had he seen them on the victims of loathsome social diseases in Fernando Po!

Zo lifted Pameta tenderly to a sitting posi-

tion, and steadied her with his arm as she
swayed.

"Pameta! Pameta!" he cried, as she gazed
at him uncomprehendingly. "This is Zo, your
husband. Don't you remember me?"

There was no light of welcome in Pameta's
eyes, only one of sorrow and regret. It hurt
her more than her pains to have her Zo see
her in such a condition after their enforced
separation of so many moons.

"Zo," she whispered weakly, "I know you
. . . but it's too late now, Zo. . . . Pameta
too sick. . . . Jackson. . . . Jackson, he do
this. . . . Jackson make me so very sick, Zo.
. . . Jackson won't give Pameta medicine.
. . . Zo, I cannot live. . . . It is too late . . .
but Jackson is up there, Zo . . . and you are
so strong."

The tears welled up in Zo's eyes and fell
upon his tunic. He carried her into the hut
and laid her on the sleeping-platform. She
coughed several times while he sat helplessly
beside her, then she vomited violently and,
with a final sigh, perhaps of relief, closed
her eyes. Alarmed, he shook her gently, then
frenziedly, but there was no response. Pameta
was dead.

Zo rose with blazing eyes, and unfastened the bush knife hanging from his belt; the same bush knife the soldiers had issued to him that morning. Walking softly, swiftly and surely, like an avenging angel, he made for the cottage of David Jackson.

How many scores he had to settle with David Jackson! He thought of the massacre at Takama, the kidnapping of his young wife, his two years in Fernando Po, and he gripped the long, sharp bush knife more tightly. Soldiers or no soldiers, he was going in that cottage.

As he approached the house, he kept cautiously out of the glare of the lights that poured from the front windows. A sentry, armed with rifle and fixed bayonet, was ambling slowly around the cottage. When he had passed and gone to the rear, Zo leaped stealthily upon the verandah and quickly entered the door.

The Director of Public Works sat, sotted and red-eyed, before his table, head on hands, staring at a nearly empty bottle and half-filled glass before him. His shirt was open, and his head kept slipping from the support of his hands. His hand shook as he reached again for his glass and, with a quick backward jerk of his head, sent the fiery fluid down his throat.

Jackson jumped up, wild-eyed, as the avenger, an insane light of hatred in his eyes, confronted him with the upraised bush knife. He did not recognize Zo.

"Wha' you want?" he shouted, in fright. "Get outta here! Hey, sentry! Sentry!"

"You know Pameta?" asked Zo, between his teeth. "Well, I am her husband. You stole her! You ruined her! You killed her! Now I kill you!"

"Sentry!" cried Jackson again, backing away from his attacker, but the cry came too late.

Zo brought down the upraised knife with an oblique, swishing blow that had the force of intense hatred and thirst for revenge behind it. The blade bit into Jackson's neck before he could raise his arm to ward off the blow. His head almost severed, the official fell heavily to the floor, the blood gushing from his wound like water from a hydrant. Zo leaped upon his inert body and hacked it a dozen times in an orgy of insane rage.

The sound of Jackson's fall brought the sentry to the door, his rifle at the ready, its cruel bayonet gleaming in the lamplight. Zo turned to escape through the nearest window, but he was just too late. Taking in the situation at a glance, the soldier leveled his rifle, fired one shot—and the young Gola lad fell back into the room, with a gaping hole in the back of his head, his brains spattering over the bloody thing that once had been David Jackson.

CHAPTER ELEVEN

ELECTION DAY in Monrovia was an exciting time. Crowds of Krus, Vais, Bassas and other tribesmen wandered through the streets from one polling place to another, steered by efficient workers of the Conservative Party. Thousands of dollars had been spent for liquor and food, and even the lowliest individual was assured of plenty to drink and eat. Clutching their fraudulent deeds, signed in blank by the thousands with the signature of Sidney Cooper Johnson, the ignorant natives voted as they were told.

According to Liberian law, only owners of property can vote. To assure the Conservative Party of continuance in power, each President signed thousands of blank deeds, which were distributed throughout the civilized section of the republic to those who could be depended upon to vote Conservative. Of course, all deeds presented for registration by members of the Liberal Party were carefully scrutinized for the slightest error.

In front of the main polling place a crowd

of three or four thousand natives and Americo-
Liberians milled around, voting as frequently
as possible and being as often challenged
ineffectually by the watchers of the Liberal
Party. Nearby was a shed from which was
being dispensed much cheap gin and steaming
hot food, all provided by the Conservative
Party. As soon as the hungry native had
filled his stomach and grown tipsy, he was cor-
ralled by party workers and taken to cast his
ballot.

Nearby stood three or four motor trucks,
ready to carry those who had already voted
to distant points in the county, where they
might vote again. Vice President Williams
was appropriately enough in charge of this
work. Sweating profusely, beaming, and
moving his hands expansively, he could be
seen steering those who had been voted out
to the trucks, and as each one was filled he
would send it away with a party worker on
the seat next to the driver.

Tom Saunders, the Presidential nominee of
the Liberal Party, went from place to place
with a group of his young men, protesting
against the open frauds that were being perpetrated. But the police and soldiers on guard
ignored him. Rufus Henderson, his attorney,

swore out dozens of warrants for the arrest of Conservative Party workers, but no one was arrested. Some of the Liberal Party workers were beaten up and thrown out of polling places and a few were arrested on charges of disorderly conduct.

The mob spirit ran high. Bands of ragged natives filled with cheap gin marched along the streets, shouting for Johnson and denouncing Tom Saunders and the Liberal Party. The band of the Frontier Force pranced up and down the rocky thoroughfares, playing discordantly but loudly. Soldiers appeared everywhere with rifles and fixed bayonets.

With nightfall came the full, red, tropical moon. It hung over the city like a huge, swollen tangerine. The polls were closed, but the celebration had just begun. In a dozen places dancing started, and went on until dawn, affording a glimpse of Monrovian night life to the drunken natives imported to cast their ballots. The thud of the drums kept on monotonously, and police, soldiers, and natives joined in a wild orgy of celebration.

Over at the government radio station, the Vice President sat in an easy chair, getting returns from the distant Maryland County.

Down from Cape Mount, and up from Sinoe
and Marshall, swift runners were bringing
the results of the balloting.

In Tom Saunders' office several of the Liberal Party workers sat glumly around. All
knew that again they had lost an election.
Four times now they had put their candidate
in the field against the Conservatives and four
times he had been defeated. It seemed a hopeless task.

"We've got to fight fire with fire," Rufus
Henderson was saying. "If we can't win by
fair means then we'll have to descend to the
Conservative Party's level."

"Well, there are only two things we can
do, Rufe," said Saunders, "we'll either have
to have an election supervised by outsiders or
else overthrow the government. There is no
other alternative."

"For my part," exclaimed a young fellow
recently returned from college abroad, "I
think the best course we can adopt is revolu-
tion. Nothing good will come from bringing
in outsiders—it's so hard to get them out
again."

The sun was high next morning when Vice
President Samuel Williams drove up to the

Executive Mansion. The soldiers straightened in salute as he strode, beaming, through the open doorway and up the red-carpeted stairway. Hailing Colonel Fitzsimmons, the aide-de-camp, he pushed open the door of the President's office and entered.

The Chief Executive was pacing back and forth, awaiting the arrival of his colleague, a light frown corrugating his forehead. President Johnson hated suspense. He knew the party had done everything to assure his re-election, and yet one could never be sure. He turned with relief as Williams came in.

"Any good news?" he asked, forcing a faint smile.

"Why, man," Williams exploded, "you're good for four more years."

"How can you be sure so soon, Sammy?" he inquired. "You know the Liberal Party put up a stronger fight than usual this time."

"Why, the Liberals never had a chance," said Williams disdainfully. "It's booze and chop that swings these elections. And of course our other little tricks help some, too. I've got the returns from Grand Cape Mount, Montserrado and Maryland Counties, and we've gone over big, gone over big, I tell you. We're sure of carrying the other places, and

if we don't it won't change the result. Rest
easy, Johnson, rest easy. It's all over but the
shouting."

"Well, that's comforting, Sammy," said the
President in a relieved tone.

"Yes, it sure is," the Vice President agreed.
"We've got nothing to worry about now for
four more years."

"What did the election cost us?" asked
Johnson, seating himself before his glass-
topped desk.

"All we had in our treasury," Williams
answered, "just about thirty-three thousand
dollars. But it's worth it, don't you think?"

"Yes, of course," Johnson agreed.

"Now, Chief," said Williams, "we've got to
get a new Director of Public Works. Things
have slowed up in the hinterland since Jackson was killed. . . . By God! It's sure too
bad about Jackson. Valuable man, he was,
and to think of him being killed by a lousy,
no 'count native! Anyhow, we've got to get
somebody up there to push that work. Think
it over, Chief, think it over."

"Yes, Sammy, I shall," the President assured him.

When the other man had gone, President
Johnson rose, walked over to the French win-

dows, and looked down on the straggling city.
It was a happy day for him. In the distance
stood his finished residence, and before it was
parked his gleaming new limousine, fresh from
America.

Hell! He wasn't sorry Jackson had been
killed when he knew Sammy Williams and the
other party men had been grooming him for
the presidency. If anything, his murder had
been a blessing. Sure, David Jackson had
been an asset to the Conservative Party in a
financial way, but he was getting entirely too
popular and powerful for Sidney Cooper
Johnson.

Now he was safe for four years more. That
meant sixty thousand dollars in salary and
whatever else came along. The opposition
was crushed, but that damned Tom Saunders
was still a menace. The idea of him trying
to have Liberia investigated by foreigners!
Why, the man ought to be shot! Guess this
country could solve its own problems.

The President turned from the window, re-
sumed his seat, and tapped the bell on his desk.
The outer door flew open and Colonel Fitzsimmons entered.

"Colonel," said Johnson, "where is Captain
Burns stationed now?"

"Still in District Number One, sir," replied the aide-de-camp.

"Well, send for him to come down here at once," the President commanded. "Don't you think he'd be a good man to handle the road building?"

"From what I know of him, sir," said the Colonel, "you couldn't have a more efficient Director of Public Works. He understands the natives so well."

"And what's more important," mused the President, half aloud, "he isn't burdened with scruples."

THE END

CATASTROPHE MODELING:
A NEW APPROACH TO
MANAGING RISK

Huebner International Series on Risk, Insurance, and Economic Security

J. David Cummins, Editor
The Wharton School
University of Pennsylvania
Philadelphia, Pennsylvania, USA
Series Advisors:
Dr. Phelim P. Boyle
University of Waterloo, Canada
Dr. Jean Lemaire
University of Pennsylvania, USA
Professor Akihiko Tsuboi
Kagawa University, Japan
Dr. Richard Zeckhauser
Harvard University, USA

Other books in the series:

CATASTROPHE MODELING: A NEW APPROACH TO MANAGING RISK

PATRICIA GROSSI

HOWARD KUNREUTHER

Managing Editors

Risk Management and Decision Processes Center
The Wharton School
University of Pennsylvania

assisted by

CHANDU C. PATEL, FCAS, MAAA (EDITOR)

Springer

Library of Congress Cataloging-in-Publication Data

A C.I.P. catalogue record is available from the Library of Congress

Catastrophe modeling : a new approach to managing risk / Patricia Grossi, Howard
    Kunreuther, editors ; assisted by Chandu C. Patel.
      p.   cm.
    Includes bibliographical references and index
    ISBN 0-387-23082-3 (hardcover)   0-387-24105-1 (paperback) 0-387-23129-3 (e-Book)
    1.Risk management. 2. Risk (Insurance) 3. Natural disasters. 4. Insurance, Disaster.
    I. Grossi, Patricia. II. Kunreuther, Howard. III. Patel, Chandu C.

Printed in the United States of America.

9 8 7 6 5 4 3 2 1   SPIN 11409342 (Hardcover) 11408208 (paperback)

springeronline.com

Contents

Contributing authors:

Weimin Dong, Risk Management Solutions
Patricia Grossi, Risk Management Solutions
Paul Kleindorfer, The Wharton School, University of Pennsylvania
Howard Kunreuther, The Wharton School, University of Pennsylvania
Dennis Kuzak, EQECAT
David Lalonde, AIR Worldwide Corporation
Tom Larsen, EQECAT
Mehrdad Mahdyiar, AIR Worldwide Corporation
Erwann Michel-Kerjan, The Wharton School, University of Pennsylvania
Beverly Porter, AIR Worldwide Corporation
Don Windeler, Risk Management Solutions

Preface and Acknowledgments

This book had its genesis in June 1996 when the Wharton Risk Management and Decision Processes Center (Wharton Risk Center) co-hosted a conference on "Information Technology and Its Impact on Catastrophic Risks". It was one of the events that year celebrating the 50th Anniversary of the first computer (ENIAC) at the University of Pennsylvania. The focus of the conference was on the challenges in dealing with natural disasters. There had been two catastrophic events several years before — Hurricane Andrew in 1992 and the Northridge earthquake in 1994 — that had raised grave concerns within the private and public sectors as to what steps should be taken to deal with future losses from these and other natural hazards. The conference featured presentations by scientific experts on assessing these risks, three leading firms [AIR Worldwide, EQECAT and Risk Management Solutions (RMS)] on modeling the risks using information technology, and the development of new strategies by insurers, reinsurers and financial institutions for managing catastrophic risks.

Over the past 8 years, representatives from all these constituencies have worked together as part of the Wharton Managing Catastrophic Risks project to examine the role of catastrophe modeling in assessing and managing natural disaster risk. This book is truly a joint effort with the modeling firms and reflects the critical commentary and evaluations from key individuals in insurance and reinsurance companies as well as financial institutions who provided funds for the research activities.

From 1996 through 2001, the project was a joint venture between the Wharton Financial Institutions Center (WFIC) and the Wharton Risk Center. We want to express our deep appreciation to Anthony Santomero, director of the WFIC during the first five years of the project, Peter Burns, project manager, and Steve Levy, project coordinator, during this period. Thanks also go to Franklin Allen, Richard Herring and Carol Leisenring who assumed leadership positions at the WFIC after Anthony Santomero and Peter Burns moved on from the Wharton School in 2000.

From the outset, our goal was to undertake state-of the-art research on the role of risk assessment in developing meaningful strategies for managing catastrophic risks. Although our focus was on natural hazards, we viewed the project as one that could be applied to a wide variety of extreme events. In fact, since 2002 the Managing Catastrophic Risks project has morphed into the Managing Extreme Events project, which is one of the major ongoing activities at the Wharton Risk Center.

To ensure the highest scientific standards, we formed a Technical Advisory Committee (TAC) whose role was to provide detailed commentary on the models developed by AIR Worldwide, EQECAT and Risk

Management Solutions. For the first few years of the project, this committee met at least once a year and several members attended the semi-annual project meetings. The TAC provided insightful comments on the use of the models as a linkage between risk assessment and risk management and urged the modeling firms to coordinate their efforts to the highest extent possible. They were principally responsible for convincing the three firms that it would be beneficial to all if a comparative study of earthquake risk were completed. As a result, a study in Charleston, South Carolina presented in this book illustrates the opportunities of utilizing these models for estimating risks, while at the same time demonstrating the degrees of uncertainty surrounding loss estimates.

Each of the three firms permitted members of the TAC to examine their models. Subsets of the TAC visited AIR Worldwide, EQECAT and Risk Management Solutions for a full day for this purpose. These TAC members then wrote up reports on the technical accuracy of the models that they shared with each firm as well as with the Wharton team. Through this process and without revealing any confidential information, the TAC members were convinced that all three firms base their models on the best scientific information available. Without this assurance from the TAC we would not be writing this book.

Most of the TAC members also commented on earlier drafts of the chapters in the book. In particular, we want to thank Roger Borcherdt (USGS), William Holmes (Rutherford & Chekene), William Iwan (Cal Tech), and Robert Whitman (MIT), who spent considerable time in going over the material on the book and writing up extensive comments for us. The other members of the TAC who provided us with advice and guidance on the project and to whom we owe a debt of gratitude are: Joe Golden (NOAA), Mark Johnson (University of Central Florida), Ralph Keeney (Duke University), Peter Sparks (University of South Carolina), Kathleen Tierney (University of Colorado, Boulder), and Susan Tubbesing (EERI).

There are numerous other individuals and firms who played a key role in this effort. Jim Tilley from Morgan Stanley and Jerry Isom from CIGNA (now ACE) convinced their organizations to provide initial seed funding for the project. Other sponsors included American Re, General Re, Goldman Sachs, Japan Property and Casualty Association, State Farm, Swiss Re, and Tokio Marine. A number of individuals from these organizations provided us with extremely helpful comments at various stages of the project. They include: James Ament (State Farm), David Durbin (Swiss Re), Carl Hedde (American Re), Robert Irvan (CIGNA/ACE), Jeff Warren (General Re), Gordon Woo (Risk Management Solutions), Yuichi Takeda (Tokio Marine). American Re (Carl Hedde, Mark Bove, and Hjortur Thraisson) provided key information on historic losses. Goldman Sachs (Vivek Bantwal and Ohi Akhigbe) also provided helpful comments on the current state of catastrophe bonds and other new financial instruments.

Special thanks go to the leadership in all three modeling firms for agreeing to share their software with the Wharton team and to open their doors to a dialog with academia: Karen Clark from AIR Worldwide; Dennis Kuzak from EQECAT; and Tom Hutton, Haresh Shah, and Terry van Gilder, who were at Risk Management Solutions when the project started.

The research on this book occurred over a span of almost 9 years, so there have been a number of individuals who have played a key role in helping to undertake the research that forms the basis for each of the chapters. At the beginning of each chapter, we list the principal authors who took the lead in writing the material, but there are others who played a role in providing data for the various chapters. In particular, we want to thank Vivek Bantwal, Jessica Binder and Jaideep Hebbar, three remarkable undergraduate students at Wharton, who were indefatigable in their efforts working with the modeling groups. Without their assistance, Chapters 8 and 9 in the book could not have been written. Paul Kleindorfer, co-director of the Wharton Risk Center, played a key role in providing inputs and guidance on the project from its very outset. He participated in all the meetings of the project and provided invaluable comments and suggests on all aspects of the research. We would also like to thank Neil Doherty and Dave Cummins from Wharton for their helpful comments and suggestions at various stages of the project. Both Neil and Dave were undertaking complementary studies of risk transfer instruments and insurance as part of the Managing Catastrophic Risks project and were also involved in the meetings with the sponsors of the project. We also had helpful discussions with Daigee Shaw of Academia Sinica in Taipei, Taiwan. Erwann Michel-Kerjan of the Wharton Risk Center has reviewed the entire book and provided insightful comments as to how the material on natural hazards linked to other extreme events, notably terrorism.

We both had a wonderful time working with our co-conspirators from the modeling companies, without whose active involvement this book would never have been written: David Lalonde, Beverly Porter, and Mehrdad Mahdyiar from AIR Worldwide, Dennis Kuzak and Tom Larsen from EQECAT, Weimin Dong and Don Windeler from Risk Management Solutions.

Chandu Patel from the Casualty Actuarial Society volunteered to play the role of editor and has gone through every chapter with a fine tooth comb, making a number of extremely helpful suggestions for improving the flow of material. We want to thank Cathy Giordano from ACE and Tara Newman from the Wharton Risk Center for their help in coordinating this effort. We were also fortunate to have Ann Perch from the Wharton School and Hannah Chervitz from the Wharton Risk Center go through the entire book to make sure it was readable to a more general audience and was in final camera-ready form for the publisher.

This has been a long journey that has taken Patricia Grossi through her doctoral dissertation at the University of Pennsylvania, to an Assistant Professor at Southern Methodist University and finally to her current position at Risk Management Solutions. On September 3, 2001, Howard Kunreuther began a one-year sabbatical at the Earth Institute (Columbia University) and has been involved in terrorism research ever since September 11th. The last chapter of the book reflects the broader objectives of catastrophe modeling by applying the concepts from natural hazards to this risk.

Our families have been part of the process from the very beginning and our spouses, Mohan Balachandran and Gail Loeb Kunreuther, deserve special thanks for their encouragement and understanding.

Patricia Grossi
Howard Kunreuther

Prelude

The aftermath of a natural disaster, such as an earthquake, flood, hurricane, can be devastating. There is a tremendous sense of personal as well as economic loss. Immediately following the disaster, the actual devastation as well as media coverage related to the event causes the affected individuals as well the general public to be keenly aware of the risk of catastrophes. Unfortunately, this awareness often fades with time and the importance of being prepared is often forgotten. There are, however, a large number of individuals who spend a great deal of time and energy modeling natural disasters and enlightening others on ways in which their impact can be managed.

The goal of this book is to bring the reader up to date on recent developments in the nature and application of catastrophe models used to manage risk from natural disasters. It describes current and potential future uses of such models. The book emphasizes natural disasters, but also discusses application of the models to the terrorist attacks of September 11, 2001. The book is targeted to individuals concerned with monitoring and managing the impact of catastrophe risks. For example:

- Senior insurance and reinsurance managers can gain insight into the policy implications of competing hazard management strategies.
- Actuaries and underwriters can learn how catastrophe modeling, in its current form of user-friendly software, can facilitate their portfolio analyses.
- Federal, state and local government employees can learn to expand their definition of risk management to include the role that insurance can play in protecting their organizations against loss.
- Structural engineers, proficient in seismic and wind resistant design, can examine the latest approaches to modeling the fragility of a building system.
- Other experts interested in catastrophe modeling, including earth scientists, computer scientists, economists, and geographers, can discover their role in creating the next generation of models.

Roadmap of the Book

Part I of this book provides an introduction to risk management and catastrophe models. Chapter 1 indicates the need to manage risk and describes the key stakeholders involved in the process. Chapter 2 provides an introduction to catastrophe models and insurance. It introduces the components of a catastrophe model and how catastrophe models aid insurers in assessing their portfolio risk. The chapter concludes by introducing a framework for integrating risk assessment with risk management strategies via catastrophe modeling.

Part II of the book delves more deeply into the complex process of linking the science of natural hazards to the output from catastrophe models. Chapter 3 discusses the components of catastrophe modeling in more detail, including the hazard, inventory, vulnerability, and loss modules. This chapter clarifies how data are incorporated into catastrophe models and how modeling techniques facilitate the assessment of earthquake and hurricane risk.

Chapter 4 discusses the treatment of uncertainty in a catastrophe model. Catastrophe modeling is an evolving science; there are assorted interpretations and approaches to the modeling process. Differences in the output from competing catastrophe models are presented for hurricane and earthquake risk. Using the Charleston, South Carolina region as an example, the chapter highlights how uncertainty in modeling risks affects estimates of future losses.

Part III examines how catastrophe modeling currently aids insurers and other stakeholders in managing the risks from natural hazards. After a general overview of current practices used by insurers, specific examples of risk management strategies are discussed in Chapters 5 though 7. Chapter 5 focuses on the actuarial principles for insurance rate making. Special emphasis is given to the role of catastrophe modeling in earthquake risk classification and rate setting for residential structures in the state of California.

Chapter 6 focuses on the role of catastrophe modeling in quantifying an insurer's portfolio risk. One of an insurer's principal concerns when constructing a portfolio of risks is to reduce the possibility of unusually large losses. Special attention is given to ways that models can address uncertainty issues and reduce the chances of highly correlated losses in an insurer's portfolio.

Chapter 7 provides a comprehensive discussion of risk financing for an organization and the regulatory basis for the design of risk transfer instruments. The chapter illustrates the role that catastrophe modeling plays in evaluating these financing schemes and discusses the reasons why there has been limited interest by investors in utilizing new financial instruments.

Part IV illustrates how catastrophe models can be utilized in developing risk management strategies for natural disasters and terrorism. In Chapter 8, insurers consider a specific risk management strategy – requiring homeowners to adopt specific mitigation measures – in determining the pricing of a policy and the amount of coverage to offer. Utilizing data provided by the three leading modeling firms (AIR Worldwide, EQECAT, and Risk Management Solutions), three hypothetical insurance companies are formed to provide earthquake or hurricane coverage to homeowners in Oakland, California, Long Beach, California and Miami/Dade County, Florida. The analyses illustrate the impact of loss reduction measures and catastrophe modeling uncertainty on an insurer's profitability and likelihood of insolvency.

Chapter 9 builds on the analyses presented in Chapter 8 by examining the role of risk transfer instruments in providing protection to insurers against losses from natural disasters. The chapter examines the impact of reinsurance and catastrophe bonds on the profitability of an insurer and the return on assets to investors in the insurance company.

Chapter 10 concludes the book by focusing on how catastrophe modeling can be utilized in dealing with terrorism. The chapter examines the challenges faced by the U.S. in providing terrorism coverage after the September 11th attacks. Given the uncertainties associated with this risk and the potential for catastrophic losses, there is a need for public-private partnerships to reduce future losses and provide financial assistance after a terrorist attack.

A Glossary at the end of the book provides definitions of scientific, engineering and economic terms used throughout the book. This should aid the reader in understanding key words that are often used to characterize and analyze risks.

PART I

FRAMEWORK FOR RISK MANAGEMENT USING CATASTROPHE MODELS

Part I of this book is an introduction to natural hazards and catastrophe risk management. Chapter 1 discusses the history of natural disaster loss and introduces the stakeholders who manage catastrophe risk, along with their motivations and relationships to one another. The chapter also discusses the role of the public and private sectors in managing risk. Chapter 2 turns to the development of catastrophe models and the use of insurance in managing catastrophe risk. The concept of an exceedance probability curve is introduced. This is a key element used throughout the book for communicating risk to a stakeholder. Finally, a conceptual framework is presented that illustrates the critical role that catastrophe modeling plays in managing risk.

San Francisco, California, Earthquake April 18, 1906. Fault trace 2 miles north of the Skinner Ranch at Olema. View is north. Plate 10, U.S. Geological Survey Folio 193; Plate 3-A, U.S. Geological Survey Bulletin 324.

Chapter 1 – Introduction: Needs, Stakeholders, and Government Initiatives

Major Contributors:
Patricia Grossi
Howard Kunreuther

1.1 Need to Manage Risk

The problem of preparing for a natural disaster is not a new one. Around the world and particularly in the more-developed countries, governments, individuals and corporations know they should prepare for a "big earthquake" or a "large hurricane" or an "extensive flood." Yet, they often do not take the necessary steps to prepare for a disaster. Only after a disaster occurs do they recognize the importance of preparing for these types of extreme events.

A major earthquake or hurricane can result in loss of life and serious damage to buildings and their contents. Bridges and roads can be damaged and closed for repair over long periods of time. Disaster victims may need to be relocated to temporary shelters or reside with friends or relatives for days or weeks. Businesses may have their activities interrupted due to facility damage or lack of utility service. For some businesses, this may result in insolvency. In August and September 2004, these challenges were obvious when Florida and other states as far north as New Jersey and Pennsylvania were deluged by Hurricanes Charley, Frances, Ivan, and Jeanne.

The need to prepare for these types of extreme events is evident when evaluating the economic consequences of natural disasters. Figure 1.1(a) and Figure 1.1(b) depict the losses due to great natural catastrophes from 1950 to 2002 throughout the world. A great natural catastrophe is defined as one where the affected region is "distinctly overtaxed, making interregional or international assistance necessary. This is usually the case when thousands of people are killed, hundreds of thousands are made homeless, or when a country suffers substantial economic losses, depending on the economic circumstances generally prevailing in that country" (Munich Re, 2002). These figures include data on the overall economic and insured losses worldwide (in 2002 dollars) from earthquakes, floods, windstorms, volcanic eruptions, droughts, heat waves, freezes, and cold waves.

Figure 1.1(a) suggests a good deal of variation in losses with time. The figure illustrates that in certain years, such as 1976, 1988, 1995, and 1999, there are peaks in the amount of loss. Furthermore, the amplitude of the peaks seems to be increasing over time. This trend is expected to continue as higher concentrations of population and built environment develop in areas susceptible to natural hazards worldwide. Additionally, worldwide losses during the 1990's exceeded $40 billion dollars each year with the exception of 1997. Losses were as high as $170 billion in 1995, primarily due to the large-scale earthquake that destroyed portions of Kobe in Japan in January of that year. Insured losses matched this growth during the same timeframe.

The volatility and trend in losses can be seen in the United States as well. Figure 1.2(a) and Figure 1.2(b) show the economic and insured losses from significant United States catastrophes from 1950 through 2002 with losses adjusted to 2002 dollars. U.S. catastrophes are deemed significant when there is an adjusted economic loss of at least $1 billion and/or over 50 deaths attributed to the event (American Re, 2002).

There are peaks in losses due to catastrophic events, as in worldwide losses (most prominently in 1989, 1992, and 1994), and the upward trend over the past 50 years is evident when broken down by decade, as seen in Figure 1.2(b). The losses from individual disasters during the past 15 years are an order of magnitude above what they were over the previous 35 years. Furthermore, prior to Hurricane Hugo in 1989, the insurance industry in the United States had never suffered a loss of over $1 billion from a single disaster. Since 1989, numerous disasters have exceeded $1 billion in insured losses. Hurricane Andrew devastated the coastal areas of southern Florida in August 1992, as well as damaging parts of south-central Louisiana causing $15.5 billion in insured losses. Similarly, on the west coast of the United States, insured losses from the Northridge earthquake of January 1994 amounted to $12.5 billion.

Residential and commercial development along coastlines and areas with high seismic hazard indicate that the potential for large insured losses in the future is substantial. The ten largest insured property losses in the United States, including the loss from 9/11, are tabulated in Table 1.1 adjusted to 2001 dollars (Insurance Information Institute, 2001). The increasing trend for catastrophe losses over the last two decades provides compelling evidence for the need to manage risks both on a national, as well as on a global scale.

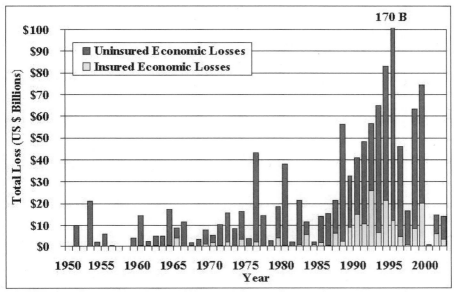

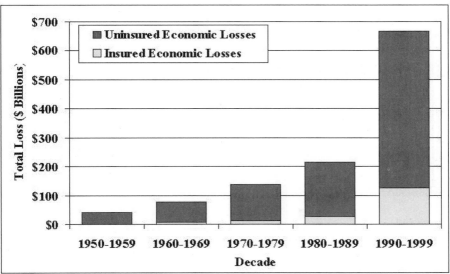

Figure 1.1. Losses due to great natural catastrophes worldwide: (a) by year; and (b) by decade (developed by the Geoscience Division of Munich Re).

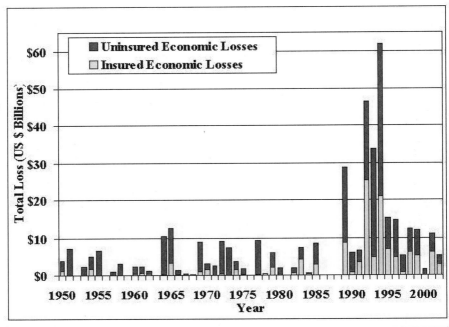

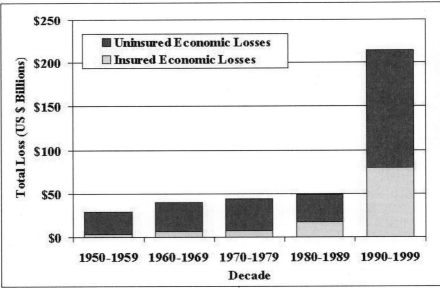

Figure 1.2. Losses due to significant U. S. natural catastrophes: (a) by year; and (b) by decade (developed by the Geoscience Division of American Re).

Table 1.1. Top 10 U.S. insured property losses (US $ billions)

Event	Dollars at year of occurrence	2001 dollars
World Trade Center (2001)	$20.3	$20.3[1]
Hurricane Andrew (1992)	$15.5	$19.6
Northridge Earthquake (1994)	$12.5	$14.9
Hurricane Hugo (1989)	$4.2	$6.0
Hurricane Georges (1998)	$2.9	$3.2
Tropical Storm Allison (2001)	$2.5	$2.5
Hurricane Opal (1995)	$2.1	$2.4
Hurricane Floyd (1999)	$2.0	$2.1
20-state winter storm (1993)	$1.8	$2.1
Oakland Firestorm (1991)	$1.7	$2.2

(Source: Insurance Information Institute)

1.2 Private Sector Stakeholders in the Management of Risk

The magnitude of economic and insured losses from natural disasters raises various questions. Who are the individuals affected by these events? What options are available to them to assess their risk? What factors influence their choices for dealing with these risks and actively managing their risk? By examining the perspectives of these individuals and groups, one can develop more effective risk management strategies for reducing potential losses from such disasters.

Figure 1.3 illustrates the key stakeholders in the management of risk that are discussed in this book. Each of the stakeholders' goals and perceptions of the risk lead them to view natural hazards from a unique perspective.

At the bottom of the pyramid are the property owners who are the primary victims of losses from natural disasters. They have to bear the brunt of the losses unless they take steps to protect themselves by mitigating or transferring some of the risk. Insurers form the next layer of the pyramid. They offer coverage to property owners against losses from natural disasters. Insurers themselves are concerned with the possibility of large claim payments from a catastrophe and turn to reinsurers, the next layer of the

---

[1] Some major claims are still in dispute; this does not include liability claims. Total insured losses due to the 9/11 attacks (including liability) are estimated around $35 billion as of July, 2004.

pyramid, to transfer some of their risk. At the top of the pyramid are the capital markets, which in recent years have provided financial protection to both insurers and reinsurers through financial instruments, such as catastrophe bonds. Of course, there are exceptions to this pyramid structure. For example, there have been two catastrophe bond issues (Concentric Re, covering Tokyo Disneyland, and Studio Re, covering Universal Studios) that offered direct protection to these property owners in place of traditional insurance arrangements.

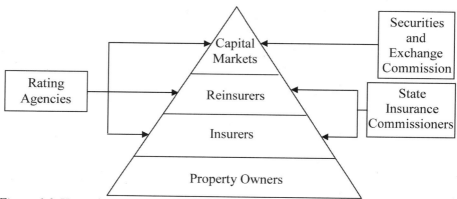

Figure 1.3. Key private sector stakeholders in the management of risk

The insurance rating agencies and state insurance commissioners are the two institutions that regulate the insurance industry. Rating agencies provide independent evaluations of the financial stability of the insurers and reinsurers. State insurance commissioners are primarily concerned that the rates charged by insurers are fair and that insurers in the market will remain solvent following a disaster. The Securities and Exchange Commission (SEC) regulates capital markets and catastrophe bonds are given bond ratings by organizations such as Fitch, Moody's Investor Service, and Standard & Poor's.

In the following sections, risk management strategies are discussed from the perspective of each stakeholder in the pyramid.

1.2.1 Property Owners

Owners of commercial and residential structures have a range of risk management strategies from which to choose. They can reduce their risk by retrofitting a structure to withstand wind or earthquake loading, transfer part of their risk by purchasing some form of insurance, and/or keep and finance their risk.

The ways in which particular individuals decide to manage risk is often a function of their perceptions. Despite a front-line position in facing the financial impacts of natural disasters, the average homeowner is one of the least active stakeholders in the process. For most, the choices are whether or not to buy insurance – if this is an option – and whether to take actions that would make their home more resistant to damage. Many homeowners do not take action even when the risk is abundantly clear and loss-reducing measures are available. It is often the case that these homeowners feel that a disaster will not affect them.

A commercial property owner's risk perception and strategies to manage risk are different from those of residential owners. A commercial establishment must concern itself not only with life safety and insolvency issues, but also with the impact of a natural hazard on the operation of its business. Often, there are extra expenses as a business tries to remain viable after a catastrophe. The company is concerned about business interruption loss – the loss or reduction of income due to the suspension of operations resulting from a natural disaster. Business owners in hazard-prone regions are normally quite interested in purchasing coverage against this type of risk.

1.2.2 Insurers

An insurer provides protection to residential and commercial property owners for losses resulting from natural disasters. Losses due to damage from fires (resulting from lightning during thunderstorms) and wind (resulting from tornadoes and hurricanes) are covered by a homeowner's insurance policy, normally required by lenders as a condition for a mortgage. In the U.S., loss due to water damage (resulting from floods) is covered under the National Flood Insurance Program (NFIP), a public-private partnership between the government and the insurance industry established in 1968. Losses due to damage from ground movement (resulting from earthquakes and landslides) are covered by a policy endorsement or by a separate policy. This separate policy is issued either by the private sector or, in California, through a state-run, privately funded earthquake insurance company, the California Earthquake Authority (CEA) that was created in 1996.

Losses from natural disasters can have a severe impact on an insurer's financial condition. Insurers, therefore, want to limit the amount of coverage they provide to property owners in hazard-prone areas. An important concern for insurers is the concentration of risk. Those who cover a large number of properties in a single geographic area face the possibility of large losses should a natural disaster occur in the area. An insurer views a portfolio with this type of highly correlated (or interrelated) risks as undesirable. Subject to regulatory restrictions, an insurer limits coverage in any given area and/or charges higher premiums in order to keep the chances of insolvency at an acceptable level.

1.2.3 Reinsurers

Reinsurers provide protection to private insurers in much the same way that insurers provide coverage to residential and commercial property owners. They traditionally supply indemnity contracts against unforeseen or extraordinary losses. In this type of arrangement, the reinsurer charges a premium in return for providing another insurance company with funds to cover a stated portion of the losses it may sustain. Most insurers, especially smaller or geographically concentrated firms, purchase reinsurance for covering natural hazard losses. Indeed, the failure to do so will likely adversely affect their financial rating and/or attract the attention of insurance regulators.

Similar to insurers, reinsurers concern themselves with concentration of risk. Hence, they too limit their exposure in catastrophe-prone areas to keep the chances of insolvency at an acceptable level. One way they achieve this is to pool the risks of several different insurers who have independent exposures in different high hazard regions. Thus, a reinsurer could take on Insurer A's hurricane risk in Florida, Insurer B's earthquake risk in California and Insurer C's earthquake risk in Tokyo, Japan. By diversifying across a number of regions and risks, the reinsurer is able to collect sufficient premiums to cover relatively large losses from a single disaster while at the same time reducing the likelihood of a catastrophic loss.

1.2.4 Capital Markets

The capital markets have recently emerged as a complement to reinsurance for covering large losses from disasters through new financial instruments known as catastrophe bonds (see Chapter 9). Several factors have led to this development. The shortage of reinsurance following Hurricane Andrew and the Northridge earthquake made it possible for insurers to offer bonds with interest rates high enough to attract capital from investors. In addition, the prospect of an investment uncorrelated with the stock market or general economic conditions is attractive to capital market investors. Finally, catastrophe models have emerged as a tool for more rigorous estimates of loss, so that disaster risk can be more accurately quantified than in the past.

Catastrophe bonds enable an insurer or reinsurer to access needed funds following a disaster. If the losses exceed a trigger amount, then the interest on the bond, the principal, or both, are forgiven. To justify the risks of losing their principal and/or interest, capital market investors demand a large enough risk-adjusted return to invest in these bonds. These investors include hedge fund managers, pension fund managers, insurers, and others, who concern themselves with the impact of the investment on their portfolio. In turn, the institutions that issue catastrophe bonds worry about their reputation should a major disaster negatively impact their investors' return.

1.2.5 Rating Agencies

Rating agencies, such as A.M. Best Company, Standard & Poor's, Moody's Investors Service, and Fitch, provide independent evaluations of reinsurers' and insurers' financial stability and their ability to meet their obligations to policyholders. The rating assigned to an insurer has significant consequences on how they do business. Many states have minimum rating requirements for an insurer to write business in their territory; similarly, insurers are less willing to cede risk to a poorly rated reinsurer. A poor rating has an impact on the premium a company can charge or the coverage it can sell, and is likely to have a negative effect on the share price of publicly traded firms.

A.M. Best Company, for example, assigns ratings through a quantitative analysis of a company's balance sheet strength, operating performance, and business profile (A.M. Best, 2001). Since at least 1997, A.M. Best Company has required insurance companies to complete a rating questionnaire that includes information on catastrophe exposures. Catastrophes play a significant role in evaluating a company's exposure, since these events could threaten the solvency of a company. Modeled loss results at specified return periods (100-year windstorm and 250-year earthquake), and the associated reinsurance programs to cover them, are important components of the rating questionnaire. A.M. Best Company's approach has been an important step forward in the incorporation of catastrophe risk into a company's capital adequacy requirements.

Investors also rely on the evaluations of catastrophe bonds by those rating agencies. These firms evaluate the quality of the risk analysis used in support of the issuance of a bond and require a variety of stress tests to check the sensitivity of the modeled losses. The resulting ratings influence the marketability and the price of a catastrophe bond. In addition, the rating can limit the potential buyer pool since some institutional investors will not participate in bonds with an unacceptable rating.

1.2.6 State Insurance Commissioners

In the United States, insurance is regulated at the state level with the principal regulatory authority residing with insurance commissioners. For insurers, two important and somewhat conflicting goals of this regulation are solvency regulation and rate regulation. Reinsurers are subject to the solvency regulation; however, they are not subject to rate regulation. Solvency regulation addresses the same concerns as rating evaluation: Is the insurer sufficiently capitalized to fulfill its obligations to its policyholders if a significant event occurs? A primary concern is the authorized control level of risk-based capital, the minimum amount of capital required below which the state has the authority to take action against the company.

Rate or market regulation attempts to ensure fair and reasonable insurance prices, products, and trade practices. Rate regulation focuses on whether insurance rates are equitable and nondiscriminatory. In all states, insurance companies are required to obtain a certificate of authority or license to underwrite policies. A license bureau provides a screening that in principle should protect the public from economic loss caused by misrepresentation, dishonesty, and incompetence of individuals seeking to sell insurance.

Solvency and rate regulation are closely related and must be coordinated to achieve their specific objectives. Regulation of rates and market practices will affect insurers' financial performance; solvency regulation ensures adequate capital. In this regard, the regulator plays a vital role in ensuring that a viable insurance market is functioning with coverage offered to consumers at affordable prices.

1.2.7 Other Stakeholders

Lenders play an essential role in managing natural disaster risk. Except for the uncommon case in which the owner pays for property outright, banks and other financial institutions enable individuals in the United States to purchase a home or business by providing mortgages. The property is the collateral in the event that the owner defaults on the mortgage.

Lenders thus have a vital stake in the risk management process, as they are unlikely to recover the full value of a loan on a piece of property destroyed by catastrophe. The 1994 Northridge earthquake, for example, generated $200-$400 million in mortgage-related losses in the Los Angeles area (Shah and Rosenbaum, 1996). Following Northridge, Freddie Mac experienced an unprecedented number of earthquake-related defaults on condominiums. As a consequence, the company retained a risk modeling firm to develop underwriting criteria that would identify high risk areas. Buyers of condominiums in these areas seeking a mortgage would then be required to buy earthquake insurance (Lehman, 1996). Interestingly enough, in 1996, the California State Legislature sought to bar this requirement, citing an undue burden on condominium owners. As a result, Freddie Mac changed its policy to require that a condominium buyer (a) purchase earthquake insurance; (b) purchase a property located in a low-risk area; or (c) pay an additional fee with the mortgage loan.

Real estate agents, developers, engineers, contractors, and other service providers also play a supporting, yet important role in the management of risk from natural disasters. In hazard-prone regions, federal or state regulations require real estate agents to inform the new owner of potential hazards. Examples include the location of a home relative to an earthquake fault line or within a 100-year flood plain. Unfortunately, it is sometimes unclear how information on natural hazard risk is being used in the purchase process. One study showed that despite the California requirement that purchasers of residential property within a certain distance of a known earthquake fault be told about the hazard, most home buyers did not understand or recall the risk warning (Palm, 1981).

Engineers and contractors can aid in the management of risk in high hazard areas. For example, structures designed and built to high standards, with inspections by reputable building officials during construction, provide good protection against life and property loss in the next earthquake or hurricane. Life and property loss are often attributable to inadequate design and construction practices. The problem of building and selling property in hazard-prone regions is exacerbated when disreputable building contractors bypass costly wind and seismic-resistant designs.

1.3 Government's Role in Management of Risk

Federal, state and local government often take the lead in managing risk from natural disasters. Policy makers at all levels of government have developed a set of programs for reducing risks from these disasters. In addition, they prioritize funding following a severe earthquake, flood, tornado, or other extreme event.

1.3.1 Types of Programs

Federal Level

At the national level, the Federal Emergency Management Agency (FEMA) coordinates many of the planning and response aspects related to catastrophes. Although specific programs come and go, FEMA has historically taken the lead in developing strategies for mitigation. For example, in December 1995, the agency introduced a National Mitigation Strategy with the objective of strengthening partnerships between all levels of government and the private sector to ensure safer communities.

This strategy was developed with input from state and local officials as well as individuals and organizations with expertise in hazard mitigation (FEMA, 1997). One of its key features was to create disaster-resistant communities through the Project Impact program. The program, begun in 1997, encouraged communities to "bring interested parties together to identify their potential natural hazards, assess the community's vulnerability, prioritize hazard risk reduction measures and communicate success to the residents" (FEMA, 2000). In 2001, over 250 communities participated in Project Impact.

Federal legislation that promotes natural disaster mitigation is another way to manage catastrophe risk. The Earthquake Loss Reduction Act of 2001 (HR.2762/S.424) and the Disaster Mitigation Act of 2000 (Public Law 106-380) are two such examples. The Disaster Mitigation Act, the latest amendment to the Robert T. Stafford Disaster Relief and Emergency Assistance Act, seeks to reduce losses to publicly owned buildings following disasters. While the federal government still provides funds to cover the majority of the cost to repair public facilities in the event of a disaster, there is a clause in the Disaster Mitigation Act of 2000 noting that the "President shall promulgate regulations to reduce the Federal share of assistance" if the eligible facility "has been damaged, on more than one occasion within the preceding 10-year-period, by the same type of event; and the owner of which has failed to implement appropriate mitigation measures to address the hazard that caused the damage to the facility." The message from the federal government is clear: local and state government officials are encouraged to mitigate.

The Earthquake Loss Reduction Act of 2001 takes a different approach to encourage mitigation. The legislation aims to "provide a number of incentives, including grants and tax credits, in order to encourage responsible state and local governments, individuals, and businesses to invest in damage prevention measures before an earthquake strikes" (Feinstein Press Release, March, 2001). As of May 2004, the Senate finance committee was still reviewing this legislation. Due to the concern of the federal government over terrorism risk, this legislation may not have the priority it had prior to 9/11.

The federal government also provides financial assistance to natural disaster victims through the Small Business Administration's (SBA) Disaster Loan Program. Over the years, the SBA has provided loans and sometimes forgiveness grants to cover homeowner and business losses from natural disasters. During the period between the Alaska Earthquake of 1964 and Tropical Storm Agnes in June 1972, the SBA was very generous in the type of disaster relief it provided. For example, those suffering uninsured losses after Agnes were eligible to receive $5,000 forgiveness grants and 30-year loans at 1% interest. In recent years, the SBA has not been as generous; disaster loans in 2003 were offered at interest rates just slightly below the existing market rate.

State Level

At the state level, an office of emergency services or a department of public safety promotes natural disaster preparedness. Additionally, seismic safety commissions have been established by earthquake-prone states to prioritize earthquake research and public policy needs. Building codes that include criteria for wind or earthquake resistance and legislation for land use management endeavor to reduce risk.

Incentive programs have been instituted to reduce losses from disaster events, especially in hazard-prone states. A good example of such legislation is California's Proposition 127. Passed in November of 1990, the law states that seismic retrofits to property completed on or after January 1, 1991, and completed on or before July 1, 2000, will not increase the property tax for a homeowner until ownership changes. The state concluded that these improvements constitute such a significant reduction in the risks to life and safety, that they should be exempt from additional property tax.

Local Level

At the local level, communities enforce building codes and have developed economic incentives, such as tax relief, for those who retrofit. Local communities have developed programs to promote awareness, provide training, and encourage self-help actions through neighborhood emergency response teams. For example, the city of San Leandro, California has set priorities to retrofit both unreinforced masonry buildings (URMs) and older wood-frame homes. The Home Earthquake Strengthening Program is a comprehensive, residential seismic strengthening program that provides homeowners with simple and cost-effective methods for strengthening their wood-frame houses for earthquake survival. The program includes earthquake-strengthening workshops for residents, a list of available earthquake contractors, as well as a tool-lending library for homeowners should they wish to do the work themselves.

Table 1.2 provides a set of examples of leadership activities at the different levels of government: for defining and prioritizing risks, for alleviating risks through legislative means, and for encouraging reduction of earthquake risk. These programs bring together diverse groups of people around a common issue, and provide needed encouragement and resources.[2]

1.3.2 Federal Disaster Insurance

The federal and state governments in the United States now play a major role in supplementing or replacing private insurance with respect to floods, hurricanes, and earthquakes. This coverage is limited to certain key stakeholders, mainly residential property owners.

Flood Insurance

Insurers have experimented over the years with providing protection against water damage from floods, hurricanes and other storms. After the severe Mississippi Floods of 1927, they concluded that the risk was too great. With the need for this type of coverage evident, Congress created the National Flood Insurance Program (NFIP) in 1968, whereby homes and businesses could purchase coverage for water damage. The stipulation for this financial protection was that the local community make a commitment to regulate the location and design of future floodplain construction to increase safety from

---

[2] See Grossi and Kunreuther (2000) for more details on earthquake programs and Moss (2002, Chapter 9) for a more general discussion of the role of the public sector in providing disaster assistance.

flood hazards. The federal government established a series of building and development standards for floodplain construction to serve as minimum requirements for participation in the program.

Table 1.2. Government leadership in managing earthquake risk (Grossi and Kunreuther, 2000)

	Define and Prioritize Risk	Legislation to Alleviate Risk	Encourage Risk Reduction
Federal Government	National Earthquake Hazards Reduction Program (NEHRP)	Robert T. Stafford Disaster Relief and Emergency Assistance Act	Federal Emergency Management Agency's Project Impact
State Government	State Seismic Safety Commissions California Earthquake Hazards Reduction Act	California Unreinforced Masonry Building Law	California Proposition 127
Local Government	Home Earthquake Strengthening Program (San Leandro, CA)	Earthquake Hazard Reduction Ordinance (Los Angeles, CA)	Tax Transfer Rebate (Berkeley, CA)

In the NFIP, private insurers market flood policies and the premiums are deposited in a federally operated Flood Insurance Fund, which then pays all legitimate claims. To encourage communities to participate in the program, and to maintain property values of structures, those residing in the area prior to the issuance of a flood insurance rate map (FIRM) have their premiums subsidized. New construction is charged an actuarial premium reflecting the risks of flood as well as efforts in mitigation (Interagency Flood Plain Management Review Committee, 1994). Additionally, the Community Rating System (CRS) was created in 1990 to recognize and encourage flood mitigation activities. The communities that are the most involved in floodplain management activities receive the greatest premium reduction; households or firms located in a community with no active risk management strategies receive no premium reductions (Pasterick, 1998).

Actuarial premiums are charged to property owners living outside the 100-year flood plain (i.e., the area where the annual chance of a flood occurring equals or exceeds 1%) or to those living within 100-year areas who build or substantially improve structures after the federal government provides complete risk information from the flood insurance rate map. Over time, the percentage of homes requiring a subsidy has declined. Whereas 41% of the 2.7 million policies were subsidized in 1993, only 30% of the 4.3 million policies were subsidized in 2000.

SIDEBAR 1: Loss estimation and policy in Oregon

For most of the 20th century, the lack of significant earthquakes in Oregon resulted in the state having minimal seismic requirements in its building code. Since the late 1980's, however, new scientific evidence reveals that massive earthquakes occurred offshore repeatedly before white settlement in the 19th century, most recently in 1700, and will likely reoccur (Clague and others, 2000; Atwater and Hemphill-Haley, 1997). While current building codes now reflect this consensus, the legacy of the older regulations leaves a building stock largely unprepared for significant earthquakes.

The Department of Geological and Mineral Industries (DOGAMI), Oregon's state geological survey, has been active in assessing the potential financial impact from the earthquake hazard. In addition to identifying and assessing sources of earthquake activity, DOGAMI has been using the federal government's loss estimation model, HAZUS, to quantify potential losses due to earthquakes on both the local and statewide levels (Wang and Clark, 1999; Vinson and Miller, 2000).

The HAZUS study was a catalyst for action within the state government. The Department of Administrative Services, which handles risk management for state-owned facilities, increased the level of earthquake insurance coverage following discussions with DOGAMI. With the growing awareness of the earthquake threat, the Oregon State Legislature drafted several bills in 2000 addressing the need for earthquake preparedness (SB 13) and retrofitting of critical structures such as schools (SB 14), hospitals, and fire stations (SB 15). HAZUS-derived statistics from Wang and Clark (1999), estimating $12 billion in losses and 8,000 casualties from a M8.5 offshore earthquake, were quoted in support of these bills. All three bills easily passed the State Legislature in 2001.

An important part of the bill's implementation will be the further incorporation of loss estimation tools. Funding for these propositions is not infinite and ideally should be allocated to targets where it will provide the most quantifiable benefit. DOGAMI will be involved in assessing the loss of life and property in communities most at risk and prioritizing these projects to optimize reduction of these losses (Beaulieu, 2001).

In January of 2003, Congress reauthorized the NFIP through the 2003 fiscal year. Also during this time, other legislation was introduced to amend the National Flood Insurance Act of 1968 to reduce losses to properties for which repetitive flood insurance claim payments have been made. At the time of the legislation's introduction in January of 2003, it was referred to subcommittee.

Hurricane Insurance

The need for hurricane insurance is most pronounced in the state of Florida. Following Hurricane Andrew in 1992, nine property-casualty insurance companies became insolvent, forcing other insurers to cover these losses under Florida's State Guaranty Fund. Property insurance became more difficult to obtain as many insurers reduced their concentrations of insured property in coastal areas.

During a special session of the Florida State legislature in 1993, a bill was enacted to handle the insurance availability crisis. It stipulated that insurers could not cancel more than 10% of their homeowners' policies in any county in one year, and that they could not cancel more than 5% of their property owners' policies statewide for each year the moratorium was in effect. At the same time, the Florida Hurricane Catastrophe Fund (FHCF) was created to relieve pressure on insurers to reduce their exposures to hurricane losses. The FHCF, a tax-exempt trust fund administered by the state of Florida, is financed by premiums paid by insurers that write insurance policies on personal and commercial residential properties. The fund reimburses a portion of insurers' losses following major hurricanes, and enables insurers to remain solvent while renewing most of their policies scheduled for non-renewal (Lecomte and Gahagan, 1998).

Earthquake Insurance

Historical earthquake activity in California convinced legislators that this risk was too great to be left solely in the hands of private insurers. In 1985, a California law required insurers writing homeowners' coverage on one to four unit residential buildings to also offer earthquake coverage. Since rates were regulated by the state, insurers felt they were forced to offer coverage against older structures in poor condition, with rates not necessarily reflecting the risk.

Following the 1994 Northridge earthquake, huge insured property losses created a surge in demand for coverage. Insurers were concerned that if they satisfied the entire demand, as they were required to do by the 1985 law, they would face an unacceptable level of risk and become insolvent following the next major earthquake. Hence, many firms decided to stop offering coverage, or restricted the sale of homeowners' policies in California.

In order to keep earthquake insurance alive in California, the State legislature authorized the formation of the California Earthquake Authority (CEA) in 1996. At the CEA's inception, all claims were subject to a 15% deductible. This meant that with full insurance on a house valued at $200,000, the property owner would have to pay the first $30,000 of repairs from future earthquake damage. In 1999, the CEA began offering wrap around policies, defined as policies with a 10% deductible, or additional contents coverage, or both. As of July 31, 2003, the CEA had 735,909 policies in force with total premiums of $428 million. Approximately 18% of those insured purchased a wrap around policy (California Earthquake Authority, 2003). In 2003, with insurers providing $743 million in cash contributions and up to $3.6 billion in possible future assessments, along with additional layers of funding from the reinsurance industry and lines of credit, the total CEA insurance pool capacity stood at $7 billion.

1.4 Summary of Chapter

This chapter provided an overview of the history of natural disasters and the nature of natural hazard risk, with a focus on the United States. Special emphasis was given to property owners at risk, the capital market, reinsurers, and insurers who provide financial protection, and the role that rating agencies and state insurance commissioners play in regulating these groups. With insured losses expected to grow in the future, this chapter serves as an introduction to the current role catastrophe models can play in helping insurers and other key stakeholders to manage this risk.

As government often takes on the responsibility of providing funds to cover damage from catastrophic disasters, it has an economic incentive to mitigate the risks from these events. While the state and federal governments often play this role, all the supporting entities in the management of risk (reinsurers, regulators, capital markets, lenders, engineers, contractors, real estate agents, and developers) have an opportunity to promote mitigation efforts and assist in the recovery after an event.

Insurers and property owners are the two stakeholders given principal consideration during the remaining chapters of this book. The next chapter presents a framework for characterizing their decision processes in choosing between competing risk management strategies. It is used throughout this book to illustrate existing and emerging solutions for managing catastrophe risk.

1.5. References

A.M. Best (2001). Preface: An explanation of Best's rating system and procedures. *2001 Best's Insurance Reports – Property / Casualty.* <http://www.ambest.com/ratings/2001/pcbirpreface.pdf >

American Re (2002). *Topics: Annual Review of North American Natural Catastrophes 2002.*

Atwater, B. and Hemphill-Haley, E. (1997). Recurrence intervals for great earthquakes of the past 3,500 years at northeastern Willapa Bay, Washington. *U.S. Geological Survey Professional Paper 1576.* 108p.

Beaulieu, J. (2001). Personal communication with Don Windeler, April 30, 2001.

California Earthquake Authority (2003). *Weekly Policy and Premium Status Report,* July 31, 2003.

Clague, J., Atwater, B.F., Wang, K., Wang, Y, and Wong, I. eds. (2000). Consensus statement. in *Penrose Conference 2000, Great Cascadia Earthquake Tricentennial. Oregon Dept. of Geol. and Mineral Industries Special Paper 33.* 17-18.

Federal Emergency Management Agency (1997). *Report on Costs and Benefits of Natural Hazard Mitigation,* Washington, D.C.

Federal Emergency Management Agency (2000). *HAZUS99 Estimated Annualized Earthquake Losses for the United States,* FEMA 366, Washington, D.C.

Feinstein Press Release (March 2001). http://feinstein.senate.gov/releases01/earthquakes.html.

Grossi, P. and Kunreuther, H. (2000). "Public Policy," Chapter 2 in *Financial Management of Earthquake Risk,* Oakland, CA: Earthquake Engineering Research Institute.

Insurance Information Institute (2001). <http://www.iii.org/media/hottopics/insurance/xxx/>

Interagency Flood Plain Management Review Committee (1994). *Sharing the Challenge: Floodplain Management into the 21st Century,* Washington, D.C: USGPO.

Lecomte, E. and Gahagan, K. (1998). "Hurricane Insurance Protection in Florida," Chapter 5 in Kunreuther, H. and Roth, R. *Paying the Price: The Status and Role of Insurance Against Natural Disasters in the United States.* Washington, D.C: Joseph Henry Press, p. 97-124.

Lehman, J. (1996). Freddie Mac takes industry lead, tackles earthquake risk head on. *Secondary Mortgage Markets: A Freddie Mac Quarterly* 13 (2): 17.

Moss, D. (2002). *When All Else Fails*, Cambridge, MA: Harvard University Press.

Munich Re (2002). *Topics: Natural Catastrophes 2002.*

Palm, R. (1981). *Real Estate Agents and Special Studies Zones Disclosure.* Boulder: Institute of Behavioral Science, University of Colorado.

Pasterick, E. (1998). "The National Flood Insurance Program," Chapter 6 in Kunreuther, H. and Roth, R. *Paying the Price: The Status and Role of Insurance Against Natural Disasters in the United States.* Washington, D.C: Joseph Henry Press, p. 125-154.

Shah, H., and Rosenbaum, D. (1996). Earthquake risk shakes mortgage industry. *Secondary Mortgage Markets: A Freddie Mac Quarterly* 13 (2): 12-19.

Vinson, B. and Miller, T.H. (2000). Pilot project: Eugene-Springfield earthquake damage and loss estimate final report, January 1999. *Oregon Dept. of Geol. and Mineral Industries Open-File Rept. O-00-02.*

Wang, Y. and Clark, J.L (1999). Earthquake damage in Oregon: Preliminary estimates of future earthquake losses. *Oregon Dept. of Geol. and Mineral Industries Special Paper 29.*

Chapter 2 – An Introduction to Catastrophe Models and Insurance

Major Contributors:
Patricia Grossi
Howard Kunreuther
Don Windeler

This chapter provides an overview of the history of catastrophe models and their role in risk assessment and management of natural disasters. It examines the insurability of catastrophe risk and illustrates how the output from catastrophe models aids insurers in meeting their goals for risk management. Throughout the chapter, there is an emphasis on understanding catastrophe modeling for earthquake and hurricane hazards and how it is used to manage natural hazard risk. In the final section, a framework for integrating risk assessment with risk management via catastrophe modeling is presented.

2.1 History of Catastrophe Models

Catastrophe modeling is not rooted in one field or discipline. The science of assessing and managing catastrophe risk originates in the fields of property insurance and the science of natural hazards. Insurers may well argue that catastrophe modeling's history lies in the earliest days of property insurance coverage for fire and lightning. In the 1800's, residential insurers managed their risk by mapping the structures that they covered. Not having access to Geographic Information Systems (GIS) software, they used tacks on a wall-hung map to indicate their concentration of exposure. This crude technique served insurers well and limited their risk. Widespread usage of mapping ended in the 1960's when it became too cumbersome and time-consuming to execute (Kozlowski and Mathewson, 1995).

On the other hand, a seismologist or meteorologist may well argue that the origin of catastrophe modeling lies in the modern science of understanding the nature and impact of natural hazards. In particular, the common practice of measuring an earthquake's magnitude and a hurricane's intensity is one of the key ingredients in catastrophe modeling. A standard set of metrics for a given hazard must be established so that risks can be assessed and managed. This measurement began in the 1800's, when the first modern seismograph (measuring earthquake ground motion) was invented and modern versions of the anemometer (measuring wind speed) gained widespread usage.

In the first part of the twentieth century, scientific measures of natural hazards advanced rapidly. By the 1970's, studies theorizing on the source and frequency of events were published. Significant analyses include the U.S. Water Resources Council publication on flood hazard (USWRC, 1967), the Algermissen study on earthquake risk (Algermissen, 1969) and National Oceanic and Atmospheric Administration (NOAA) hurricane forecasts (Neumann, 1972). These developments led U.S. researchers to compile hazard and loss studies, estimating the impact of earthquakes, hurricanes, floods, and other natural disasters. Notable compilations include Brinkmann's summary of hurricane hazards in the United States (1975) and Steinbrugge's anthology of losses from earthquakes, volcanoes, and tsunamis (1982).

These two separate developments – mapping risk and measuring hazard – came together in a definitive way in the late 1980's and early 1990's, through catastrophe modeling as shown in Figure 2.1. Computer-based models for measuring catastrophe loss potential were developed by linking scientific studies of natural hazards' measures and historical occurrences with advances in information technology and geographic information systems (GIS). The models provided estimates of catastrophe losses by overlaying the properties at risk with the potential natural hazard(s) sources in the geographic area. With the ability to store and manage vast amounts of spatially referenced information, GIS became an ideal environment for conducting easier and more cost-effective hazard and loss studies.

Around the same time, several new modeling firms developed computer software for analyzing the implications of natural hazard risk. Three major firms emerged: AIR Worldwide was founded in 1987 in Boston; Risk Management Solutions (RMS) was formed in 1988 at Stanford University; and EQECAT began in San Francisco in 1994 as a subsidiary of EQE International. In 2001, EQE International became a part of ABS Consulting.

When introduced, the use of catastrophe models was not widespread. In 1989, two large-scale disasters occurred that instigated a flurry of activity in the advancement and use of these models. On September 21, 1989, Hurricane Hugo hit the coast of South Carolina, devastating the towns of Charleston and Myrtle Beach. Insured loss estimates totaled $4 billion before the storm moved through North Carolina the next day (Insurance Information Institute, 2000). Less than a month later, on October 17, 1989, the Loma Prieta Earthquake occurred at the southern end of the San Francisco peninsula. Property damage to the surrounding Bay Area was estimated at $6 billion (Stover and Coffman, 1993).

These two disasters sent a warning signal to the insuranc
On the heels of these two events, Hurricane Andrew made lan
Southern Florida in August of 1992. Within hours of landfall, AIR World
issued a fax to its clients to the effect that losses, as estimated in real time b
the AIR Worldwide hurricane model, might reach the astonishing amount of
$13 billion. It was not until months later that the final tally, $15.5 billion, was
issued by the Property Claim Services Office.

Nine insurers became insolvent as a result of their losses from
Hurricane Andrew. Insurers and reinsurers realized that, in order to remain in
business, they needed to estimate and manage their natural hazard risk more
precisely. Many companies turned to the modelers of catastrophe risk for
decision support. The modeling companies grew and catastrophe models
increased in number, availability, and capability. By 2001, other organizations
joined these front-runners in developing catastrophe models for assisting
insurers and reinsurers in pricing their insurance policies and determining
how much coverage to offer in hazard-prone areas of the country.

The series of natural disasters in 1989 and 1992 also sent a warning
signal to the public sector of the United States. The government recognized
the need for an accurate assessment of the impact of disasters for mitigation
and emergency planning purposes. In 1992, the Federal Emergency
Management Agency (FEMA) funded a study to assess the latest loss
estimation methodologies for earthquakes. The agency issued a report in 1994
on the results of this study entitled: Assessment of the State of the Art
Earthquake Loss Estimation Methodologies (FEMA 249, 1994).

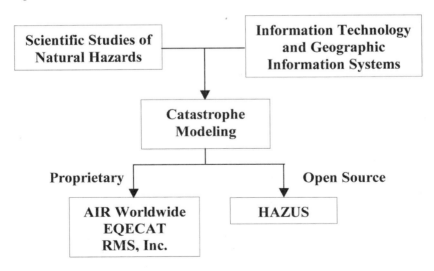

Figure 2.1. Development of catastrophe modeling.

inced FEMA to fund the development of "Hazards
strophe model in the public domain. HAZUS is
irce model in Figure 2.1. From the outset, one of
reate a methodology that was the "standard national
ssessing losses from natural hazards" (FEMA, 2002).
ZUS was developed with a combination of public and
stimate earthquake losses and was released in 1997
s to the HAZUS earthquake model have been in the
form of data and soft are integration; methodologically, the software remains
the same. In 2004, the latest HAZUS multi-hazard methodology, relabeled
HAZUS-MH, integrates the earthquake module with two new modules for
estimating potential losses from wind and flood (riverine and coastal) hazards.

2.2 Structure of Catastrophe Models

The four basic components of a catastrophe model are: hazard,
inventory, vulnerability, and loss as depicted in Figure 2.2. First, the model
characterizes the risk of natural hazard phenomena. For example, an
earthquake hazard is characterized by its epicenter location and moment
magnitude, along with other relevant parameters. A hurricane is characterized
by its projected path and wind speed. The frequency of certain magnitudes or
frequencies of events also describes the hazard in question.

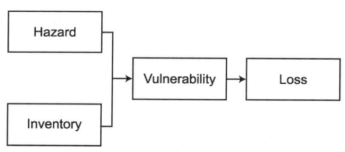

Figure 2.2. Structure of catastrophe models.

Next, the model characterizes the inventory or portfolio of properties
at risk as accurately as possible. Arguably, the most important parameter used
to characterize the inventory is the location of each property at risk. A process
called geocoding is normally used to assign geographic coordinates such as
latitude and longitude to a property based on its street address, ZIP code or
another location descriptor. With a property's location in spatial terms, other
factors that could aid in estimating the vulnerability of a property are added to
its characterization. For a building, these parameters include such features as
its construction type, the number of stories in the structure, and its age. If the

property is insured, information on the nature of the policy, such as the deductible and coverage limit, is also recorded.

The hazard and inventory modules enable the calculation of the vulnerability or susceptibility to damage of the structures at risk. In essence, this step in the model quantifies the physical impact of the natural hazard phenomenon on the property at risk. How this vulnerability is quantified differs from model to model. For example, the HAZUS model classifies a structure as being in a Slight, Moderate, Extensive, or Complete damage state. Other models construct damage curves and relate structural damage to a severity parameter, such as peak gust wind speed or spectral acceleration. In all models, damage curves are constructed for the building, its contents and time element losses, such as business interruption loss or relocation expenses.

From this measure of vulnerability, the loss to the inventory is evaluated. In a catastrophe model, loss is characterized as direct or indirect in nature. Direct losses include the cost to repair and/or replace a structure. Indirect losses include business interruption impacts and relocation costs of residents forced to evacuate their homes. Proprietary models include the ability to analyze insurance policies, so that the loss can be properly allocated. More details on these elements of a catastrophe model are provided in Chapter 3.

2.3 Uses of a Catastrophe Model for Risk Management

A catastrophe model is employed to assess catastrophe risk and improve risk management decisions. But how is this accomplished? Briefly, the model output is quantified and presented in a way that is useful to the stakeholder. Once these metrics are in hand, alternate risk management strategies, such as mitigation, insurance, reinsurance and catastrophe bonds, can be assessed. Currently, insurers and reinsurers are the stakeholders with the most widespread interest and integrated use of catastrophe models. Reinsurance brokers in particular have enhanced the use of catastrophe models. It is fairly common for a broker to collect data for potential clients, run the models on that data, and provide the output to interested reinsurers.

The capital markets have also been eager users of this technology in order to more accurately price catastrophe bonds. In fact, their recent interest and involvement in natural hazards have been made possible by the quantification afforded by catastrophe modeling. Property owners are less likely to use catastrophe models themselves, but their decision processes are directly or indirectly influenced by the outcomes. At the governmental level, catastrophe modeling presents both a positive opportunity and a political dilemma for regulators and emergency management agencies.

As an example of a positive use of the models, consider the use of HAZUS to measure the impact of an earthquake. One model output option is to create a GIS map of the potential loss. Given the definition of the hazard, including the earthquake's epicenter location, and the concentration of the properties at risk, Figure 2.3 depicts a map of the displaced households for the Charleston, South Carolina region subject to an M 7.3 earthquake. The largest concentration of loss, measured by the number of individuals seeking shelter following the disaster, is near the scenario's epicenter. This map is potentially useful to emergency response and recovery officials responding to a disaster.

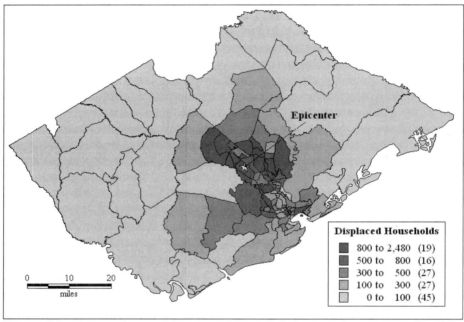

Figure 2.3. Catastrophe model output: Map of shelter requirements predicted by HAZUS for M 7.3 events in Charleston, South Carolina region.

Another output option is the exceedance probability (EP) curve. For a given portfolio of structures at risk, an EP curve is a graphical representation of the probability that a certain level of loss will be surpassed in a given time period. Special attention is given to the right-hand tail of this curve where the largest losses are situated. Figure 2.4 depicts an EP curve for an insurer with a portfolio of residential earthquake policies in Long Beach, California. In contrast to a GIS map of loss, which presents loss in a spatial manner, an exceedance probability curve portrays loss in a temporal manner.

An EP curve is particularly valuable for insurers and reinsurers to determine the size and distribution of their portfolios' potential losses. Based on the EP curve, they can determine the types and locations of buildings they would like to insure, what coverage to offer, and what price to charge. To keep the probability of insolvency at an acceptable level, insurers can also use an EP curve to determine what proportion of their risk needs to be transferred to either a reinsurer and/or the capital markets.

For example, suppose an insurer in Long Beach offers residential earthquake coverage and the insurer's exceedance probability curve for its portfolio is as depicted in Figure 2.4. Further suppose the insurer specifies $10 million as an acceptable level of loss at a 1% (1-in-100) probability of exceedance. Based on the graph, it can be seen that loss profile of the current portfolio would be unacceptable since the 1-in-100 loss for the portfolio is $15 million. The insurer would need to look for ways to reduce its portfolio, transfer $5 million of loss to a reinsurer, or purchase a catastrophe bond to cover it.

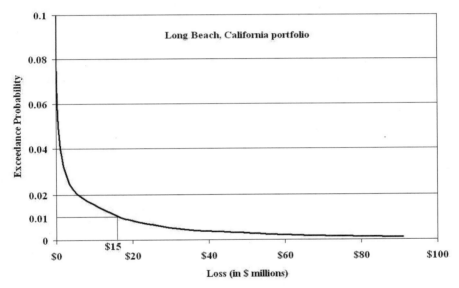

Figure 2.4. Catastrophe model output: Right-hand tail of exceedance probability curve predicted by EQECAT for all possible events.

2.4 Derivation and Use of an Exceedance Probability Curve

Given the importance of how insurers use catastrophe modeling and the EP curve to manage risk, it is essential to understand how the EP curve can be created from the loss output.

2.4.1 Generating an Exceedance Probability Curve

For the purposes of illustration, some simplifying assumptions are made to generate an EP curve. Suppose there is a set of natural disaster events, E_i, which could damage a portfolio of structures. Each event has an annual probability of occurrence, p_i, and an associated loss, L_i. The number of events per year is not limited to one; numerous events can occur in the given year. A list of 15 such events is listed in Table 2.1, ranked in descending order of the amount of loss. In order to keep the example simple and calculations straightforward, these events were chosen so the set is exhaustive (i.e., sum of the probabilities for all of the events equals one).

The events listed in Table 2.1 are assumed to be independent Bernoulli random variables, each with a probability mass function defined as:

$$P(E_i \text{ occurs}) = p_i$$
$$P(E_i \text{ does not occur}) = (1 - p_i)$$

If an event E_i does not occur, the loss is zero. The Expected Loss for a given event, E_i, in a given year, is simply:

$$E[L] = p_i L_i$$

The overall expected loss for the entire set of events, denoted as the average annual loss (AAL) in Table 2.1, is the sum of the expected losses of each of the individual events for a given year and is given by:

$$AAL = \sum_i p_i L_i$$

Assuming that during a given year, only one disaster occurs, the exceedance probability for a given level of loss, $EP(L_i)$, can be determined by calculating:

$$EP(L_i) = P(L > L_i) = 1 - P(L \le L_i)$$
$$EP(L_i) = 1 - \prod_{j=1}^{i}(1 - p_j)$$

The resulting exceedance probability is the annual probability that the loss exceeds a given value. As seen in the equation above, this translates into one minus the probability that all the other events below this value have not occurred. The exceedance probability curve for the events in Table 2.1 is shown in Figure 2.5. Sidebar 1 explains how the EP curve can be used to determine probable maximum loss (PML).

Table 2.1. Events, Losses, and Probabilities

Event (E_i)	Annual probability of occurrence (p_i)	Loss (L_i)	Exceedance probability $[EP(L_i)]$	$E[L] = (p_i * L_i)$
1	0.0020	$25,000,000	0.0020	$50,000
2	0.0050	15,000,000	0.0070	75,000
3	0.0100	10,000,000	0.0169	100,000
4	0.0200	5,000,000	0.0366	100,000
5	0.0300	3,000,000	0.0655	90,000
6	0.0400	2,000,000	0.1029	80,000
7	0.0500	1,000,000	0.1477	50,000
8	0.0500	800,000	0.1903	40,000
9	0.0500	700,000	0.2308	35,000
10	0.0700	500,000	0.2847	35,000
11	0.0900	500,000	0.3490	45,000
12	0.1000	300,000	0.4141	30,000
13	0.1000	200,000	0.4727	20,000
14	0.1000	100,000	0.5255	10,000
15	0.2830	0	0.6597	0
			Average Annual Loss (AAL) =	$760,000

SIDEBAR 1: PML as a function of the EP Curve

The exceedance probability curve illustrated in Figure 2.5 enables an insurer to determine his PML or Probable Maximum Loss for a portfolio of structures in a given time period. The term PML is a subjective risk metric and is associated with a given probability of exceedance specified by the insurer. For example, suppose that an insurer specifies its acceptable risk level as the 0.4% probability of exceedance. The insurer can use the EP curve to determine how large a loss will occur at this probability level. Often, PML limits are framed in terms of a return period. The return period is simply the inverse of the annual probability of exceedance. In this example, a 1-in-250 year PML is the lower limit on the loss at a 0.4% probability of exceedance on the EP curve. From the inset of Figure 2.5, it can be seen that the PML is approximately $21 million.

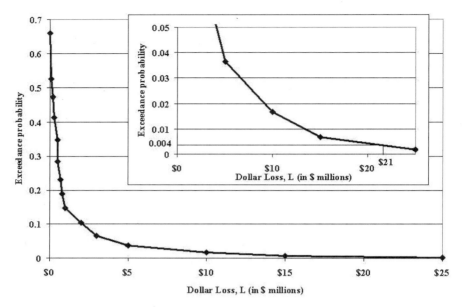

Figure 2.5. Exceedance probability curve

2.4.2 Stakeholders and the Exceedance Probability Curve

The exceedance probability curve can also be used to distribute the losses between stakeholders. Suppose there are three stakeholders who share the losses from a particular disaster. The owner retains the first part of the loss, a second party covers the middle portion and a third party covers the extreme portion. This scenario could represent a portfolio of homes with the homeowners having deductibles on their insurance policies such that they cover the first portion of the loss, an insurer covers the middle portion and a reinsurer handles the losses above a certain amount. Figure 2.6 shows a simple illustrative example. The potential loss for a portfolio with a total value of $100 million is split between three participants: P1, P2, and P3. The first $5 million of loss (L1) would be borne by P1 (homeowners), losses between $5M and $30M (L2) by P2 (insurer), and losses in excess of $30M (L3) by P3 (reinsurer). If the events facing the three parties were those given in Table 2.1, then the reinsurer would never experience any claim payments because the maximum loss would be $25 million.

Now suppose the three parties face the set of events in Table 2.1, but there is some uncertainty associated with the losses from each of the first 14 events (E_{15} has a loss of zero). In other words, the losses in Table 2.1 represent the mean estimates of loss; each event E_i has a distribution of loss associated with it. There is now a range of possible outcomes for each event, and some of these will penetrate the higher layer L3 (Figure 2.7). By combining the loss distributions for all the events, the probability of exceeding a specific loss level can be calculated. This then becomes the basis for developing EP curves for each of the parties with resources at risk.

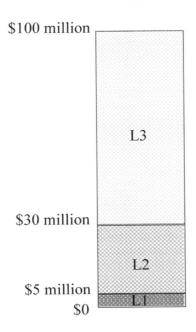

Figure 2.6. Layering for hypothetical portfolio, total value $100 million.

Figure 2.7 shows a set of loss-causing events with a high level of uncertainty in the loss distributions where the coefficient of variation (CV) on the event losses is 1.0.[1] By definition, the coefficient of variation is the ratio of the standard deviation to the mean. The effect of this high uncertainty is clearest on L3. If there were no variability in the losses, L3 would not be affected because no event is capable of reaching a $30 million loss, as previously stated. Based on the assumption (CV = 1.0), there is an annual probability of 0.28% that an event would cause some loss to L3.

This illustrative example shows how catastrophe modeling provides a means of both quantifying risks and allocating them among stakeholders. Using these metrics, it is possible to make rational, informed decisions on how to price risks and determine how much coverage is needed based on an

---

[1]Note that the assumption of a constant coefficient of variation for all events is not realistic and is used only for ease of illustration. The CV on the event loss generally decreases as the size of the loss increases; a portfolio CV of 1.0 for the most damaging event in this example is highly unlikely.

34

acceptable level of risk. However, there are uncertainties inherent in the catastrophe modeling process that can have a large impact on the distribution of risk among stakeholders. The quantification and disaggregation of uncertainty provides opportunities for stakeholders to reduce risk. As will be discussed in Part II, some of this uncertainty can be reduced by better data, but a significant component is an intrinsic part of the physical process.

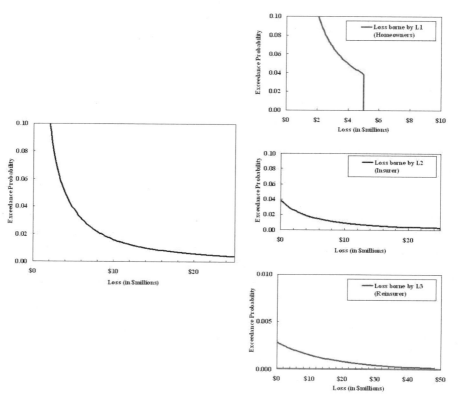

Figure 2.7. Exceedance probability curves for total portfolio and individual participants.

2.5 Insurability of Catastrophe Risks

In most developed countries, insurance is one of the principal mechanisms used by individuals and organizations to manage risk. Insurance allows the payment of a relatively small premium for protection against a potentially large loss in the future. In the United States, some property insurance coverage is required by law or by the lending institution. For example, homeowners normally have to purchase fire coverage as a condition for a mortgage. Automobile liability insurance is also required in most states as a condition for licensing a car. However, earthquake insurance is usually not required by lenders on single-family residences.

Insurance pricing can be a signal of how risky certain activities are for a particular individual. To illustrate, consider automobile insurance. For cars that are the same price, younger, inexperienced drivers of sporty vehicles pay more in premiums than older drivers of more conservative cars. For life and health insurance, smokers pay more for coverage than nonsmokers. This allocation of risk seems appropriate since it is tied to the likelihood of outcomes resulting from the nature of an individual's lifestyle. If one individual is more susceptible to a specific risk, then the cost for coverage against a loss from that risk is greater. Of course, since insurance rates are subject to regulation, the price of the policy may not fully reflect the underlying risk.

The key challenge is how to allocate catastrophe risk among stakeholders in a manner similar to what is done for more frequent, non-extreme events. For automobile coverage, considerable historical data are available and utilized to estimate insurance premiums for individuals with different risk characteristics. The large number of data points and the absence of correlation between accidents allow the use of actuarial-based models to estimate risk (Panjer and Willmot, 1992). With respect to natural disasters, there are limited data available to determine the probabilities of events occurring and their likely outcomes. In the absence of past data, there is a need for insurers to model the risk. Catastrophe models serve this purpose by maximizing the use of available information on the risk (hazard and inventory) to estimate the potential losses from natural hazards.

2.5.1 Conditions for Insurability of a Risk

Consider a standard insurance policy whereby premiums are paid at the start of a given time period to cover losses during this interval. Two conditions must be met before insurance providers are willing to offer coverage against an uncertain event. The first condition is the ability to identify and quantify, or estimate at least partially, the chances of the event occurring and the extent of losses likely to be incurred. The second condition is the ability to set premiums for each potential customer or class of customers.

If both conditions are satisfied, a risk is considered to be insurable. But it still may not be profitable. In other words, it may be impossible to specify a rate for which there is sufficient demand and incoming revenue to cover the development, marketing, operating, and claims processing costs of the insurance and yield a net positive profit over a prespecified time horizon. In such cases, the insurer will opt not to offer coverage against this risk.

To satisfy the first condition, estimates must be made of the frequency of specific events and the likely extent of losses. Such estimates can be based on past data or catastrophe modeling, coupled with data on what experts know about a particular risk. The insurer can then construct an exceedance probability (EP) curve that depicts the probability that a certain level of loss will be exceeded on an annual basis.

With respect to the second condition, if there is considerable ambiguity or uncertainty associated with the risk, insurers may wish to charge a much higher premium than if they had more precise estimates of the risk (Kunreuther, Hogarth and Meszaros, 1995). Moreover, if the capacity of the insurance industry is reduced due to recent large losses, then premiums will rise due to a shortage in supply. The situation will be exacerbated if the recent losses trigger an increase in demand for coverage, as was the case after Hurricane Andrew in 1992 and the Northridge earthquake in 1994 (Kunreuther and Roth, Sr. 1998).

Once the risk is estimated, the insurer needs to determine a premium rate that yields a profit and avoids an unacceptable level of loss. There are a number of factors that influence an insurer's decision on what premium to set. State regulations often limit insurers in their rate-setting process, and competition can play a role in what may be charged in a given marketplace. Even in the absence of these influences, there are a number of issues that an insurer must consider in setting premiums: uncertainty of losses, highly correlated losses, adverse selection, and moral hazard. Neither adverse selection nor moral hazard appears to be a major problem with respect to natural hazard risks. Adverse selection occurs when the insurer cannot distinguish (or does not discriminate through price) between the expected losses for different categories of risk, while the insured, possessing information unknown to the insurer, selects a price/coverage option more favorable to the insured. Moral hazard refers to an increase in the expected loss caused by the behavior of the policyholder. One example of moral hazard is moving unwanted furniture into the basement so an impending flood can destroy it, but this behavior occurs very infrequently. Given the difficulty uncertainty of losses and highly correlated losses pose in setting premiums, they are discussed below.

2.5.2 Uncertainty of Losses

Natural disasters pose a set of challenging problems for insurers because they involve potentially high losses that are extremely uncertain. Figure 2.8 illustrates the total number of loss events from 1950 to 2000 in the United States for three prevalent hazards: earthquakes, floods, and hurricanes. Events were selected that had at least $1 billion of economic damage and/or over 50 deaths (American Re, 2002).

Looking across all the disasters of a particular type (earthquake, hurricane or flood), for this 50-year period, the median loss is low while the maximum loss is very high. Given this wide variation in loss distribution, it is not surprising that there is a need for catastrophe models to aid insurers and reinsurers in estimating the potential loss from events that have not yet occurred but are scientifically credible.

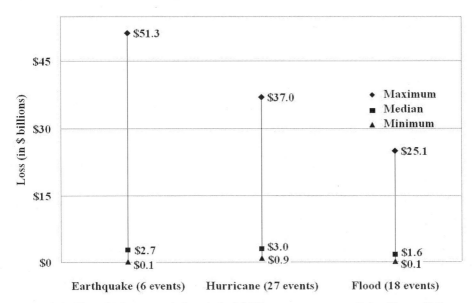

Figure 2.8. Historical economic losses in $ billions versus type of significant U.S. natural disaster. 1950-2000 (Source: American Re)

2.5.3 Highly Correlated Losses

Natural disasters involve spatially correlated losses or the simultaneous occurrence of many losses from a single event. If insurers sell a block of residential policies in a neighborhood, they could potentially experience a large (spatially correlated) loss should a disaster occur in the region. For example, due to their high concentration of homeowners' policies in the Miami/Dade County area of Florida, State Farm and Allstate Insurance paid $3.6 billion and $2.3 billion in claims respectively in the wake of Hurricane Andrew in 1992. Given this unexpectedly high loss, both companies began to reassess their strategies of providing coverage against wind damage in hurricane-prone areas (Lecomte and Gahagan, 1998).

In general, insurance markets flourish when companies can issue a large number of policies whose losses are spatially and otherwise independent. The portfolio follows the law of large numbers, and is thus predictable. This law states that for a series of independent and identically distributed random variables, the variance around the mean of the random variables decreases as the number of variables increases. Losses from natural hazards do not follow the law of large numbers, as they are not independent.

2.5.4 Determining Whether to Provide Coverage

In his study, James Stone (1973) sheds light on insurers' decision rules as to when they would market coverage for a specific risk. Stone indicates that firms are interested in maximizing expected profits subject to satisfying a constraint related to the survival of the firm. He also introduces a constraint regarding the stability of the insurer's operation. However, insurers have traditionally not focused on this constraint in dealing with catastrophic risks.

Following the disasters of 1989, insurers focused on the survival constraint in determining the amount of catastrophe coverage they wanted to provide. Moreover, insurers were caught off guard with respect to the magnitude of the losses from Hurricane Andrew in 1992 and the Northridge earthquake in 1994. In conjunction with the insolvencies that resulted from these disasters, the demand for coverage increased. Insurers only marketed coverage against wind damage in Florida because they were required to do so and state insurance pools were formed to limit their risk. Similarly, the California Earthquake Authority enabled the market to continue to offer earthquake coverage in California.

An insurer satisfies the survival constraint by choosing a portfolio of risks with an overall expected probability of insolvency less than some threshold, p_1. A simple example illustrates how an insurer would utilize the survival constraint to determine whether the earthquake risk is insurable. Assume that all homes in an earthquake-prone area are equally resistant to damage such that the insurance premium, z, is the same for each structure. Further assume that an insurer has \$A dollars in current surplus and wants to determine the number of policies it can write and still satisfy its survival constraint. Then, the maximum number of policies, n, satisfying the survival constraint is:

$$\text{Probability } [\text{Total Loss} > (n \cdot z + A)] < p_1$$

Whether the company will view the earthquake risk as insurable depends on whether the fixed cost of marketing and issuing policies is sufficiently low to make a positive expected profit. This, in turn, depends on how large the value of n is for any given premium, z. Note that the company also has some freedom to change its premium. A larger z will increase the values of n but will lower the demand for coverage. The insurer will decide not to offer earthquake coverage if it believes it cannot attract enough demand at any premium structure to make a positive expected profit. The company will use the survival constraint to determine the maximum number of policies it is willing to offer.

The EP curve is a useful tool for insurers to utilize in order to examine the conditions for meeting their survival constraint. Suppose that an insurer wants to determine whether its current portfolio of properties in Long Beach is meeting the survival constraint for the earthquake hazard. Based on its current surplus and total earthquake premiums, the insurer is declared insolvent if it suffers a loss greater than $15 million. The insurer can construct an EP curve such as Figure 2.4 and examine the probability that losses exceed certain amounts. From this figure, the probability of insolvency is 1.0%. If the acceptable risk level, $p_1 < 1.0\%$, then the insurer can either decrease the amount of coverage, raise the premium and/or transfer some of the risk to others.

2.6 Framework to Integrate Risk Assessment with Risk Management

Figure 2.9 depicts a framework for integrating risk assessment with risk management and serves as a guide to the concepts and analyses presented in this book. The risk is first assessed through catastrophe modeling. Catastrophe modeling combines the four components (hazard, inventory, vulnerability, and loss) to aid insurers in making their decisions on what type of protection they can offer against a particular risk.

The key link between assessing risk via catastrophe models and implementing risk management strategies is the stakeholders' decision processes. The types of information stakeholders collect and the nature of their decision processes are essential in developing risk management strategies. With respect to insurers, catastrophe models are the primary sources of information on the risk. Their decision rule for developing risk management strategies is to maximize expected profits subject to meeting the survival constraint. Property owners in hazard prone areas utilize simplified decision rules in determining whether or not to adopt mitigation measures to reduce future losses to their property and/or to purchase insurance.

For purposes of this book, risk management strategies are broadly classified as either risk reduction measures, such as mitigation, or risk transfer measures, such as reinsurance. For example, strategies for residential property owners often involve a combination of measures, including mitigation, insurance, well-enforced building codes, and land-use regulations. In California and Florida, all these initiatives exist in some form. Strategies for insurers could involve charging higher rates to reflect the uncertainty of the risk, changing their portfolio so they can spread the risk across many areas, or reassigning the risk using risk transfer instruments such as reinsurance and/or catastrophe bonds.

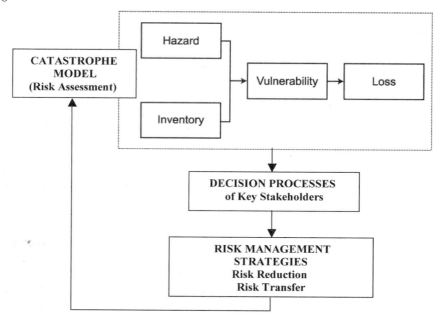

Figure 2.9. Framework for linking risk assessment with risk management.

2.7 Summary and Relationship to Parts II-IV

This chapter examined the history of catastrophe modeling and the role catastrophe models play in making a risk insurable. Part II provides a more detailed discussion of catastrophe modeling for earthquakes and hurricanes. The output from catastrophe models provides important information for insurers to manage their risk. By modeling the risk, insurers can more accurately estimate the premiums to charge for insurance coverage from natural disasters. In addition, insurers and reinsurers are able to tailor their coverage to reduce the chances of insolvency. They can develop new strategies for managing their portfolios so as to avoid losses that might otherwise cause an unacceptable reduction in surplus. These strategies are discussed in Part III of the book.

The impact of insurers' risk management strategies on profitability and probability of insolvency are explored further in Part IV of the book. Exceedance probability curves are constructed using real market data for insurers in Oakland, California, Long Beach, California and Miami/Dade County, Florida and alternative strategies are examined, including requiring mitigation to homes in these disaster-prone areas and using risk transfer instruments to satisfy an insurer's survival constraint. The book concludes with a chapter on the future role of catastrophe models in dealing with the risks associated with terrorism as an extreme event.

2.8 References

American Re (2002). *Topics: Annual Review of North American Natural Catastrophes 2001.*

Algermissen, S.T. (1969). *Seismic risk studies in the United States*, 4th World Conference on Earthquake Engineering Proceedings, Chilean Association for Seismology and Earthquake Engineering, Santiago, Chile.

Brinkmann, W. (1975). *Hurricane Hazard in the United States: A Research Assessment.* Monograph #NSF-RA-E-75-007, Program on Technology, Environment and Man, Institute of Behavioral Sciences, University of Colorado, Boulder, Colorado.

FEMA 249 (1994). *Assessment of the State of the Art Earthquake Loss Estimation Methodologies,* June.

FEMA (2002). *HAZUS99 SR2 User's Manual*, Federal Emergency Management Agency.

Insurance Information Institute (2000). Catastrophes [online]. The Insurance Information Institute 10 June 2000 <http://www.iii.org/media/issues/catastrophes>.

Kozlowski, R. T. and Mathewson, S. B. (1995). "Measuring and Managing Catastrophe Risk," *1995 Discussion Papers on Dynamic Financial Analysis*, Casualty Actuarial Society, Arlington, Virginia.

Kunreuther, H., R. Hogarth, J. Meszaros and M. Spranca (1995). "Ambiguity and underwriter decision processes," *Journal of Economic Behavior and Organization*, 26: 337-352.

Kunreuther, H. and Roth, R. (1998). *Paying the Price: The Status and Role of Insurance Against Natural Disasters in the United States.* Washington, D.C: Joseph Henry Press.

Neumann, C.J. (1972). *An alternate to the HURRAN tropical cyclone forecast system.* NOAA Tech. Memo. NWS SR-62, 24 pp.

NIBS (1997). *HAZUS: Hazards U.S.: Earthquake Loss Estimation Methodology.* NIBS Document Number 5200, National Institute of Building Sciences, Washington, D.C.

Panjer, H. H. and Willmot, G.E. (1992). *Insurance Risk Models.* Illinois: Society of Actuaries.

Steinbrugge, K. V. (1982). *Earthquakes, Volcanoes, and Tsunamis: An Anatomy of Hazards.* Skandia America Group: New York, New York.

Stone, J. (1973). "A theory of capacity and the insurance of catastrophe risks: Part I and Part II," *Journal of Risk and Insurance*, 40: 231-243 (Part I) and 40: 339-355 (Part II).

Stover, C.W. and Coffman, J.L (1993). *Seismicity of the United States, 1568-1989.* U.S. Geological Survey Professional Paper 1527, United States Government Printing Office, Washington, D.C.

USWRC (1967). *A Uniform Technique for Determining Flood Flow Frequencies*, U.S. Water Resource Council, Hydrology Committee, Bulletin 15, Washington, D.C.

PART II
NATURAL HAZARD RISK ASSESSMENT

Part II of this book discusses the inner workings of catastrophe models and how they assess risk from natural hazards. Readers will learn more about the components of catastrophe models, including the hazard, inventory, vulnerability, and loss modules. In Chapter 3, these components are discussed in detail, and the complexities of the process are illuminated. This chapter also emphasizes the importance of data quality in determining earthquake and hurricane hazards, as well as exposure risk. Chapter 4 turns to the role of uncertainty in catastrophe models by examining the sources, nature, and impact of uncertainty on assessing natural hazard risk. Illustrative examples of assessing hurricane risk in Florida and earthquake risk in South Carolina enable readers to understand how uncertainty in the modeling process affects the allocation of risk between stakeholders.

Hurricane Andrew on its approach to Florida, 1992.

Chapter 3 – The Risk Assessment Process: The Role of Catastrophe Modeling in Dealing with Natural Hazards

Major Contributors:
Mehrdad Mahdyiar
Beverly Porter

3.1 Introduction

Probabilistic risk analysis has long played an important role in engineering design for natural hazards. For example, the lateral loads imposed by hurricanes or earthquakes, and characterized by a specified probability of exceedance, are used by structural engineers to design buildings that minimize injuries and fatalities. More recently, these techniques have been extended to estimate the damage to existing building inventories and, ultimately, to estimate the economic and insured losses that result from the occurrence of natural catastrophes. Catastrophe loss estimation techniques, known collectively as catastrophe modeling, have gained widespread acceptance by the insurance and risk management industries and are now heavily relied upon to support a wide range of financial decisions.

A probabilistic approach to catastrophe loss analysis is the most appropriate way to handle the abundant sources of uncertainty inherent in all natural hazard related phenomena. As pointed out in Chapter 2, the relative infrequency of catastrophe events results in a scarcity of historical loss data. Hence statistical techniques used by actuaries for estimating future losses stemming from automobile or fire insurance policies, for example — techniques that rely on a wealth of available claims data — are not appropriate for estimating future losses from natural catastrophes. Furthermore, the usefulness of the limited historical loss data that do exist cannot be easily extrapolated to estimate the economic impact of disasters because of the ever-changing landscape of properties. Property values change, as do the costs of repair and replacement. Building materials, design and practice change along with building codes. Therefore new structures may be more or less vulnerable to catastrophe events than existing ones.

While it is generally agreed that the probabilistic approach is the most appropriate, it is highly complex and multifaceted. It requires modeling complex physical phenomena in time and space, compiling detailed databases of building inventories, estimating physical damage to various types of structures and their contents, translating physical damage to monetary loss and, finally, summing over entire portfolios of buildings. From the modeler's perspective, the task is to simulate, realistically and adequately, the most important aspects of this very complex system. Risk managers need to familiarize themselves with the underlying assumptions of the models and understand the implications and limitations of their output in order to utilize the results effectively.

Briefly, the hazard component of catastrophe models estimates the probability that the physical parameters that define the hazard will exceed various levels. In the case of earthquakes, for example, the model estimates the probability that parameters such as peak ground acceleration or spectral acceleration (defined as the maximum acceleration experienced by a simple oscillator, used as a representation for building response) will exceed various levels at a particular site. The model's vulnerability component deals with the potential for the hazard to damage structures and their contents. It estimates the probability that building damage will exceed various levels as a result of ground motion. The loss module translates physical damage into monetary loss and estimates the probability of exceeding various levels of loss.

Together, the hazard and vulnerability modules comprise what is traditionally known as probabilistic risk analysis. This approach to modeling earthquake risk is based on the pioneering work of Cornell (1968) and is now well established in the literature. Catastrophe loss models can be thought of as one application of probabilistic risk analysis, characterized by their refinement of the financial loss estimation component. The final result of the catastrophe model, commonly used in financial analysis, is the exceedance probability, or EP, curve introduced in the preceding chapter. At each stage in the process, the model takes into consideration the uncertainty in the various parameters that describe the model.

All catastrophe models require substantial amounts of data for model construction and validation. In addition, the reliability of such models depends heavily on our understanding of the underlying physical mechanisms that control the occurrence and behavior of natural hazards. While no one would claim to have a complete understanding of all of the intricacies of these physical systems, scientists and engineers, aided by increasingly sophisticated instrumentation and computing capabilities, have accumulated vast amounts of information and knowledge in these areas. By incorporating this information and knowledge, the sophisticated theoretical and empirical models currently being developed can reasonably simulate these complex phenomena.

This chapter explores in detail the building blocks of catastrophe models introduced in Chapter 2: hazard, inventory, vulnerability, and loss (see Figure 3.1 below). Chapter 4 focuses on the sources, nature and impact of the uncertainties that characterize each of these modules.

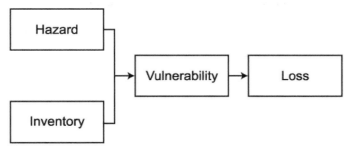

Figure 3.1. Catastrophe model components.

3.2 Hazard Module

All catastrophe models must address three basic issues regarding the source parameters of the hazard: the most likely locations of future events, their frequency of occurrence and their severity. These three elements are closely related and, in many cases, their modeling and validation require very similar sets of data. Probability distributions are developed based on historical data for each variable that defines these elements. The selection and subsequent refinement of these distributions is based not only on the expert application of statistical techniques, but also on well-established scientific principles and an understanding of how natural hazards behave. By sampling from these probability distributions, the model produces a large catalog of simulated events.

Once the model generates the source parameters of each simulated event, it propagates the resulting intensity over the affected area. That is, for each location within the affected area, local intensity is estimated. What follows is a more detailed discussion of each of these elements of the model's hazard module.

3.2.1 Locations of Potential Future Events

To achieve reliable estimates of catastrophe loss, the modeler must first define the model domain, or the region over which the sources of the hazard need to be identified.

Earthquakes

In conducting a catastrophe analysis for earthquakes in southern California, those faults and seismic source zones that have measurable impact on the building inventory of interest must be identified. Much of this information becomes available through direct observation and measurement of the physical parameters of actual earthquakes and their impact upon their environment. Typically, the rate at which ground motion attenuates with distance will determine the appropriate geographical extent of the region to be modeled.

In certain cases, however, the issue becomes more complex. In 1985, an earthquake of magnitude 8.1 occurred at the Pacific coast of Mexico, fully 400 kilometers away from Mexico City. Ordinarily, this distance would be too great to pose any significant threat to that city. Yet this earthquake caused serious damage there and killed some 20,000 people. This happened because the soft soils that comprise the former lake basin over which Mexico City is built, trapped and strongly amplified the very weak incoming ground motion that had traveled from hundreds of kilometers away (Mendez and Anderson, 1991).

This type of information is critical in identifying a model domain that captures all relevant sources of hazard. In this example, physical damage and loss can be better predicted with a thorough knowledge of the region's geological features and an understanding of the physics of wave propagation through soft soils and ground motion-structure interaction.

After defining the boundaries of the model domain, all sources of hazard within those boundaries need to be identified. In the case of earthquakes, that task is greatly facilitated when the locations of faults are known and mapped. In some regions, faults can easily be seen on the surface of the earth — the San Andreas Fault in California is a prime example. For the most part, records of historical seismicity (both instrumental and pre-instrumental), such as those depicted in Figure 3.2, play a key role in the process of identifying active faults. These data are supplemented by information obtained through methods such as fault trenching, subsurface sounding techniques and aerial photography (designed to detect the surface expression of faults). In general, an identified fault that has exhibited no earthquake activity within the current Holocene time period (roughly within the last 10,000 years) can be considered inactive and therefore excluded from earthquake hazard analysis.

Not all earthquakes happen on known faults, however. In such cases, seismicity is often modeled using area (polygonal) source zones rather than faults. The spatial distribution of past earthquakes within the zone is used to estimate the spatial distribution of future earthquakes. However, because of the uncertainty surrounding the exact locations of the underlying faults (which are inferred from the seismic activity of the area), catastrophe models typically allow simulated earthquakes to occur not only where they have occurred in the past, but also, with some probability, anywhere within the seismic source zone. This is accomplished by statistically smoothing the historical data.

For regions where there has been little or no historical seismic activity, larger zones of so-called "background seismicity" are typically defined. Using these concepts, seismic hazard is ultimately modeled as some weighted combination of seismicity as generated by faults, area source zones, and background seismicity. The United States Geological Survey (USGS) seismologists have used this technique to develop the present U.S. Seismic Hazard Maps that are used in the International Building Code (IBC).

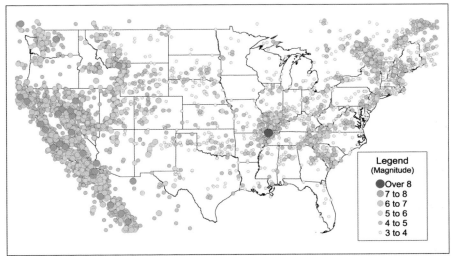

Figure 3.2. Spatial distribution of historical earthquakes since 1700. (Source: USGS)

Historical seismicity catalogs alone cannot identify all regional seismic sources. One reason is that large earthquakes associated with particular faults have sometimes very long recurrence intervals, while our historical and instrumentally recorded earthquake catalogs are of relatively short duration. Thus, in many cases, if the modeler relies only on earthquake catalog data, active faults can remain unidentified because of the lack of any record of earthquakes having occurred there. The historical earthquake catalog can be augmented with other auxiliary information, such as paleoseismic data. Paleoseismology is the study of prehistoric earthquakes, particularly their location, timing and size. Paleoseismologic evidence of prehistoric earthquakes includes offsets in geologic formations found in exhumed fault zones, evidence of rapid uplift or subsidence near coastal areas, laterally offset stream valleys, and liquefaction artifacts such as sand boils.

The principal challenge with this approach is to assign magnitudes to the paleoearthquakes. This requires locating contemporaneous sites exhibiting evidence of paleoseismicity, estimating the total affected area and converting this area to a magnitude. The last step is typically based on empirical relationships derived from the few earthquakes of sufficient size that have occurred historically in the region. Consequently, there is considerable uncertainty regarding estimates of recurrence rates derived from paleoseismic data. Nevertheless, paleoseismology is a major source of data used to estimate return periods of large magnitude earthquakes. For example, paleoseismic studies (Johnston and Schweig, 1996) have provided some of the most compelling evidence for estimating the magnitudes and return periods of large earthquakes in the New Madrid Seismic Zone of the Central United States.

Another more recent technique for identifying potentially active seismic sources is the use of geodetic survey data. Geodetic surveys, and in particular data derived from Global Positioning System (GPS) networks, which reveal relative movements of the earth's crust, provide information that can be used to identify regions under strain (SCEC, 1995). Theory and observation indicate that elastic materials relieve strain by producing earthquakes. In that sense, geodetic data can provide valuable information for identifying regions under strain and thus with high potential for earthquake activity.

Hurricanes

Weather-related sources of potential hazard, like seismic sources, are more prevalent in some regions than in others. Tropical cyclone genesis, for example, requires a large expanse of warm ocean water; therefore these cyclones are most likely to form between 5 degrees and 20 degrees latitude. Hurricanes are the most severe manifestation of tropical cyclones, and are characterized by wind speeds of 74 miles per hour or greater.

Approaches used to quantify the geographical distribution of hurricanes include defining various parameters such as storm tracks, landfall location, and track angle at landfall. Other more sophisticated approaches, such as physically-based numerical weather prediction models, are being used increasingly and may ultimately replace parametric models, particularly for very complex weather events (Kurihara et al., 1992). Storm tracks are the manifestation of the temporal and spatial interaction between complex and dynamic atmospheric systems. Nevertheless, observations of past storm tracks reveal clear patterns and are therefore important pieces of information when constructing stochastic, or simulated, storm catalogs for catastrophe loss analysis.

Scientific and fully probabilistic procedures have been developed to simulate storm tracks for each ocean basin of concern. Historical track data are used to generate probability matrices that answer the question: "If the direction of storm movement at some location is *a*, what is the probability that its next direction will be *a, b, c, d,* etc.?" The advantage of this probabilistic approach is that the storm tracks generated for simulated hurricanes more closely resemble the curving and recurving tracks that are actually observed.

Furthermore, the simulated storm tracks are fully probabilistic, which means that any possible storm track can be generated, not just historical tracks.

Figure 3.3 depicts the observed number of land-falling hurricanes from 1900 to 2000 per 50-mile segment of the Atlantic and Gulf Coasts of the United States. This historical distribution suggests where future hurricanes are most likely to make landfall. Yet, discontinuities in landfall frequency between adjacent coastline segments may occur not for meteorological reasons, but rather due simply to the small size of the historical sample. The historical data are therefore smoothed, using algorithms well established in the meteorological literature, to allow for the possibility of future hurricanes making landfall where none have occurred in the past. This kind of information is used to construct the stochastic storm catalogs that become part of the catastrophe model's hazard module. Also shown in Figure 3.3 are the cumulative probability distributions of both actual and simulated hurricanes making landfall in Florida.

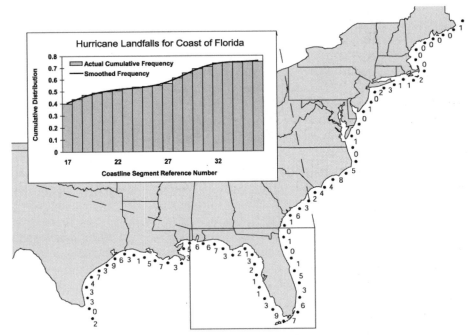

Figure 3.3. Number of Historical Landfalls Per 50-Mile Coastline Segments from 1900 to 2000. (*Source: National Hurricane Center*)

3.2.2 Frequency of Occurrence

Closely related to the likely locations of potential future catastrophe events is their frequency of occurrence. The determination of the annual probability of occurrence of catastrophe events is, in general, the most critical and uncertain aspect of the model's hazard module. It is critical because the damage and loss probabilities are directly related to this value. The uncertainty results, in part, from the scarcity of historical data necessary to construct reliable statistical recurrence models for these events. Furthermore, what really determines the probability of occurrence of natural hazards within any time period are the underlying physical mechanisms and boundary conditions over which, despite enormous advances, scientists still have only a loose grasp.

Earthquakes

The statistical interpretation of past earthquakes on the San Bernardino Mountain segment of the San Andreas Fault in Southern California suggests a mean recurrence interval of about 150 years for large magnitude earthquakes. The last such occurrence was in 1812, or 189 years ago. Using a time-independent model of earthquake occurrence (that is, one that makes no assumption regarding the temporal pattern of earthquake occurrence), the estimated 1/150 annual rate of occurrence on this fault implies a 6.5% probability that another large earthquake will occur in the next 10 years. In fact, the present state of stresses on the fault, and the forces resisting rupture, control the next occurrence of a large magnitude earthquake. The state of stress on a fault can be influenced by the rupture of adjacent faults or, as new findings suggest, even the occurrence of large earthquakes on distant faults. Therefore the stress history of the fault must be known in order to assess its present condition and its rupture potential.

It is a common practice to model the relationship between the frequency of occurrence of earthquakes and their magnitude as a combination of so-called characteristic earthquakes and the Gutenberg-Richter magnitude distribution. When a fault or fault segment ruptures at fairly regular intervals, producing earthquakes of similar magnitude, the fault is said to have a characteristic earthquake. In general, faults do not rupture with such predictability. However, the concept of a characteristic earthquake is a useful tool for formulating a fault's strain accumulation and subsequent release. Characteristic earthquakes can be identified either by a single magnitude or by a magnitude range with some distribution.

The Gutenberg-Richter relationship, which holds over a wide range of magnitudes (M), is depicted in Figure 3.4 and can be written as:

$$log\ (N) = a - b\ M$$

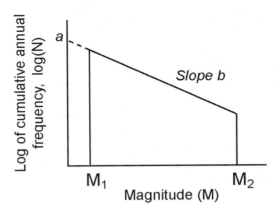

Figure 3.4. Frequency-magnitude relationship of a typical seismic zone.

The defining parameters, which depend upon seismic characteristics of the region under consideration, are:

- Lower and upper bound magnitudes, M_1 and M_2
- The occurrence rate of earthquakes of magnitude greater than or equal to some reference magnitude, characterized by the so-called a-value
- The rate at which the log of the cumulative annual frequency of earthquakes decreases as the magnitude increases, characterized by the b-value.

The level of effort to determine these parameters varies from region to region, depending on the availability and reliability of various types of data. Where there are long and reliable historical and instrumentally recorded earthquake data, parameters can be directly calculated from such information. Where historic and recorded data are not available or are unreliable, the common practice is to estimate this distribution based on relevant physical parameters, such as those obtained from GPS data.

The choice of the upper bound magnitude in the above formulation has an important implication for the frequency-magnitude distribution of earthquakes. A unit increase in earthquake magnitude translates to about 32 times greater energy release. This means, for example, that the occurrence of 32 earthquakes of magnitude 6 release about the same amount of energy as one magnitude 7 earthquake. This is an important consideration in source modeling. An unrealistic choice of upper bound magnitudes for a seismic source could result in the model producing either too few or too many small and moderate magnitude earthquakes, rates that may not be supported by the observed data.

All available earthquake-related data for a source zone are integrated into a coherent representation of seismic hazard. The most recent example of such an effort is the USGS National Seismic Hazard Mapping Project (Frankel, et al., 1996). USGS has compiled geologic, paleoseismic and geodetic data for all major seismic sources in the U.S. Based on the available data, seismic sources were categorized as either faults or as area seismic zones. For certain faults, paleoseismic data were used to estimate the magnitudes and recurrence rates of their characteristic earthquakes. Regional earthquake catalogs were used to calculate both the rates and spatial probability distribution of earthquakes within different geographic areas. Geologic and seismic data were used to estimate fault slip rates. GPS data were used to estimate regional and local strain rates. All of this information is synthesized into seismic hazard maps that show earthquake ground motions that have a specified probability of being exceeded in 50 years. Among the uses of these maps are the creation and update of the seismic design provisions of building codes.

Hurricanes

For a particular weather hazard, frequency of occurrence may reflect the regional climate. Hurricanes form where there is a convergence of the necessary conditions. Two such conditions are a large expanse of warm ocean water (generally, water temperatures must be at least 80 degrees Fahrenheit), and the relative absence of vertical shear, or winds that change appreciably in either magnitude or direction with height. Too great a distance from the equator means that water temperatures will not be sufficiently warm for cyclonic formation.

The likelihood of vertical shear increases with distance from tropical latitudes. Neither will hurricane formation occur in very close proximity to the equator because of the absence of the Coriolis Force there, which is required for the spiraling circulation of surface winds. The most active months are when the oceans are at their warmest: August and September in the Northern Hemisphere, and January and February in the Southern Hemisphere. Figure 3.5 indicates average annual frequency of hurricane formation in each of the world's ocean basins. Note that these numbers include all hurricane formations, and not just those storms that make landfall or come close enough to land to cause damage.

3.2.3 Parameterizing Severity at the Hazard's Source

After identifying all regional hazard sources, the model generates the primary characteristics, whether meteorological or seismological, of all simulated events within each source zone. That is, the model quantifies the physical parameters that describe the hazard at its source. The basic parameters for characterizing the severity of hurricanes include central barometric pressure (the primary determinant of wind speed), forward or translational speed, radius of maximum winds and track angle at landfall. For the purpose of seismic hazard analysis, simulated events are typically characterized by earthquake magnitude, focal depth, and various fault-rupture characteristics.

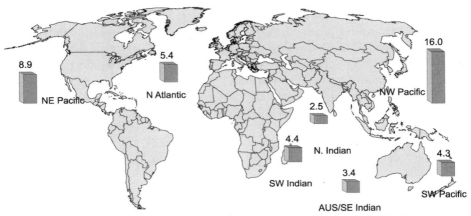

Figure 3.5. Average number of hurricane formations per year by ocean basin.

Earthquake models impose a limiting (upper bound) magnitude for simulated earthquakes on individual modeled faults. This limiting magnitude is usually determined either by examining the magnitudes of historical earthquakes on that fault or by using an estimate of the fault's largest expected rupture dimension. In the latter case, empirical equations that describe the relationship between magnitude and rupture dimension are used to estimate the limiting magnitude.

Determining limiting values for weather hazards involves a similar process. Hurricane models, for example, fit theoretical probability distributions to historical data on central pressure. A lower bound (higher intensity) is determined by analyzing the historical data in conjunction with meteorological expertise regarding what is physically possible.

3.2.4 Parameters for Local Intensity and Site Effects

To estimate the damage potential of natural hazards, the model must estimate their physical parameters not only at the source, but also at the sites of the affected building inventory. This part of the model's hazard module is designed to capture how intensity changes as the simulated catastrophe propagates over the affected area.

Earthquakes

Upon its rupture, a fault releases energy and creates disturbances within its source region. These disturbances propagate away from the source through the region in the form of seismic waves, as illustrated in Figure 3.6.

Damage to structures is sensitive to the amplitude and the frequency content of those waves, parameters that are controlled by the earthquake's source mechanism, characteristics of the intervening geological materials through which the waves travel and, finally, by the complexities of the local soil materials underlying each affected site.

Constructing physical models that realistically simulate variations in earthquake ground motion over a region is difficult. For catastrophe modeling purposes, a common practice is to employ empirical relationships, called attenuation equations, which mathematically describe the rate at which the amplitude of the seismic waves decreases as the waves propagate outward from the source of the rupture. A typical attenuation equation in its general form can be written as:

$$Y = F(f, M, r, Source, Site)$$

where Y is ground motion amplitude at frequency f, M is the earthquake magnitude, and r is the source-to-site distance. The terms Source and Site in the attenuation equation above reflect source rupture mechanisms and the local site effects of soils on ground motion, respectively.

The amplitude of high frequency waves decays faster than that of low frequency waves. The rate of decay is a function of the propagating materials. That is, crustal heterogeneities, such as fractures, and a variety of regional geological complexities all have their effect on attenuation rates. For these and other reasons, empirical attenuation equations are region-specific.

The results of many years of data gathering and interpretation indicate that earthquakes with similar magnitudes but different types of source mechanisms systematically create quantitatively different levels of ground motion. Earthquakes with thrust and reverse faulting mechanisms are, in general, observed to produce higher levels of ground motion than earthquakes with strike-slip and normal faulting mechanisms. Also, the ground motion at sites equidistant from the rupture but with different local soil conditions can be very different, even when the source parameters of the underlying earthquakes are similar.

For example, soft soil materials that lie within a large bowl-like structure of underlying bedrock characterize certain parts of Los Angeles. Such so-called basins of soft soils can trap seismic waves and create very complex amplification and deamplification patterns for low frequency ground motions. The shallow soil materials, on the other hand, mostly affect high frequency components of ground motion. In general, both large-scale basin effects, if present, and shallow soil conditions are important for the estimation of earthquake ground motion at individual sites.

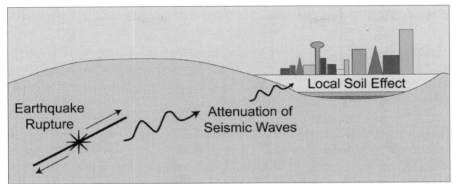

Figure 3.6. Attenuation and local soil/site effects.

Hurricanes

In weather-related hazards, the propagation of intensity across the affected region is determined by the interaction between the source and its environment. In the case of hurricanes, once the model probabilistically generates the storm's source parameters, including its primary meteorological characteristics, it simulates the storm's movement along a track. To generate local windfields, the maximum over-water wind speed is calculated. Adjustments are then made for the effects of storm asymmetry, filling (the rate at which central pressure increases as the storm moves inland), and local surface terrain.

Differences in surface terrain can have a significant effect on wind speeds. Wind velocity profiles typically show higher wind speeds at higher elevations. Winds travel more slowly at ground level because of the horizontal drag force of the earth's surface, or surface friction. The addition of obstacles, such as buildings or trees, will further degrade wind speed. Models often employ a friction coefficient for each location of interest to obtain an estimate of the surface roughness. These estimates are based on digital land use/land cover data, plus exposure information at the site. In general, the rougher the terrain, the more quickly wind speeds dissipate.

Wind duration is also an important consideration in determining local intensity and therefore in damage estimation. Consider the effects of two storms of equal intensity but of different forward speeds and thus different site duration. At any given site, damage resulting from the storm of longer duration (slower forward speed) will be higher because of the cumulative effects of wind. A recent example of this is the 1998 Hurricane Georges, which stalled over the Gulf Coast, battering the area around Biloxi and Gulfport with hurricane and tropical storm force winds over an unusually prolonged period of time resulting in significantly higher losses than might be expected of a hurricane of its intensity (Category 2 on the Saffir Simpson scale).

3.3 Inventory Module

Building inventory is a key input for the catastrophe model to estimate potential future losses to structures and their contents. Catastrophe models can be used to estimate aggregate insured or insurable losses for the entire insurance industry, for individual company portfolios, or for individual buildings.

For aggregate analysis, modelers develop annually updated databases from governmental and private sources that include estimates of total property exposures within the modeled region at the postal code level. The data include the number of properties, or risks, and their values, broken down by line of business (residential, commercial and industrial), by coverage (building, appurtenant structures, contents and time element, or loss of use) and by occupancy and construction type. Building damage is primarily a function of construction type. Masonry buildings, for example, typically perform poorly when subjected to violent ground shaking, but perform quite well in the face of hurricane winds. Engineered buildings typically perform better than non-engineered buildings, whatever the peril. Inventory data should also reflect regional differences in both construction practice and building code. Damage to contents is typically a function of both occupancy class and structural damage. Occupancy class provides insight into the kinds of contents contained in the building and hence their relative vulnerability.

When estimating losses on individual insurance company portfolios, modelers must work closely with clients identifying missing or erroneous data and testing for reasonability. The more detailed the information provided by the client and entered into a catastrophe model, the more detailed and reliable the output. Catastrophe models can take full advantage of risk-specific structural details, such as roof pitch or floor-wall connection, as well as occupancy, age, and height. They can also take advantage of information, if available, on the presence of mitigation devices and retrofit.

For particularly important or valuable buildings, a site-specific analysis may be appropriate. In such cases, the level of detail of the inventory data can increase by an order of magnitude. Typically, engineers make on-site inspections and incorporate information provided in actual design documents, including specifications of the physical dimensions of individual components (beam, column, joints, partitions, etc.) and their material properties. The vulnerability component of the catastrophe model is then developed to mathematically describe the behavior of the building when subjected to the forces imposed by earthquakes or windstorms.

3.4 Vulnerability Module

The vulnerability module estimates the level of building damage expected for different levels of severity of the oncoming external forces imposed, such as earthquake ground motion or high winds. The likelihood that any level of external forces is experienced at any given site identified in the inventory module (Section 3.3) is the result of the hazard module (Section 3.2).

Many different approaches have been devised to link ground motion or wind intensity to the expected level of damage or, more ambitiously, directly to the level of monetary loss. These approaches are based either on engineering judgment or, in more sophisticated models, on building response analyses performed using a wide variety of techniques. The former approach – combining the opinions of experts – is not easily updated when more or new information becomes available. It is, by definition, somewhat arbitrary in nature. The latter approach has been generally recognized by the engineering community to be superior and constitutes one of the most prolific fields of current research.   See, for example, the Pacific Earthquake Engineering Research Center website at http://peer.berkeley.edu.

While the most advanced engineering-based techniques can provide a fairly accurate estimate of building response, they are tailored for application to specific buildings at specific locations. Direct application of these techniques to portfolio risk assessment is impractical, at best. For one thing, the information needed for performing any truly sophisticated engineering analysis is usually missing. For most portfolios of insurance companies, the information collected for each property rarely goes beyond its address, the type of construction, the number of stories, and the age. Portfolios of reinsurance companies often contain even less information.

Thus, engineering methods were modified to make possible their application to portfolio risk assessment. The building stock is divided into many typical building classes (e.g., unreinforced masonry building) with different characteristics (e.g., two stories, built between 1976 and 1998). This process may categorize the building stock in the United States into, for example, 50 different building classes. Each class is then subdivided according to different modifiers to account for details that may have an impact on the building response under loads imposed by wind or ground motion (e.g., the presence of a cripple wall in wood frame structures impacts its performance during earthquakes, as does roof pitch during hurricanes).

For each building class, one typical building is analyzed using the structure-specific techniques mentioned above. The response of the typical building for different levels of ground motion or wind intensity is then applied to any property in the portfolio that belongs to that class. Although the performance of any given building within a class may deviate considerably from the performance of the typical building, this approach generally leads to accurate estimates of mean damage (and monetary losses after the loss module is applied) on a portfolio basis. This assumes that typical buildings are appropriately selected to avoid any source of bias. It is important to emphasize that portfolio risk analyses aim at estimating the distribution of potential losses (i.e., the EP curve) to ensembles of large numbers of properties, rather than for any single property.

There are two major steps in the application of such engineering-based vulnerability approaches to portfolio risk analyses:

1) Identification and definition of typical buildings in the modeled region.
2) Calculation of building performance to ground motion or winds of different intensities. This will be referred to here as vulnerability analysis.

3.4.1 Identification of Typical Buildings

In surveying the inventory of buildings in a region, the most important aspect is evaluating the size of the statistical populations of different types of structures within the building stock. Data collection needs to be conducted for all relevant occupancy types such as residential, commercial, industrial, and agricultural, as well as insurance coverages for buildings and contents.

From the perspective of a portfolio analysis, more effort needs to be devoted to estimating the performance of the more widely represented building classes. Other aspects include evaluating the homogeneity of structures within the same building class, addressing construction types unique to the region, adoption and enforcement of regional building codes for the perils of interest, and construction practices. All these aspects lead to the definition of as many building classes as is reasonably practical to represent the statistical population of structures in the region.

The building classes are identified by considering the most important factors affecting structural response to the perils under consideration. These could be building material (e.g., steel or reinforced concrete), structural system (e.g., moment frame versus braced-frame) and height (e.g., two versus 10 stories). Each building class is further subdivided based on parameters sometimes called secondary modifiers (e.g., roof and foundation type).

3.4.2 Evaluation of Building Performance

Building performance is described by a relationship between the intensity of the imposed force, that is, the external excitation, and the level of expected damage caused to the building. Because there is considerable uncertainty in this step, this relationship, besides being a predictive equation for mean damage, also carries a measure of the error of estimation.

Damage to buildings from earthquakes is typically both structural and non-structural in nature and primarily due to the lateral building deformation caused by ground shaking. Engineers have used objective measures of building lateral response, such as the maximum interstory drift (the ratio of the maximum relative lateral displacement of the two adjacent stories to the inter-story height) to predict the level of damage to the components at that story. For earthquakes, structural damage can be severe even for engineered buildings designed according to code. There were examples of this in the Northridge earthquake in California (1994) and the Kobe earthquake in Japan (1995), both places where seismic building codes are among the most advanced in the world. Damage patterns from these two earthquakes revealed that engineers had been overestimating the performance of steel construction.

Wind, on the other hand, results primarily in damage to non-structural elements, involving different components of the building envelope and, in most cases, is localized in nature. The exception to this is mobile homes, where severe roof damage can lead to partial collapse. Structural collapse can occur under extreme wind conditions, but is usually restricted to non-engineered buildings, such as wood frames. In such cases, roofs and openings in the façade (e.g., windows and garage doors) are typically the first elements to be damaged by wind. Loss of the first shingle allows wind to penetrate and lift the next shingle. Unsecured slates may peel off; metal roofs may roll up and off.

Similarly, the loss of the first window, either because of extreme pressure or of wind-induced projectiles, can create a sudden build-up of internal pressure that can blow off roof shingles from inside even if they are properly secured. In structures where the roof provides the lateral stability by supporting the top of the building's walls, the integrity of the entire structure can be compromised. Even if the structure remains intact, once the building envelope is breached, contents are vulnerable either due to the wind itself or to accompanying rain.

Engineered structures, such as those built of commercial reinforced concrete and steel frame, fare relatively well, though they may experience damage to roof coverings, glass, and cladding. At very high wind speeds, these buildings can experience major damage to non-structural elements but rarely to components that would compromise the integrity of the structure.

There is a relative scarcity of test data on component or envelope resistances to wind. Most present-day knowledge of wind damage comes from damage investigations conducted in the aftermath of an event and from wind tunnel data obtained in laboratories around the world. Actual damage investigations are not always reliable, as the final damage state of a house is often caused by the initial failure of windows, doors, or shingles that may not have been properly installed. Furthermore, wind tunnel studies require very expensive testing facilities and are usually obtained by testing structures and/or components built according to high-quality standards rather than actual construction practice. The main drawback of wind damage estimation prediction is the lack of reliable wind recordings at or close to structures that have experienced different levels of damage. The relative scarcity of such observations is therefore often supplemented with engineering experience and knowledge when developing relationships for wind-induced damage.

In the case of earthquakes, the relationship linking the severity of the external excitation to building damage is captured by a fragility curve for given structural damage states (minor, moderate, severe damage, or collapse). A fragility curve for a given damage state provides the probability that the specified damage state will be reached or exceeded as a function of the severity of ground motion at the site. The use of fragility curves started in the 1980s (Kennedy et al., 1980; Kennedy and Ravindra, 1984) with the application of probabilistic risk analysis to nuclear power plants and facilities for the storage of hazardous materials.

In portfolio risk assessment studies, the same information contained in the fragility curve format is typically expressed in a roughly equivalent form called the damage function. A damage function is an equation that relates the expected structural damage state of the entire building to the intensity of the event. The standard deviation divided by the mean, the coefficient of variation, is often used to capture the uncertainty in the prediction of damage.

For financial analysis, building damage is ultimately expressed in terms of a damage ratio, the ratio of repair cost to the replacement cost of the building. The damage ratio can range from 0% to 100%, or total loss. Figure 3.7 shows a typical damage function. The distributions sketched in dotted lines in the figure reflect the fact that both the intensity of the external excitation and the level of damage given the level of excitation are uncertain quantities. Therefore, the damage ratio of the building is an uncertain quantity as well.

The damage state of the entire building for a given level of external excitation is given by the cumulative damage of its structural components, non-structural components, and contents. Structural components are, for example, beams and columns, while non-structural components include items such as cooling and heating systems, partition walls, plumbing, exterior walls, and suspended ceilings. For earthquake excitation, the damage level of most of the building components depends, loosely speaking, on the maximum deformation of the story where the component is located. Contents have instead been found to be more sensitive to maximum floor acceleration than to building deformation.

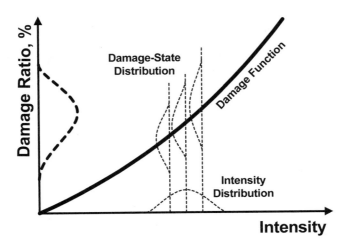

Figure 3.7. Illustration of a typical damage function.

For each typical structure within each building class, engineering analyses are performed to evaluate the level of building deformation and floor acceleration that are imposed on the structure by different levels of ground shaking. The damage inflicted to structural and non-structural components by building deformation and to contents by floor acceleration can be estimated either via a damage survey of instrumented buildings that have experienced past earthquakes or by laboratory tests. The expected damage ratio for the entire building for a certain level of deformation can be computed by considering the sum of the damage ratios of all the components and contents.

The level of physical damage inflicted on each component by a certain level of building deformation can be repaired according to strategies that range from "do nothing" to "complete replacement." Each repair strategy has a cost associated with it. (The next section in this chapter discusses the loss module and describes the process by which physical damage is translated into monetary costs.)

The engineering analyses performed to estimate the level of building deformation for a given level of ground shaking typically entails building a computer model of the structure. The virtual building is then either subjected to ground acceleration recordings of different intensities or pushed in lateral increments until collapse to mimic the lateral response of the building during different size earthquakes. At each increment, the force is redistributed to the elements that remain functional. Figure 3.8 shows a schematic flow of the damage calculation process. The procedure is performed for each site and for each event.

The procedure estimates separate damage states for the building and its contents, as well as a time-element damage state, which determines the

64

amount of loss associated with the loss of use of the building. The structure type is a key element in determining the building damage state. The building's occupancy type is a key element to determine contents damage and time-element damage states. These states of damage are combined to estimate the overall damage to the building as a system.

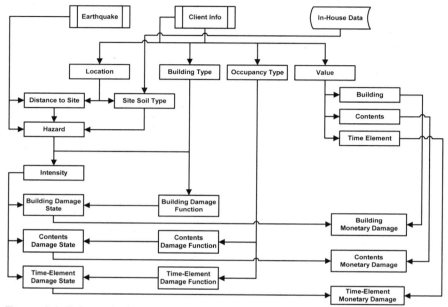

Figure 3.8. Schematic for process of damage calculation.

3.5 Loss Module

As was mentioned in the previous section, one approach taken by catastrophe modelers has been to link ground motion or wind intensity directly to the level of monetary loss. In this case, damage functions are developed based on the opinions of experts and not on actual engineering analysis of building types.

Noted structural engineers from private industry and academia are asked to estimate the damage ratio that would result to a typical building of a specific construction type were that building subjected to a given intensity of earthquake or hurricane. Their responses, which are based on their personal knowledge and experience, are statistically combined. One shortcoming of this approach is that the damage functions based on this method cannot be easily updated to reflect new construction techniques, building codes, repair costs or information gained in the aftermath of actual events.

A recent development in earthquake loss modeling has been the employment of cost models that translate estimates of physical damage into monetary loss. The model produces estimates of the cost of repair or replacement for each damaged structural and non-structural component as identified by the engineering analysis. Repair cost depends on the strategy utilized to replace or restore the structure. This depends, in turn, on the degree of damage to each component. In the case of a reinforced masonry wall with only minor cracks, for example, only cosmetic measures need be taken and the associated costs of repair would be minimal. If cracks are wider, removal and patching of damaged masonry and loose concrete, and injection of cracks with epoxy are needed to restore structural performance. At high levels of damage, full replacement of the affected component may be called for, increasing costs dramatically. The repair costs of each individual component are combined, along with the cost of inspection, set up and debris removal, to achieve an estimate of the monetary loss to the building as a whole.

Once total losses are calculated, estimates of insured losses are computed by applying policy conditions to the total loss estimates. Policy conditions include deductibles by coverage, site-specific or blanket deductibles, coverage limits and sublimits, loss triggers, coinsurance, attachment points and limits for single or multiple location policies, and risk specific reinsurance terms. The estimates of insured loss are validated, and damage functions fine-tuned, using loss data from actual events. This is particularly true in the case of wind perils, where loss data are relatively plentiful. Loss data for actual events normally consists of claims and paid losses by ZIP code and by line of business. However, data are also frequently available by construction type, and insurance coverage. Such detailed data, when available, are extremely useful to the modeler who is engaged in a continual process of validation and calibration.

3.6 Summary

Probabilistic catastrophe loss models incorporate detailed databases and scientific understanding of the highly complex physical phenomena of natural hazards, and engineering expertise about how buildings and their contents respond to the effects of those hazards.

Catastrophe models are typically composed of four primary components, or modules. The hazard module estimates the location, severity and frequency of occurrence of potential future catastrophe events. It also propagates the event across the affected region and calculates local intensity at each affected site.

The inventory module consists of detailed databases of property values and the number of structures, broken down by line of business, occupancy, and construction type. The vulnerability module employs mathematical relationships, called damage functions, that describe the interaction between structures and the intensity of the event to which they are exposed. In the loss module, physical damage is translated to total, or ground up (in insurance industry parlance) losses. Insured losses are calculated by applying policy conditions to the estimates of total loss.

After the loss estimations have been completed, they can be analyzed in ways of interest to risk management professionals. For example, the model produces probability distributions of losses, as well as the exceedance probability (EP) curve. As explained in Chapter 2, the EP curve reveals, for a particular portfolio of buildings, the probability that a certain level of loss will be surpassed in a given time period. Output includes probability distributions of total monetary loss, as well as net losses after the application of insurance policy conditions for both annual aggregate and annual occurrence losses. The probabilities can also be expressed in terms of return periods. That is, the loss associated with a return period of twenty years is likely to be exceeded only 5% of the time or, on average, in one year out of twenty.

Output may be customized to any desired degree of geographical resolution down to location level, as well as by line of business, and within line of business, by construction class, coverage, etc. The model can also provide summary reports of exposures, comparisons of exposures and losses by geographical area, and detailed information on potential large losses caused by the extreme events that make up the right-hand tail of the loss distribution.

3.7 References

Algermissen, S.T., Perkins, D.M., Thenhaus, P.C., Hanson, S.L., and Bender B.L. (1982). *Probabilistic Estimates of Maximum Acceleration and Velocity in Rock in the Contiguous United States*, United States Geological Survey Open-File Report 82-1033.

ATC-13 (1985). *Earthquake Damage Evaluation Data for California,* Applied Technology Council, Redwood City, California.

Cornell, C.A. (1968). "Engineering Seismic Risk Analysis," *Bulletin of Seismological Society of America*, 58(5): 1583-1606.

Electric Power Research Institute (1986). *Seismic Hazard Methodology for the Central and Eastern United States*, 10 volumes, EPRI report NP-7426, Electric Power Research Institute, Palo Alto.

Ellsworth, W.L. (1990). *Earthquake History in The San Andreas Fault System*, USGS Prof. Paper 1515.

Engdahl, E.R. and Rinehart, W.A. (1991). *Seismicity Map of North America*, in Slemmons, D.B., Engdahl, E.R., Zoback, M.D., and Blackwell, D.D. (eds.), "Neotectonics of North America", Boulder, CO, The Geological Society of America, Decade Map Volume 1, 21-27.

Engineering Sciences Data Unit (1994). *Wind Speed and Turbulence*, Vols. 1a. 1b.

Frankel, A., Mueller, C., Barnhard, T., Perkins, D., Leyendecker, E., Dickman, N., Hanson, S., Hopper, M. (1996). *Interim National Seismic Hazard Maps: Documentation,* United States Geological Survey, MS 966, Box 25046, Denver Federal Center, Denver, CO 80225, draft: January 18.

Georgiou, P.N. (1985). Design Wind Speed in Tropical Cyclone-Prone Regions, Boundary Layer Wind Tunnel Laboratory, Research Report # BLWT-2.

Johnston, C.A., and Schweig, E.S. (1996). *The Enigma of The New Madrid Earthquakes of 1811-1812*, Annu. Rev. Earth Planet. Sci., 24: 339-384.

Kaplan, J. and DeMaria, M. (1995). *A Simple Empirical Model for Predicting the Decay of Tropical Cyclone Winds After Landfall*, Journal of Applied Meteorology.

Kennedy, R.P., Cornell, C.A., Campbell, R.D., Kaplan, S., and Perla, H.F. (1980). *Probabilistic Seismic Safety Study of an Existing Nuclear Power Plant*, Nuclear Engineering and Design, Vol. 59: 315-338.

68

Kennedy, R.P. and Ravindra, M.K. (1984). *Seismic Fragilities for Nuclear Power Plant Risk Studies*, Nuclear Engineering and Design, 79: 47-68.

Kurihara, Y., Tuleya, R.E., Bender, M.A., and Ross R (1992). *Advanced Modeling of Tropical Cyclones*, Proceedings of the ICSU/WMO International Symposium on Tropical Cyclone Disasters, pp.190-201.

Mendez, A. and Anderson, J. G. (1991). *The temporal and spatial evolution of the 19 September 1985 Michoacan earthquake as inferred from near-source ground motion records*, Bulletin of the Seismological Society of America 81: 844-861.

Reiter, L. (1990). *Earthquake Hazard Analysis*, New York, Columbia University Press, New York.

SCEC (Southern California Earthquake Council) (1995). Working Group on California Earthquake Probabilities, *Seismic hazards in southern California: probable earthquakes, 1994-2024*, Bull. Seis. Soc. Am., 85: 379-439.

Schwerdt, R.W., Ho, F.P., Watkins, R.R. (1979). *Meteorological Criteria for Standard Projects Hurricane and Probable Maximum Hurricane Windfields, Gulf and East Coast of the united States*, United States Department of Commerce, National Oceanic and Atmospheric Administration, NOAA Technical report NWS23, September.

Simiu, E. and Scanlan, R.H. (1996). *Wind Effects on Structures- Fundamentals and Applications to Design*, Wiley Interscience.

USGS (1996). *National Seismic Hazard Maps Documentation: USGS Open-File Report 96-532*.

USGS (1999). *Earthquake Probabilities in the San Francisco Bay Region: 2000 to 2030 - A Summary of Findings, USGS Open-File Report 99-51*.

Wells, D.L., and Coppersmith, K.J. (1994). *New Empirical Relationships Among Magnitude, Rupture Length, Rupture Width, Rupture Area and Surface Displacement*, Bulletin of the Seismological Society of America, 84: 974-1002.

Chapter 4 – Sources, Nature, and Impact of Uncertainties on Catastrophe Modeling

Major Contributors:
Patricia Grossi
Don Windeler

4.1 Introduction

Catastrophe modeling is a complex tool used to assess the risk from natural hazards. The four components of hazard, inventory, vulnerability, and loss depicted in Figure 3.1 and discussed in detail in Chapter 3 require information from a range of sources and the expertise of an array of professionals. Natural hazard, engineering and economic data are the foundation of catastrophe models. Limitations in data and assumptions about the model's parameters, in the hazard, inventory, and vulnerability modules, affect a catastrophe model's loss estimates and the uncertainty associated with these estimates.

This chapter explores the sources, nature, and impact of uncertainties in a catastrophe model. Prevalent methods to represent and quantify uncertainty through the components of the catastrophe model are discussed. Finally, the impact of uncertainty on exceedance probability (EP) curves used by risk managers to quantify their catastrophe risk potential is illustrated by examining potential losses to residential property from hurricanes in Florida and earthquakes in Charleston, South Carolina. Quantification and classification of uncertainty provides opportunities to reduce risk. With accurate measures of uncertainty, stakeholders can potentially lower the cost of dealing with catastrophe risk. Furthermore, since the risk affects stakeholders in dissimilar ways, the robustness of a risk management strategy can be made clear to each stakeholder if uncertainty is delineated.

4.2 Classifications of Uncertainty

As indicated in Chapter 3, there is a great deal of information needed to develop the hazard, inventory, vulnerability, and loss components of a catastrophe model. Therefore, all stakeholders in the management of risk value new information regarding these modules. For example, an insurer values additional information on the likelihood of disasters and potential damage to properties in its portfolio in order to more accurately manage the risk. Local government officials value a thorough understanding of hazards in their regions in order to plan for emergency response and recovery efforts following a disaster. Model developers value any additional information to validate and calibrate their catastrophe models.

Since catastrophe modeling is a fairly new field of application, there are no historical classifications of catastrophe modeling uncertainty, per se. However, building on the concepts from probabilistic hazard analyses, uncertainty can be characterized as either aleatory or epistemic in nature (Budnitz et al., 1997). Aleatory uncertainty is the inherent randomness associated with natural hazard events, such as earthquakes, hurricanes, and floods. It cannot be reduced by the collection of additional data. In contrast, epistemic uncertainty is the uncertainty due to lack of information or knowledge of the hazard. Unlike aleatory uncertainty, epistemic uncertainty can be reduced by the collection of additional data.

While the advantage of differentiating between aleatory and epistemic uncertainty in an analysis is clear (only epistemic uncertainty can be reduced), the necessity of distinguishing between aleatory and epistemic uncertainty is not. "Epistemic and aleatory uncertainties are fixed neither in space...nor in time. What is aleatory uncertainty in one model can be epistemic uncertainty in another model, at least in part. And what appears to be aleatory uncertainty at the present time may be cast, at least in part, into epistemic uncertainty at a later date" (Hanks and Cornell, 1994). Therefore, developers of catastrophe models do not necessarily distinguish between these two types of uncertainty; instead, model developers concentrate on not ignoring or double counting uncertainties and clearly documenting the process in which they represent and quantify uncertainties.

4.3 Sources of Uncertainty

Limited scientific knowledge, coupled with a lack of historical data, leave open several possible and competing explanations for the parameters, data, and mathematical models underlying each of the components in a catastrophe model. Simply put, the science and impact of natural hazards are not completely understood; in addition, the cross-disciplinary nature of a catastrophe model leads to complexity. Experts in seismology or meteorology who model the hazard must interact with structural engineers who model the vulnerability; similarly structural engineers who model the vulnerability must interact with actuaries who model the loss. Basically, as each discipline's modeling assumptions are added to the process, more uncertainty is added to the estimates.

In catastrophe modeling, both epistemic and aleatory uncertainties are reflected in the four basic components of a model. Aleatory uncertainty is reflected via probability distributions. The frequency of a hazard occurrence and the fragility of a building, as discussed in Chapter 3, are examples of aleatory uncertainty. Since the exact time of occurrence and the precise level of structural damage cannot be known in advance of a hazard event, the recurrence rate and the vulnerability of the inventory exposed to the natural hazard are characterized using probability distributions. Similarly the capacity of individual structural elements of a building during a severe event, and the resulting cost of repair cannot be determined beforehand. Probability distributions are also used to characterize these parameters in a catastrophe model.

A larger issue in quantifying uncertainty is the lack of data for characterizing the four components in a catastrophe model. For example, as discussed in Chapter 3, the recurrence of earthquake events on fault sources can be modeled using a magnitude-frequency model (Richter, 1958), a characteristic earthquake model (Youngs and Coppersmith, 1985), or a combination of both models. In California, estimates of ground shaking probabilities on certain fault segments are established by combining the two recurrence models for earthquake magnitude-frequency distributions (Peterson et al. 1996). Historical earthquake records are used to establish a recurrence curve, or the Gutenberg-Richter relationship, for the smaller magnitude events, while geologic data (most importantly, a fault's slip rate) is used to estimate the recurrence of the larger, characteristic events.

The availability of seismological data describing earthquake occurrence in California for only a few hundred years makes the updating of the recurrence distributions problematic. When more data become available, in the form of fault slip rates or seismograph recordings, these relationships could potentially be improved. Similar issues arise in modeling the recurrence of hurricane events. Past data describing the location and occurrence of hurricanes on the eastern seaboard of the United States are also limited to a few hundred years (Powell and Aberson, 2001).

The deficiency of information regarding repair costs and business interruption costs affect the accuracy of the loss component of a catastrophe model. For example, the increased cost to repair or rebuild after an event is often taken into account using a demand surge adjustment. This is simply the percentage increase in costs due to the limited supply of construction material and labor immediately following a disaster. Further, due to the growing understanding of indirect losses, estimates of business interruption costs to commercial property owners are continually validated and calibrated with the latest loss information.

Another source of epistemic uncertainty in a catastrophe model is the lack of available data to create the Geographic Information Systems (GIS) databases within the modeling software. For any model, recognizing the importance of input data is essential. The "garbage in, garbage out" principle holds irrespective of how advanced or state-of-the-art a model may be. GIS maps of hazard sources, geologic features and topographic landscape characterize hazards. GIS maps of the locations of structures characterize inventory.

An incomplete description of a hazard source, the geology or the topography can cause erroneous results. For example, in earthquake modeling, having accurate information on the underlying soil in a region is very important. A structure built on rock-like material is likely to sustain much lower losses compared to a structure built on soft clay-like material. Inaccurate information on soil conditions can lead to large errors in estimation of loss due to an earthquake.

In fact, past observations from earthquakes confirm that soil condition plays a very important role in building performance. As expected, buildings on soft ground or steep slopes usually suffer more significant damage in comparison to those on firm and flat ground. Since soil condition may vary dramatically within a small area, such as the Marina District in San Francisco (where soil conditions vary from bay mud to rock site), using ZIP code to identify a location may not be sufficiently accurate. At a particular location, high-resolution geocoding should be used as it can more accurately pin down the soil condition.

Partial information on a structure's characteristics can also result in an inaccurate estimate of future damage. For example, most structural engineers would agree that the construction type, age, height, occupancy, assessed value, and the location of a structure are needed – at a minimum – for the inventory component of a catastrophe model. If more specific information regarding the structure such as its location relative to other structures and previous damage to the structure were available, a more accurate estimate of damage or vulnerability would result.

Lack of accurate data on true market values of the properties under consideration is an additional source of epistemic uncertainty in the modeling process. For determining the appropriate coverage limit, many residential policies use property tax assessment data, which are generally outdated and under-valued. Under-valued exposures will result in under-estimating potential loss. For example, suppose a home's property value is assessed at $600,000 when its true worth is $1 million. Furthermore, suppose it is insured with a 15% deductible and full coverage based on the lower assessed value. If an earthquake occurs and causes major damage and the cost to repair the structure is 35% of the true value of the home, the resulting monetary loss is $350,000. A $600,000 insurance policy with a 15% deductible translates to the homeowner being responsible for $90,000, with the insurer covering the remaining $260,000 of the loss. If the insurance coverage had been based on the home's true worth of $1 million, the homeowner would have to cover the first $150,000 of the loss and the insurer would only have claim payments of $200,000.

Incomplete or inaccurate information on an inventory's description is a concern not only to insurers but also to all risk management stakeholders. To improve on the amount of such information available, an effort to document the types of housing structures worldwide was initiated in 2000 to assess the vulnerability of the world's population to earthquake hazard. Under the guidance of the Earthquake Engineering Research Institute (EERI) and the International Association of Earthquake Engineering (IAEE), the World Housing Encyclopedia has a web-based listing of housing construction types from earthquake-prone countries around the world (EERI, 2003). In addition, the Institute for Business and Home Safety (IBHS) relies on INCAST, a data inventory tool used in conjunction with the HAZUS catastrophe model, to store inventory information on the homes that are a part of their "Fortified...for safer living" program. These homes are reinforced to withstand many natural hazards, including high winds, wildfire, flood, hail, and earthquake.

Epistemic uncertainty is also found in the use of laboratory testing (shake table tests for earthquake hazard or wind-tunnel tests for hurricane hazard) and expert opinion to develop the vulnerability component of a catastrophe model. For a portfolio risk assessment, damage functions such as the one illustrated in Figure 3.7 in Chapter 3, have traditionally been constructed using these sources along with damage surveys of actual structures. Given that laboratory testing has been restricted to certain types of structural materials, there is a limited understanding of how other materials withstand lateral loading.

In the earliest versions of catastrophe models, damage ratios were estimated using the Applied Technology Council report of Earthquake Damage Evaluation Data for California (ATC-13, 1985). This report was generated using the Delphi method of collecting information from a group of experts (Dalkey, 1969). In this method, a series of questionnaires interspersed with controlled opinion feedback resulted in a group judgment. In the ATC-13 study, 71 earthquake engineering experts were asked to indicate their low, best, and high estimates of damage ratios for 78 types of structures subject to earthquakes with Modified Mercalli Intensity (MMI) levels of VI through XII. Catastrophe model developers used these estimates in their earliest versions of their earthquake loss software, skewing estimates of damage due to the use of the Delphi Method and limiting the interpretation of damage due to the use of MMI. More recent models employ cost models that translate estimates of physical damage into direct monetary loss rather than depending on damage ratios.

4.4 Representing and Quantifying Uncertainty

Guidelines do exist for identifying the sources of uncertainty and incorporating them into catastrophe models. The Senior Seismic Hazard Analysis Committee (SSHAC) Report is a comprehensive study addressing this issue and the use of expert opinion in a probabilistic seismic hazard analysis (Budnitz et al., 1997). This report can also be used for the incorporation of uncertainty of other natural hazards. Additionally, guidelines set forth by the Environmental Protection Agency (EPA), requiring that all risk assessments possess the core values of "transparency, clarity, consistency, and reasonableness," are relevant for the modeling of natural hazards (Browner, 1995).

The most common methods for incorporating uncertainty into catastrophe modeling are logic trees and simulation techniques. These two methods are standard approaches for quantifying and propagating uncertainty when there is intrinsic aleatory uncertainty, lack of consensus among experts, and lack of data used to estimate parameters.

4.4.1 Logic Trees

In the logic tree approach, alternative parameter values or mathematical relationships are identified within the catastrophe model, relative weighting schemes are assigned to each alternative, and estimates of parameters or relationships are calculated using a weighted, linear combination of the outcomes. Weighting schemes are numerous, with the weights representing the credibility of that alternative in relation to the available data. For example, one can use equal weights, weights proportional to the ranking of alternatives, or weights based on some comparison of previously assessed estimates with actual outcomes. Weights are often established through the use of expert opinion, and therefore, are biased towards an expert's judgment.

Figure 4.1 depicts a simple example of how a logic tree can be used in a catastrophe model. Suppose that there is an earthquake fault that generates a characteristic magnitude event. This event is estimated using a recurrence model with two alternatives for the fault's slip rate, λ_1 and λ_2, weighted w_1 and $1-w_1$, respectively. Next, suppose a single family residential structure is the only structure to be assessed in the inventory. However, there is a lack of consensus regarding the type of underlying soil at the site. Thus, there are two alternatives for the soil parameter, denoted S_1 and S_2 with respective weights w_2 and $1-w_2$ in Figure 4.1.

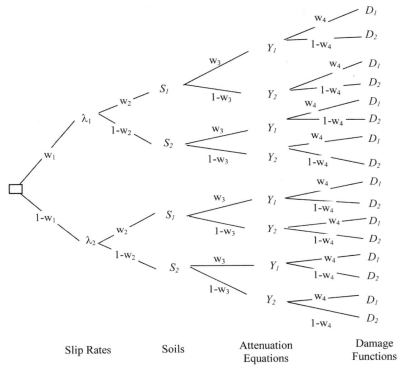

Slip Rates   Soils   Attenuation   Damage
                          Equations   Functions

Figure 4.1. Logic tree approach to catastrophe modeling.

In the next branch of the logic tree, the two estimates of recurrence for a characteristic magnitude event and the two alternatives for site-specific soils are combined with two competing attenuation equations describing the rate at which the amplitude of the seismic waves decreases as the waves propagate outward from the source of the rupture. For example, the Frankel, et al. (1996) attenuation relationship and the Toro, et al. (1997) relationship can be used as two competing models of strong ground motion in the Central and Eastern United States. These two models, denoted Y_1 and Y_2 in Figure 4.1 (using similar notation introduced in Chapter 3 for characterizing ground motion attenuation), are weighted w_3 and $1-w_3$, respectively. This combination results in estimates of earthquake ground motion for certain magnitude events at a certain frequency of occurrence, under certain site conditions, and at certain distances from the event's epicenter.

Finally, these ground motion estimates are combined with two competing models for damage functions, one created using expert opinion and one based on laboratory testing. These functions, D_1 and D_2, relate the expected damage state of the residential building (minor, moderate, severe damage, or collapse) to the level of ground motion at the site. Each is weighted accordingly, denoted w_4 and $1-w_4$ in Figure 4.1. The final results of this simple example are sixteen calculations of structural damage to a single-family dwelling based on alternative assumptions of characteristic fault slip rates, underlying soils, and empirical attenuation models. As is evident, the costs of repair have not yet been incorporated.

The logic tree approach to incorporating uncertainty is utilized often in practice because of its tractability and its usefulness as a tool to communicate risk to stakeholders. While a set of results grows with each alternative assumption added to the analysis, advances in computing power allow the handling of large databases; therefore, both parameter and model alternatives can be identified within this type of approach. Although the preceding example shows two alternatives at each branch, a larger (yet finite) number of alternatives can be considered, as is typically the case in a catastrophe model.

4.4.2 Simulation Techniques

Simulation is a method for learning about a real system by experimenting with a model that duplicates the essential behavior of the system. It is one of the most widely used quantitative approaches to decision making. In contrast to a logic tree, which requires a set of simplifying assumptions, simulation can model extremely complex processes. An uncertain parameter is represented by a discrete or continuous probability distribution, multiple simulations are run which sample from the distribution, and the analyses are completed using these sample values. The results are statistically analyzed to estimate important performance measures of the system. In the case of catastrophe modeling, a performance measure is, for example, exceedance probability loss.

Although most distributions in catastrophe modeling are continuous, a simulation using a discrete distribution is presented here for simplicity. Suppose that a single-family residential structure is subject to a hurricane hazard and five levels of damage states are defined (none, minor, moderate, severe, or collapse) in a catastrophe model. Suppose further that damage functions are available that represent the probability of being in, or exceeding, a certain damage state level given a certain level of wind speed. Now suppose that the residential insurer wants a probabilistic estimate of being in a certain damage state given that the wind speed is 100 mph.

Simulation can be used to generate this probability distribution. First, the probability of being in one of the five damage states is calculated based on the given set of damage functions, indicated by damage state probability in Table 4.1. For example, there is a 5% probability that there will be no damage and a 7% probability that the building will collapse. In this case, an arbitrary range from 00-99 (100 digits) is used, with 5% representing the probability of having no damage (00-04), 24% representing minor damage (05-28), 48% representing moderate damage (29-76), 16% representing severe damage (77-92), and 7% representing collapse of the structure (93-99). Then the cumulative probabilities are calculated for the ordered damage states and random numbers are assigned in proportion to these cumulative probabilities as shown in Table 4.1.

Table 4.1. Simulation example in catastrophe modeling

Damage State	Damage State Probability	Cumulative Probability	Random Number Lower Bound	Random Number Upper Bound
None	0.05	0.05	00	04
Minor	0.24	0.29	05	28
Moderate	0.48	0.77	29	76
Severe	0.16	0.93	77	92
Collapse	0.07	1.00	93	99

To start the simulation, a random number between 00 and 99 is generated. Based on the resulting value, a damage state is projected. For example, if the random number is 36, the structure has moderate damage; if the random number is 21, the structure sustains minor damage. This random number generation is repeated, for example, 1,000 times, and the levels of damage are stored. At the end of the 1,000 sample runs, a histogram of the sample damage state frequencies is created (Figure 4.2). This histogram is an approximation to the distribution of damage, given a level of wind speed.

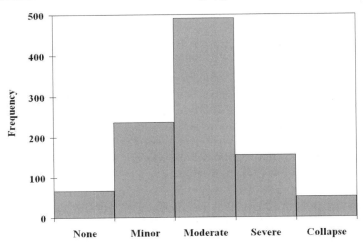

Figure 4.2. Histogram of damage state frequency for 1000 simulation runs.

While this is a simple example of a Monte Carlo simulation (actual simulations in catastrophe modeling are much more complicated), it should be noted that this type of modeling is computationally intensive and requires a large number of samples. If the time and computer resources required to run a full-blown simulation are prohibitively expensive, a degree of computational efficiency can be found through the use of modified Monte Carlo methods, such as Latin Hypercube Sampling, that sample from the input distribution in a more efficient manner (Inman and Conover, 1980). In this way, the number of necessary runs, compared to the Monte Carlo method, is significantly reduced.

4.4.3 Uncertainty and the Exceedance Probability Curve

As defined in Chapter 2, an exceedance probability curve is a graphical representation of the probability that a certain level of loss will be exceeded over a future time period. A widely used technique to create an exceedance probability curve in a catastrophe model is a combination of a logic tree with Monte Carlo simulation. Building on the simple examples presented earlier, each branch of the logic tree represents an alternative that samples from a probability distribution rather than assuming a simple point estimate alternative. For example, consider the competing attenuation equations for ground motion presented earlier, denoted $Y_1 = F_1(f, M, r, Source, Site)$ and $Y_2 = F_2(f, M, r, Source, Site)$. Instead of using the mean estimates of ground motion amplitude based on these functions for each branch of the logic tree, Monte Carlo methods can be used to sample from the attenuation functions along the branches of the tree.

This blended approach allows the creation, in a systematic way, of a set of curves that represent various confidence levels in exceedance probabilities. For example, suppose that there are a set of assumptions, A_1, $A_2...A_n$, which represent an exhaustive set of all possible assumptions about the parameters, data, and mathematical models needed to generate an exceedance probability curve in a catastrophe model. Further, suppose that each set of assumptions is an alternative on one branch of a logic tree and each logic tree branch results in an EP curve that is generated when the assumptions A_i are made, characterizing the loss L, as shown in Figure 4.3 (i.e., $EP(L,A_i) = P(Loss > L, A_i)$). If each of the sets of assumptions are weighted with subjective probabilities, w_1, $w_2...w_n$, that add up to one and the assumptions, A_1, $A_2...A_n$, give rise to a monotonic ordering of their respective EP curves, the mean, median, and a confidence interval for the resulting collection of EP curves, can be defined.

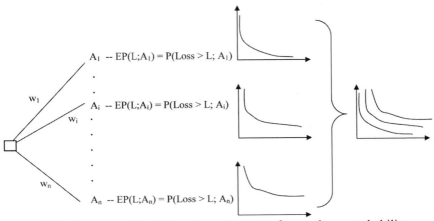

Figure 4.3. Logic tree and simulation to create a set of exceedance probability curves.

4.5 Case Studies in Uncertainty

Given the complexity of catastrophe modeling and the preceding discussion of the sources and techniques to incorporate uncertainty in a model, it is not surprising that competing catastrophe models will generate different EP curves for the same portfolio of structures. When first used in practice, the degree to which these curves could differ is surprising to the users of catastrophe models. With more experience, a user expects a range of possible EP curves.

4.5.1 Hurricane Hazard: Florida

Hurricane losses in Florida provide an interesting example of dissimilar exceedance probability curves for an identical residential inventory. Following the exorbitant losses to the insurance industry after Hurricane Andrew in 1992, the state of Florida resolved to use catastrophe models for residential insurance ratemaking. Prior to Hurricane Andrew, property insurance rates in Florida, including the provision for hurricane losses, were based on historical loss data in combination with the excess wind procedure developed by the Insurance Services Office (ISO), the primary property insurance rating organization in Florida (Florida Insurance Council, February, 1998). This procedure relied on the examination of the prior 30 years wind loss experience in the state and produced an average loss cost to be used in the rate filing application by the insurer.

Prior to Hurricane Andrew, ISO estimated a required catastrophic wind premium for Florida homeowners totaling $80 million using the excess wind procedure. The premium structure proposed by ISO would have required over 100 years to pay for the losses from Hurricane Andrew alone - without considering any other hurricanes that could make landfall. In retrospect, ISO's rate setting process grossly understated the actual risk, shocking the insurance and reinsurance industry with losses far greater than they ever imagined.

In 1995, in response to the insurance crisis in the state and to use a more appropriate procedure to calculate property rates, the Florida Legislature authorized the creation of the Florida Commission on Hurricane Loss Projection Methodology (FCHLPM). The commission consisted of eleven experts, independent of the insurance industry and the Department of Insurance, with responsibility to review the commercially available catastrophe models with regard to their accuracy and reliability (FCHLPM, November 2001). This supported the Legislature's findings that "reliable projections of hurricane losses are necessary to assure that rates for residential insurance are neither excessive nor inadequate, and that in recent years computer modeling has made it possible to improve upon the accuracy of hurricane loss projections" (FCHLPM, 2001).

To be certified for use in establishing residential insurance rates, a catastrophe model undergoes a rigorous yearly review process. Prior to the yearly review and approval by the FCHLPM, a professional team conducts on-site audits of the models. This team consists of five members, including a statistician, an actuary, a computer scientist, a civil engineer and a meteorologist. This professional team is under the authority of the FCHLPM, which is mandated by the state to "consider any actuarial methods, principles, standards, models or output ranges that have the potential for improving the accuracy of or reliability of the hurricane loss projections used in residential property rate filings" (FCHLPM, 2001).

In 1996, AIR Worldwide was the first model certified. In 1997, a total of three models were certified -- AIR Worldwide, EQECAT, and Risk Management Solutions. Since 1997, additional models such as Applied Research Associates have been certified. The Florida Hurricane Catastrophe Fund (FHCF), a residual risk wind pool established in 1993 to maintain insurance availability following Hurricane Andrew, utilizes rate calculations based on computer models that have been certified for use in Florida by the FHCLPM. Typically, rates are based on averaging the outputs from multiple models. In 1999, for example, three models were used, with 50% weight to the middle result, and 25% weight to the high and low results.

While the FHCF must use the Commission's findings regarding models in establishing rates, individual insurers are not required to do so in their own rate filings. If they do, the findings are admissible and relevant in rate filings, arbitration, and judicial proceedings. However, the Department of Insurance has the authority to review and approve rate filings using any methodology, and is not obligated to approve filings based on model-based analyses. The use of models in Florida rate filings is increasing, but public and regulatory acceptance is still far from universal. In fact, some insurers have stated their objection to model based rates, and the public opposition to model rates is especially high in the coastal areas of Broward and Dade County.

As part of a model's certification process, each firm must submit an exceedance probability curve from its catastrophe model for a portfolio of residential structures in Florida. The portfolio includes one $100,000 building for each of three construction types (wood frame, masonry, and mobile home) in each ZIP code in Florida. Additional insured values are added for appurtenant structures, contents, and additional living expense. Table 4.2 and Figure 4.4 present a summary of this information for three competing catastrophe models, denoted Model A, Model B, and Model C, submitted to the Florida Commission in 2001. All models must submit estimates of expected loss for eleven exceedance probability levels, ranging from 0.01% (0.0001) to 20% (0.20). Additionally, a model may or may not present a loss estimate for a top event, defined by the modeler to be the largest exceedance probability/loss combination that can possibly occur. In this case, Model A did not present a top event while Models B and C did, as shown in Table 4.2.

In Table 4.2, a weighted linear combination of the three competing loss estimates for each exceedance probability level is shown to illustrate how all of the information can be used to make an informed decision on setting insurance rates. In this example, a 50% weight is given to the middle result, and 25% weights are given to the high and low results. Thus, the expected loss for this residential portfolio for the 1-in-100 year event could be estimated as: (0.25*$28.5 + 0.50*$31.7 + 0.25*$39.1) = $32.75 million. Other weighting schemes such as equal weights could be utilized to estimate the expected losses for each event.

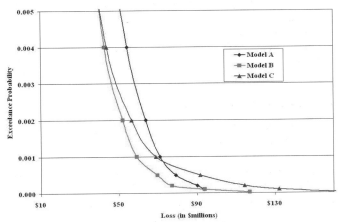

Figure 4.4. Exceedance probability curves from competing models (Source: Florida Loss Commission Data, Form E, 2001).

82

Table 4.2. Exceedance probabilities versus estimated loss (in millions) across models

Return Time (years)	Exceedance Probability	Estimated Loss Model A	Estimated Loss Model B*	Estimated Loss Model C**	Weighted Linear Combination***
Top Event	---	---	$116.8	$165.9	---
10,000	0.01%	$93.3	$93.7	$131.9	$103.15
5,000	0.02%	89.9	77.1	114.3	92.80
2,000	0.05%	79.0	69.7	91.6	79.83
1,000	0.10%	71.0	59.0	68.8	66.90
500	0.20%	63.7	52.0	56.5	57.18
250	0.40%	54.2	42.7	43.9	46.18
100	1.00%	39.1	31.7	28.5	32.75
50	2.00%	27.8	22.8	18.6	23.00
20	5.00%	16.3	12.5	9.4	12.68
10	10.00%	8.7	6.6	4.7	6.65
5	20.00%	2.9	2.4	1.7	2.35

* top event exceedance probability = 0.002% (Return time of 50,000 years)
** top event exceedance probability = 0.001% (Return time of 100,000 years)
*** 50% weight on middle result and 25% weight on high and low results (no result shown for top event due to differences in exceedance probability and limitations of data)

Looking more closely at the data provided, at the 1-in-20 year event or 5% annual probability of exceedance, the loss estimates range from about $9.4 million to $16.3 million. At the 1-in-1,000 year event or annual probability of exceedance of 0.1% (0.001), loss estimates range from $59 million to $71 million. In this example, as the probability of exceedance increases, the absolute range of losses across the competing model curves consistently decreases. This trend is often seen in the development of exceedance probability curves in high hazard areas. Of course, with the lower dollar figures, the percentage difference can be much higher than at the larger, catastrophic loss levels.

4.5.2 Earthquake Hazard: Charleston, South Carolina

While hurricane risk in Florida is useful to understand the range of differences in loss between competing catastrophe models in the expected or mean case, a different approach must be used to represent confidence levels for various loss/probability combinations on an EP curve. In the summer of 1999, a meeting was held among representatives of Risk Management Solutions, EQECAT, AIR Worldwide and the Wharton School to discuss a sensitivity analysis regarding catastrophe models' estimates of earthquake loss (Grossi, et al., 1999). In this section, a case study of earthquake hazard in Charleston, South Carolina is presented using data from four catastrophe models: models developed by each of the three modeling firms involved in this study (similarly denoted Model A, Model B, and Model C as in the earlier hurricane example), along with FEMA's catastrophe model, HAZUS. A list of the common assumptions were specified for each modeling firm to conduct an assessment of the Charleston region, along with the key elements of uncertainty for the Wharton team to consider in an analysis they would undertake using the HAZUS model.

Composite Model Curves

The first goal of this case study was to discover not only the range of differences between results generated by the three competing catastrophe models, but also to compare a set of exceedance probability curves that represent the 5th percentile, mean, and 95th percentile level of loss. With these curves, a 90% confidence interval on loss is created. In other words, each model created three EP curves for comparison: a best estimate of loss, defined by its mean exceedance probability curve, and two additional curves representing a symmetric 90% confidence level about the mean loss.

As in the case of the hurricane hazard in Florida, the exceedance probability curves produced were expected to be dissimilar, given the degree of uncertainty associated with earthquake recurrence in the Charleston, South Carolina region. In fact, the degree of uncertainty amongst the models was expected to be greater than in the Florida case due to the lack of understanding of the seismic sources in this region. Charleston region is a low earthquake hazard area and the moment magnitude 7.3 earthquake event in 1886 is the only known historical event of note.

The assumptions for the analysis are summarized in Table 4.3. Four counties in the southeastern region of South Carolina, which surround the city of Charleston, comprised the study region. One hundred and thirty four census tracts are contained within the counties of Berkeley, Dorchester, Charleston, and Colleton. The HAZUS database of structures, as defined by the HAZUS97 release (NIBS, 1997), was assumed for the inventory at risk. This database consists of seven occupancy classes of structures, namely residential, commercial, industrial, agricultural, religious, government, and educational occupancies. There were roughly 170,000 buildings in the data set, with approximately 97% of them classified as residential structures.

Table 4.3. Charleston, South Carolina earthquake hazard analysis assumptions

Component	Assumptions
Hazard	o Fault and area sources defined by model o Recurrence defined by model o Site specific characteristics defined by model
Inventory	o 134 census tracts containing 170,000 structures o 97% residential structures
Vulnerability	o Damage functions/fragility curves defined by model
Loss	o Repair costs defined by model o Building damage loss only

Using this common inventory database, each catastrophe model was run unaltered. In other words, no additional common information was used to define the hazard component, the vulnerability component, and the loss component of each model; the proprietary portion of each model remained as such for the study. The generated exceedance probability curves with the relevant confidence intervals were constructed by each of the modeling firms for the loss associated with building damage only (i.e., ground-up loss); no insurance parameters were considered in the analysis.

Given the proprietary nature of the competing models, each model's set of curves is not presented here. Instead, composite curves developed by the Wharton research team are shown[1]. In Figure 4.5, a composite EP curve for the mean loss is shown that represents an equally weighted linear combination of the data (1/3 of each). For example, suppose an estimate of the probability of exceeding a loss of $1 billion (EP(L) = P(Loss > $1 billion) is needed for the study area. Model A's probability of exceedance of 0.0091 is combined with Model B's exceedance probability of 0.0051 and Model C's exceedance probability of 0.0053 to estimate: P(Loss > $1 billion) = (0.0091 + 0.0053 + 0.0051)/3 = 0.0065 or 0.65% probability of exceedance (a 1-in-154 year return period), as seen in Figure 4.5.

Bounding the composite mean EP curve are composite symmetric 90% confidence interval curves: a lower bound on loss, representing the 5th percentile loss, and an upper bound on loss, representing the 95th percentile loss. Since the range of exceedance probabilities varied greatly for a particular loss level for these bounded curves, an equally weighted linear combination was not used (as it was in the mean case). Instead, the extreme value points across the three models were utilized in constructing the

---

[1] The individual and composite curves were reviewed by Professor Robert Whitman of the Massachusetts Institute of Technology, as part of the Technical Advisory Committee input to the project.

confidence intervals. Thus, the tendency to favor one model over the other two models was avoided.

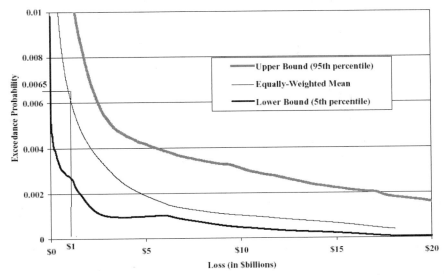

Figure 4.5. Composite exceedance probability curves for Charleston region.

To illustrate the difference between the two approaches, consider the following example. Suppose that the 5th percentile of exceeding a loss of $15 billion (EP(L) = P(Loss > $15 billion)) is required to determine a risk management strategy, which represents a large loss on the right-hand tail of the EP curve. Model A estimates a return period of 5,080 years, Model B estimates a return period of 1,730 years, but Model C's curve does not extend beyond 1,000 years because there is too much modeling uncertainty beyond this point. If the weighted linear combination of these two estimates were calculated equally, ignoring Model C, the result would be a return period of 3,405 years or 0.029% (0.00029) probability of exceedance.

Using the extreme value points for the lower and upper bound curves, the 5th percentile loss of $15 billion has a return period of 5,080 years or approximately 0.02% (0.0002) probability of exceedance rather than the average of 0.029% (0.00029). In this way, the 90% confidence level on the mean curve is an envelope of the three model curves, capturing the true bounds on the uncertainty across the three models.

Reconsidering the loss levels presented earlier for these curves, the probability that the loss to the inventory of structures in the Charleston region will exceed $1 billion or EP(L) = P(Loss > $1 billion) is, on average, 0.0065 or 0.65% with lower and upper bounds of 0.27% (0.0027) and 1.17%

(0.0117), respectively. The mean probability that the loss to the inventory of structures will exceed $15 billion = P(Loss > $15 billion) = 0.064% (0.00064) with a lower bound of 0.02% and an upper bound of 0.22%.

A specific loss level for the region could be determined, given a probability of exceedance, using the same data. Using the example of the range of losses for the 0.2% (0.002) probability of exceedance or the 1-in-500 year event, it can be determined from Figure 4.5 that the mean loss to these structures is $4.6 billion with a lower bound of $1.5 billion and an upper bound of $17.1 billion. It should be clear that in dealing with catastrophe modeling, there is a wide variation in the probability of exceedance given a level of monetary loss and a wide variation in loss given a probability of exceedance.

HAZUS Analysis

A related objective of the Charleston analysis was to generate an exceedance probability curve utilizing the HAZUS model and to test the sensitivity of the loss output to a few key assumptions in the model. (For more details and the complete analysis, see Grossi and Windeler, 2000.) While the HAZUS methodology is more transparent than the approaches used in the three competing proprietary models, it requires the development of additional software to create an EP curve (Grossi, 2000). The 1997 HAZUS earthquake model, in its basic form was not designed to create an exceedance probability curve (NIBS, 1997). It could create either an estimate of loss based on one scenario event or based on a probabilistic seismic hazard map, such as the ones created by a USGS team of researchers (Frankel, et al., 1996).

The software tools that enable the creation of an exceedance probability curve using the HAZUS model consist of a pre-processor, designated Scenario Builder and a post-processor, designated HAZUS-EP. As shown in Figure 4.6, Scenario Builder defines a finite set of earthquake events, j = 1,2...N, which represent a minimum set of data points needed to create an EP curve. Each event *j* is defined by its source, magnitude, rupture location, recurrence and attenuation (the hazard component of a catastrophe model). The data and assumptions used to develop the stochastic event set generally follow those described in the USGS National Seismic Hazard Mapping project (Frankel et al., 1996). Notably, the attenuation relationship to describe the rate at which ground motion decays from source to site is an equally weighted linear combination of the Frankel et al., (1996) and the Toro et al., (1997) empirical equations. In this way, all information available is incorporated into the model.

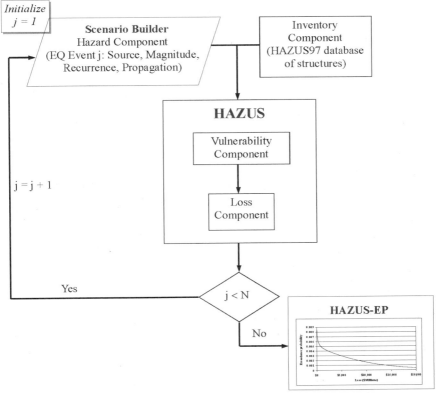

Figure 4.6. Scenario Builder-HAZUS-HAZUS-EP to create an exceedance probability curve.

The total set of events, N = 156, was chosen so that there was a wide enough spectrum of events capable of affecting the Charleston study region. The operative assumption in defining events was that variation in losses would decrease with distance from the study area. Therefore, the greatest number of events would be required within the study counties; the seismicity of progressively larger areas outside these counties could be represented by single events. Similarly, smaller magnitude events were eliminated with increasing distance. As in the earlier analysis to create the composite set of EP curves from Models A, B, and C, the database of inventory structures are defined by the HAZUS97 release (NIBS, 1997), consisting of approximately 170,000 buildings of various occupancy classes.

With the portfolio of structures in Charleston, South Carolina, the HAZUS model is run for each event *j* with *j* = 1,2,...156. The model calculates the damage to the structural and nonstructural building components and the resulting direct economic losses, as defined by the HAZUS methodology (the vulnerability and loss components of a catastrophe model). The results of each run, including losses by census tract and by occupancy type, are stored in a database file for input into the post-processor, HAZUS-EP. HAZUS-EP consolidates the losses to form an exceedance probability curve for the region.

In the complete analysis of the Charleston region using HAZUS, a collection of exceedance probability curves was generated under various assumptions in the hazard and inventory components of the model (Grossi and Windeler, 2000). In this sensitivity analysis, such things as the occupancy mapping of structures, the attenuation relationships, the earthquake duration, and the soils mapping schemes were analyzed. Since a sensitivity analysis of every assumption in a catastrophe model cannot be presented here due to the large number of parameters, a single example demonstrating the sensitivity of loss to a site's underlying soil conditions is discussed. The underlying soils across the entire region are classified as stiff soils or soil class D, as defined by the NEHRP provisions (FEMA, 1997) and assumed in the default mode of HAZUS. To test the sensitivity of this assumption, a different GIS map was used which showed underlying soils in the region to be rock, stiff soils, and soft soils (soil classes B through E in the NEHRP provisions). This latter scheme, which considers varying soil classes, can be considered as a reduction in epistemic uncertainty due to the addition of new data on the geology of the region.

The two curves presented in Figure 4.7 are the mean exceedance probability curves assuming stiff soils and assuming a range of soil types (rock, stiff soils, and soft soils). Interestingly, for a given probability of exceedance, the loss assuming all stiff soils in the region is greater than the loss assuming a range of soil types. It is therefore a conservative assumption in the default mode of HAZUS. For example, at the 0.2% (0.002) probability of exceedance or the 1-in-500 event, the stiff soils mean loss is $8.4 billion and the mean loss assuming other soil types is $6.7 billion. Therefore, the assumption of stiff soils everywhere in the region serves to establish a conservative estimate of loss. These curves show no expected loss above the 1% probability of exceedance level.

Finally, the probability of exceeding a loss of $1 billion using the HAZUS model can be compared with the probability of exceeding this same loss calculated from the equally weighted linear combination of the three competing catastrophe models. The HAZUS analysis, assuming stiff soils everywhere in the region, estimates P(Loss > $1 billion) = 0.0048 or 0.48% or 1-in-208 year event. As noted earlier and shown on Figure 4.5, the composite mean EP curve has P(Loss > $1 billion) = 0.0065 or 0.65% probability of exceedance or a 1-in-154 year return period. These two return periods are not very different, a surprising result given the uncertainty in the seismicity of the Charleston region.

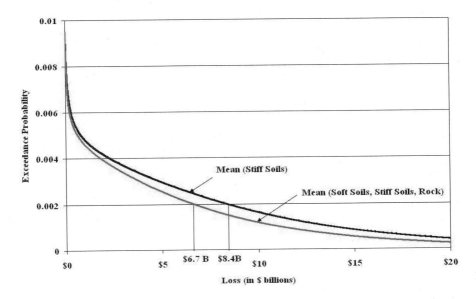

Figure 4.7. HAZUS mean exceedance probability curves for Charleston region.

4.6 Summary and Conclusions

This chapter examined the complexities of catastrophe modeling, mathematical constructs that allow the generation of exceedance probability curves, and the uncertainties inherent in the modeling process. By introducing the concepts of epistemic and aleatory uncertainty, the chapter explored how to quantify uncertainty through the use of logic trees and simulation techniques. Two case studies in Florida and South Carolina indicated the importance of understanding where uncertainty lies in a catastrophe model and how it can be captured and utilized in the risk assessment process. By constructing exceedance probability curves with confidence intervals, the degree of uncertainty associated with natural hazard events, such as an earthquake in Charleston or a hurricane in Florida, can be appreciated.

4.7 References

ATC-13 (1985). *Earthquake Damage Evaluation Data for California*, Applied Technology Council, Redwood City, CA.

Browner, C. (1995). "Guidance for Risk Characterization," Environmental Protection Agency, February.

Budnitz, R.J., Apostolakis, G., Boore, D.M., Cluff, L.S., Coppersmith, K.J., Cornell, C.A., and Morris, P.A. (1997). *Recommendations for Probabilistic Seismic Hazard Analysis: Guidance on Uncertainty and Use of Experts*, Senior Seismic Hazard Analysis Committee, NUREG/CR-6372, U.S. Nuclear Regulatory Commission, Washington, DC.

Dalkey, N.C. (1969). *The Delphi Method.* Rand Corporation: Santa Monica, California.

EERI (2003). World Housing Encyclopedia. <http://www.world-housing.net/>.

Federal Emergency Management Agency (1997). *FEMA 303 - NEHRP Recommended Provisions for Seismic Regulations for New Buildings and Other Structures*, 1997 Edition, Developed by The Building Seismic Safety Council (BSSC) for the Federal Emergency Management Agency (FEMA).

Florida Commission on Hurricane Loss Projection Methodology (2001).

Frankel, A., Mueller, C., Barnhard, T., Perkins, D., Leyendecker, E.V., Dickman, N., Hanson, S., and Hopper, M. (1996). *National Seismic Hazards Maps: Documentation*, June 1996, USGS Open-File Report 96-532: United States Geological Survey.

Grossi, P., Kleindorfer, P., and Kunreuther, H. (1999). "The Impact of Uncertainty in Managing Seismic Risk: The Case of Earthquake Frequency and Structural Vulnerability," Risk Management and Decision Processes Working Paper 99-03-26, Department of Operations and Information Management, The Wharton School.

Grossi, P. (2000). *Quantifying the Uncertainty in Seismic Risk and Loss Estimation.* Doctoral Dissertation, University of Pennsylvania.

Grossi, P. and Windeler, D. (2000). "Sensitivity analysis of earthquake risk in the Charleston, South Carolina region," EERI's Sixth International Conference on Seismic Zonation, November 12-15, 2000.

Hanks, T.C. and C. A. Cornell (1994). "Probabilistic Seismic Hazard Analysis: A Beginner's Guide." *Proceedings of the Fifth Symposium on Current Issues Related to Nuclear Power Plant Structures, Equipment and Piping, I/1-1 to I/1-17*, North Carolina State University, Raleigh, N.C.

Inman, R.L. and Conover, W.J (1980). "Small Sample Sensitivity Analysis Techniques for Computer Models, with an Application to Risk Assessment," *Communications in Statistics, Part A. Theory and Methods,* 17: 1749-1842.

NIBS (1997). HAZUS: Hazards U.S.: Earthquake Loss Estimation Methodology. NIBS Document Number 5200: National Institute of Building Sciences.

Peterson, M.D., Bryant, W.A., Cramer, C.H., Cao, T., Reichle, M.S., Frankel, A.D., Lienkaemper, J.L., McCrory, P.A., and D.P. Schwartz (1996). *Probabilistic Seismic Hazard Assessment for the State of California*, USGS Open-File Report 96-706: United States Geological Survey, Menlo Park, California.

Powell, M.D. and Aberson, S.D. (2001). "Accuracy of United States Tropical Cyclone Landfall Forecasts in the Atlantic Basin (1976-2000)." *Bulletin of the American Meteorological Society*, 82(12): 2749-2767.

Richter, C.F. (1958). *Elementary Seismology.* W.H. Freeman and Company: San Francisco, California.

Toro, G.R., Abrahamson, N., and Schneider, J. (1997). "Model of strong ground motions from earthquakes in the Central and Eastern North America: best estimates and uncertainties," *Seismological Research Letters* 68: 41-57.

Youngs, R.R., and K.J. Coppersmith (1985). "Implications of Fault Slip Rates and Earthquake Recurrence Models to Probabilistic Seismic Hazard Estimates." *Bulletin of the Seismological Society of America*, 75 (4): 939-964.

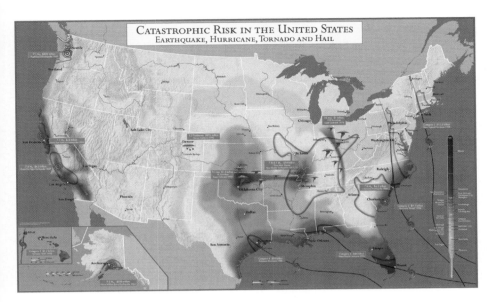

PART III

LINKING RISK ASSESSMENT WITH INSURANCE

Part III of this book explores applications of catastrophe modeling tools by linking the risk assessment process discussed in Part II, with the risk management strategies practiced by insurers. More specifically, the next three chapters address how insurers can take advantage of the scientific advances in evaluating the risks of earthquakes, hurricanes and other natural disasters, to develop strategies for reducing their losses. These strategies should help insurers avoid insolvency or significant loss of surplus following future catastrophic events.

Insurers' risk management strategies are designed to increase their expected profits, while at the same time meeting an acceptable level of risk, characterized in Chapter 2 as a survival constraint. Part III examines how catastrophe models can be used to support insurers in this regard.

As a way of introducing the topic of risk management, a set of EP curves is presented in Figure III for a hypothetical insurer's catastrophe risk. This company is assumed to have $100 million in surplus to cover hurricane losses, and would like this loss level to have an annual probability of 0.4%

(250-year return period) or less. A risk analysis for their portfolio yields an EP curve depicted in Figure III(A), indicating that the likelihood of exceeding $100 million under the insurer's current risk management plan is approximately 0.6%. What options does this company have to improve its situation? More formally, what options does this company have to meet its survival constraint while still maintaining a high expected profits?

Three possible strategies are shown in Figures III(B) through III(D), each one reflecting a topic covered in one of the next three chapters and ordered with an increasing degree of external involvement: rate making, portfolio management, and risk financing. It should be noted that the examples presented are highly simplified and do not consider how the cost of a strategy might reduce the capital available to pay out losses. Some strategies require time to implement and thus are long-term solutions rather than immediate fixes.

Rate Making (Chapter 5)

The rate-making process is concerned with the most basic of insurance questions: when the company decides to provide coverage for a given risk, how much should it charge? The insurer must first consider whether the rates are adequate to cover expected annual losses, plus other administrative expenses. The insurer must then decide whether the premiums are adequate to cover the possible losses following a catastrophic disaster. The answer to this question depends on the nature of the insurer's portfolio.

An alternative to raising premiums is exposure reduction, so that the insurer's EP curve shifts downward as shown in Figure III(B). The two most common ways of doing this are by increasing the deductible or reducing the maximum coverage limits. In either case, if there is a large-scale disaster that destroys many structures, the insurer will have smaller amounts to pay.

Portfolio Management (Chapter 6)

It is the role of an insurer's portfolio manager to examine the scope of the company's risks and determine the likelihood that losses from a catastrophic disaster will exceed $100 million. Through an analysis of its portfolio, the insurer may find that a significant fraction of its loss curve is driven by events affecting one geographic area. By redistributing its exposure such that potential losses are less correlated, the insurer can maintain the total value of its portfolio while reducing the potential for any single event to exceed its surplus. Over time, the firm can develop a plan to strategically shrink its concentrations of exposure contributing to large loss events, and expand coverage in other parts of the country.

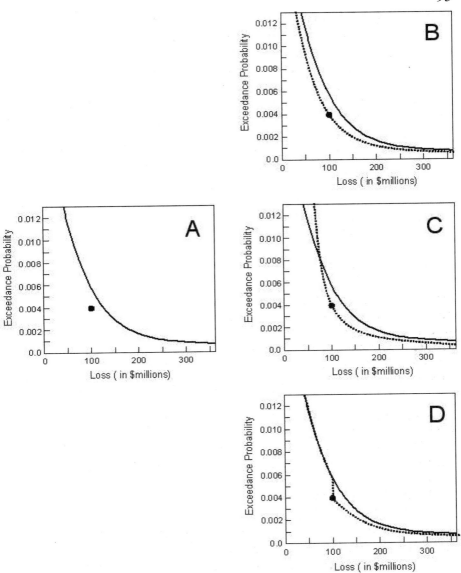

Figure III. Illustrating the effects of alternative strategies for risk. Base case (A) shows the loss curve relative to the company portfolio prior to implementation of any strategy. Dotted lines show modified EP curve relative to original after (B) exposure reduction through an increased deductible, (C) diversification, and (D) transfer. Note that the effects of most management strategies have been exaggerated for display and that the costs of implementation have not been reflected.

Diversification need not only be geographic, however. In Figure III(C), the insurer has arranged a swap with a company writing earthquake insurance, exchanging some of its policies for another risk with identical loss probabilities, but uncorrelated with the existing portfolio. This swap reduces the EP curve so that the likelihood of a loss of $100 million or more is below 0.4% --- the acceptable level of risk specified by the firm.

Risk Financing   (Chapter 7)

The traditional method for reducing risk by an insurer has been to transfer it to another party for a fee through reinsurance. In Figure III(D), the insurer purchases a reinsurance treaty that covers the first $30 million of loss above $100 million, reducing its 250-year loss to an acceptable target value. In determining how much reinsurance to purchase, the insurer has to take into account the impact that the costs of this coverage will have on its surplus. More recently, insurers have begun to transfer risk by investing in new financial instruments such as catastrophe bonds.

Summary

The examples highlighted here illustrate how risk assessment tools, via the EP curve, can be used to quantify the effectiveness of different management strategies discussed in the next three chapters. In practice, insurers are likely to utilize some combination of the strategies presented: rate making, portfolio management, and risk financing.

An important value of catastrophe modeling is its ability to examine an appropriate mixture of these three risk management strategies. Thus, an underwriter can link into a company-wide database and not only determine what premium it should charge for a new account, but also how this risk correlates with others in the company's portfolio. The portfolio manager can implement underwriting guidelines to determine what premiums to charge for new policies as a function of their location and potential hazards.   Different risk transfer programs can be priced and evaluated in conjunction with an existing portfolio of risk. Decisions can then be made as to whether it is advisable for the company to reduce its exposure, raise its premiums, purchase a catastrophe bond, and/or transfer some of its risk to a reinsurer.

Chapter 5 – Use of Catastrophe Models in Insurance Rate Making

Major Contributors:
Dennis Kuzak
Tom Larsen

5.1 Introduction

This chapter explores the use of catastrophe models in insurance rate making. Before examining the use of models, a brief discussion of the rate-making process and the actuarial principles underlying rate making is presented. The chapter then discusses how catastrophe models are utilized in both setting rates and differentiating between risks as a function of structure attributes, location and hazard conditions. The chapter concludes with a discussion of some of the regulatory aspects associated with catastrophe modeling and rate making, using the determination of rates for the California Earthquake Authority (CEA) as a case study.

The chapter concentrates on how modeling is used in the rate-making process, but it is not about rate making per se. However, in order to see how modeling can play its supporting role, a brief review of the rate-making process is presented. Insurance rates are, as all economic products, the result of supply and demand forces. On the demand side, the rates must be sufficiently attractive relative to the insured's estimate of the expected loss such that buying insurance is an attractive option.

On the supply side, the premium must be sufficiently high for investors to expect an acceptable return on their invested capital given the risk characteristics of the insurer. Moreover, the rates must be sufficient to ensure that the insurer has an acceptably low ruin probability and high credit rating so that demand is not eroded by credit risk. Catastrophe modeling provides the technical inputs into a wider planning process associated with financial management. Figure 5.1 illustrates how catastrophe modeling can be used in conjunction with data on capital allocation to undertake financial modeling for an insurance company. For example, the exceedance probability curve developed through catastrophe modeling can be integrated with a capital allocation analysis and run through a financial model of the firm, such as Enterprise Risk Management (ERM) in which the implications of risk-financing strategies can be evaluated using risk versus return criteria.

Figure 5.1. Role of catastrophe modeling in an insurance company's financial management.

5.2 Actuarial Principles

According to the Actuarial Standard of Practice (ASOP), rate-making is "the process of establishing rates used in insurance or other risk transfer mechanisms" and "is prospective because …rates must be developed prior to the transfer of risk" (Actuarial Standards Board, 1991). While the definition is short, the process of rate making can be long and complex, dictated by the determination of numerous costs associated with risk transfer including claims and claims settlement expenses, operational and administrative expenses, and the cost of capital.

Catastrophe risk models provide significant inputs into the process of determining rates by providing estimates of future claims costs or loss costs. These are the expenditures arising directly from the occurrence of a catastrophic event and are a function of the underlying frequency and severity of the disaster.

Actuarial principles and practice dictate that insurance rates for a catastrophe hazard be based on estimated future costs that are determined in a manner that is fair and equitable. To the extent possible, these rates should reflect individual risk characteristics. The following is a summary of the relevant actuarial principles for determining whether a rate is actuarially sound, reasonable and not unfairly discriminatory (Actuarial Standards Board, 1991).

Principle 1: A rate is an estimate of the expected value of future costs.
Rate making should provide for all costs so that the insurance system is financially sound.

Principle 2: A rate provides for all costs associated with the transfer of risk.
Rate making should provide for the costs of an individual risk transfer so that equity among insureds is maintained. When the experience of an individual risk does not provide a credible basis for estimating these costs, it is appropriate to consider the aggregate experience of similar risks. A rate estimated from such experience is an estimate of the costs or the risk transfer for each individual in the class.

Principle 3: A rate provides for the costs associated with an individual risk transfer.
Rate making produces cost estimates that are actuarially sound if the estimation is based on Principles 1, 2, and 3. Such rates comply with four criteria commonly used by actuaries: reasonable, not excessive, adequate, and not unfairly discriminatory.

Principle 4: A rate is reasonable and not excessive, adequate, or not unfairly discriminatory if it is an actuarially sound estimate of the expected value of all future costs associated with an individual risk transfer.

Additional commentary on rate setting that has special significance to catastrophe modeling is the suggestion by the Actuarial Standards Board that "the determination of an appropriate exposure unit or premium basis is essential" and that such units should vary with the hazard and should be practical and verifiable. In this context, practical and verifiable means that the exposure unit is directly related to the underlying catastrophic loss potential and that it can be measured objectively in a transparent manner.

Accordingly the criteria used to determine an earthquake or hurricane residential rate should include such factors as the location of the property, size of the home, age of the home, type of construction, replacement cost and mitigation measures. Catastrophe models can also show the effect on losses due to differences in proximity to hazards, construction materials and methods, occupancy, and line of business. If information for an individual risk is insufficient, data for a group of risks with similar risk characteristics can be used. Catastrophe models thus have the ability to estimate future costs based on these actuarial principles and therefore have become a valuable tool in establishing insurance rates.

5.3 Use of Catastrophe Models in Rate Making

Although catastrophe models facilitate the application of actuarial principles to rate making, the process is not a simple one. In contrast to standard perils such as fire and automobile, natural hazards challenge the role of insurance as a means to efficiently transfer risk between parties. Perhaps the most notable feature is highly correlated losses resulting in significant financial hardship to the insurer.

A comprehensive rate-making exercise involves the identification of all of the relevant costs to determine sufficient and equitable rates. In this regard, catastrophe models are essential for the calculation of two components: the Average Annual Loss (AAL) and the Surplus Cost. To adequately insure a basket of risks, an insurer must maintain sufficient liquid assets or surplus to cover potential catastrophic losses. The surplus can take the form of cash and liquid securities, reinsurance (indemnification) contracts, catastrophe bonds, or contingent debt offerings. The insurer will want to charge a higher premium to reflect the opportunity cost associated with holding surplus capital in a more liquid form than normal. This additional premium is the surplus cost or the cost of capital component.

5.3.1 A Simple Rate Making Model

The price or premium that the insurer should charge to policyholders is based on the sum of the following three components:

$$Premium = AAL + Risk\ Load + Expense\ Load$$

The AAL reflects the actuarial principle that the rate be based on risk. As discussed in Chapter 2, AAL is calculated as:

$$AAL = \sum_i p_i L_i$$

where p_i is the probability that an event occurs and L_i is the associated loss. The Risk Load is determined by the uncertainty surrounding the AAL. While several measures of risk exist, the standard deviation (σ) of the EP curve is used as an example. The risk load is an important component of the pricing equation. It reflects the insurer's concern with the survival constraint and the need for additional surplus capital. The Expense Load reflects the administrative costs involved in insurance contracts and is comprised of factors such as loss adjustment expense, processing fees, premium taxes, commissions and profits.

There are numerous methods that can be used to calculate the standard deviation of the loss, but a computationally efficient form is:

$$\sigma = \sqrt{\sum_i (L_i^2 p_i) - AAL^2}$$

Table 5.1 shows the loss rates for homeowners' risks within the state of Florida using the above formulation. As an example, the table shows the mean and standard deviation from the EP curves for each county within the state.

Table 5.1. AAL and standard deviation rate calculations.

County	AAL Rate ($AAL / $1000 Value)	Standard Deviation
Monroe	$ 9.02	$ 45.98
Dade	6.56	33.98
Palm Beach	5.38	28.38
Okeechobee	1.67	9.41
Hillsborough	1.10	6.69
Dixie	0.36	2.21
Duval	0.32	2.05
Sarasota	2.18	15.46

Based on the data in Table 5.1, estimated insurance rates can be constructed for homeowners (i.e., single family dwelling occupancy) in each county as shown in Table 5.2. These rates are derived using a theoretical basis for pricing described in Kreps (1998), where the derived premium is calculated considering the expected loss, its volatility, as well as administrative costs. As noted by Kreps, these rates can be viewed as an upper, but useful, bound on what insurers should charge assuming investment returns based on current financial market conditions and portfolio composition. It does not take into account the benefits of diversifying risks through portfolio selection across counties. The table shows the tremendous range in rates that can exist across counties, reflecting the underlying catastrophe potential.

Table 5.2. Annual homeowner insurance rates by county.

County	Insurance rate per $1000 value (no expenses or credits)
Monroe	$ 32.01
Dade	$ 23.55
Palm Beach	$ 19.57
Okeechobee	$ 6.37
Hillsborough	$ 4.45
Dixie	$ 1.47
Duval	$ 1.35
Sarasota	$ 9.91

5.3.2 Differentiating Risk

There are many risk factors that are important to the calculation of equitable rates. These factors can be characterized as directly related to the inputs of a catastrophe model. Two of the most critical factors in differentiating risks for rate setting are the structure attributes of a portfolio (the inventory component of a catastrophe model) and the location attributes of a portfolio (proximity or susceptibility to hazard). Each of these is now considered in turn.

Structure Attributes

Structure attributes are those features of the insured risk related to the physical performance of a building in an extreme event. Structural materials, building codes, year of construction modification, and occupancy fall under this category and impact the rates charged for insurance.

First, construction plays a major role in determining susceptibility to natural hazard risk. Construction materials and structural systems determine how a building responds to the hazard. Some materials perform better for some hazards and worse for others. For example, wood frame construction is generally thought of as superior for earthquake resistance due, in part, to its light weight and flexibility. During an earthquake, masonry is considered inferior due to its high weight and non-ductile behavior. With respect to the hurricane peril, masonry is superior to wood frame due to its mass and resistance to projectile damage.

Building codes in existence at the time of construction are a reflection of potential building performance. Newer codes reflect the latest advances in science, research, and loss experience. The 1933 Long Beach, California earthquake highlighted the risks to life and property from collapsing unreinforced masonry buildings. The inelastic nature of the masonry-mortar connection makes these structures prone to catastrophic collapse. Similarly, the partial collapse of the brand new Olive View Hospital from the 1971 San Fernando, California earthquake revealed inadequate design of large open areas on the first floor and demonstrated the need for ductile framing connections in structures subjected to earthquake forces. The lessons learned in this earthquake triggered substantial changes to future building codes.

Revised codes apply only to new construction and to those structures that are undergoing voluntary retrofits. For this reason, the year of construction offers insights into the design and detailing methods for particular structures. For example, riveted steel buildings in the 1800's gave way to welded structures in the late 1900's. Higher standards of living led to houses with larger rooms (i.e., fewer crossing walls added stability to structures), changing the way that buildings respond to earthquakes (Bertero, 1989). In recognition of age-related earthquake response, the state of California Department of Insurance approved insurance rates that varied by year of construction as well as by construction materials with the formation of the CEA in 1996. Similarly, in hurricane-prone areas, higher standards of living also led to houses with larger windows and doorways, increasing the exposure to wind borne hazards.

Finally, building occupancies can indicate how susceptible a structure is to damage. Experience with natural catastrophe claims, and engineering reviews of risks, demonstrate the varying damage patterns expected, based on occupancy. Building occupancy effectively changes the layouts of buildings, types of contents and values, and their locations within and outside buildings.

The effect of occupancy is greatest in estimating business interruption losses. Natural catastrophes impact not only the business, but also its suppliers and customers in the region. For example, a processing plant that requires significant amounts of water to operate chillers is effectively interrupted if the water supply is cut off by an earthquake that caused significant damage to underground utilities. Another example is the vulnerability of many retailers to communications outages. Many communications lifelines rely on above-ground distribution, which is susceptible to damage from high winds.

Occupancy can also affect the layout of walls, windows, doors, and equipment within a building. This layout can affect building performance. For example, manufacturing facilities with assembly lines will tend to have long spans with significant amounts of equipment suspended from the ceiling, which increase the potential loss from a catastrophe.

Location Attributes

Location attributes reflect the degree to which structures are subject to damage from hazards as a function of where they are built. For example, one very commonly understood underwriting tool for flooding is whether or not the building is in a 100-year flood plain. Other examples include proximity to known earthquake faults, distance from the coast with respect to hurricane hazard, local soil conditions as they relate to ground motion during an earthquake, and surface roughness and topography as they relate to wind speed during a hurricane.

One important aspect of the differentiation of risk is a structure's proximity to known sources of hazard. As shown in Figure 5.2, the AAL for an idealized risk situated in various locations throughout Southeastern Florida would have a varying loss rate directly related to its proximity to the coastline. The state of Florida Wind Underwriting Authority (FWUA) allows wind insurance rates in southern Florida to vary based on distance from the coastline. This is also done in other states, most notably Texas. The coastal counties in Texas are designated as catastrophe areas by the Texas Department of Insurance. These zones define what construction criteria a structure must meet to be considered for windstorm insurance. Similarly, the State of California identified special earthquake zones in the Alquist-Priolo Act of 1990.

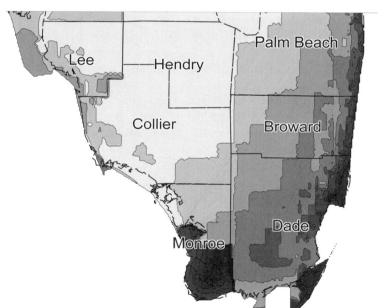

Figure 5.2. Expected annual damage rate contours, State of Florida. (Dark shading is high risk, light shading is low risk)

Local soil conditions play a key role in the determination of risk from earthquakes. One notable type of soil failure is landslide, where a building collapses because its foundation loses its ground support. Ground failure is often excluded from earthquake insurance policies due to its potential catastrophic impact.

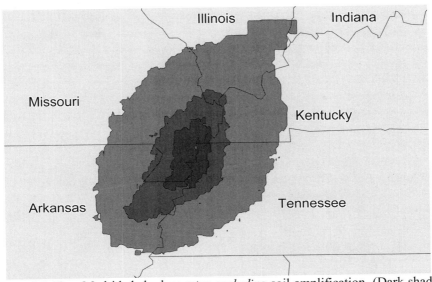

Figure 5.3. New Madrid shake loss rates *excluding* soil amplification. (Dark shading indicates high loss rates, light shading indicates low loss rates)

The 1989 Loma Prieta, California earthquake demonstrated very clearly the effects of soil amplification upon building performance. Although approximately 70 miles from the epicenter of the earthquake, several areas within the city of San Francisco experienced significant levels of damage. One of the most notable pockets of damage was the San Francisco Marina district, where the structures that suffered the highest losses were located in the area of a lagoon that was filled in for the San Francisco World's Fair in the early 1900's (EQE International QuickLook Report, 1989).

Comparing Figure 5.3, which shows the loss rates for the New Madrid Seismic Zone *excluding* soil amplification, to Figure 5.4, which shows the loss rates *including* soil amplification, one can see the significant difference in the Average Annual Loss in the New Madrid region using local soils amplification factors. Both figures depict a very strong dependence in loss rates with distance to the largest source zone in the area. However, the New Madrid region overlays a portion of the Mississippi River and associated tributary streams. Alluvial river valleys such as these are characterized by large depositions of unconsolidated silty and sandy soils (soft soils), which will result in increased earthquake ground shaking similar to the soft soils in the San Francisco Marina District. Hence, as demonstrated in Figure 5.4, losses are much greater when soil amplification is taken into account.

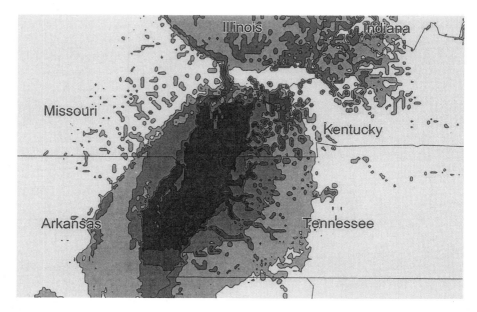

Figure 5.4. New Madrid shake loss rates *including* soil amplification. (Dark shading indicates high loss rates, light shading indicates low loss rates)

5.4 Regulation and Catastrophe Modeling

This book is not directly concerned with the details of the regulatory process. However, catastrophe modeling can play an extremely important role in educating regulators and their constituents of the rationale behind their expected loss costs and the resulting premium structures. Because of intense economic and political pressures, state governments have intervened in catastrophe insurance markets in significant ways.

Insurers and insurance markets are regulated primarily at the state level (Klein, 1998). Hence, the laws and regulations governing insurance transactions are set by the individual state legislatures and insurance commissioners, with legal disputes generally adjudicated by state courts. Regulatory policies vary among states based on market conditions, differing regulatory philosophies, and political factors. As a result, state regulatory authorities respond differently to the use of catastrophe modeling in support of rate making. This is evident in the California case study described in the next section.

To date, regulators have not been supportive of having model-generated information introduced in support of the regulatory process, possibly because it imposes an additional constraint on their already difficult job of finding acceptable recipes for rate regulation. At the same time, they have to develop an understanding of catastrophe models, as insurers increasingly integrate these tools into their day-to-day operations. These models present a conflict for the regulators. On the one hand, they provide a scientifically rational approach for quantifying an insurer's risk. By requiring insurers to report modeled loss estimates, the regulator can assess whether the company has been responsible in controlling their accumulations. Rates can be based on an integration of all possible events, not just a limited historical record. On the other hand, the regulator may view a model with some suspicion if they perceive it as a tool for justifying higher rates.

Catastrophe models are complex products that require specialized expertise to evaluate thoroughly and, for competitive reasons, modeling firms usually want to protect proprietary aspects of their models. This is particularly true for states with sunshine laws that require government documents be publicly available. Differences in model assumptions can cause loss results to vary considerably between modeling firms, as indicated in the case studies presented in Chapter 4. Each model may be reasonable given the data constraints, but the range of uncertainty can be disconcerting when compared to estimates for lines such as life or automobile insurance.

As the states most at risk from earthquakes and hurricanes, California and Florida have been in the forefront with respect to the role that catastrophe models play regarding rate setting. As discussed in Chapter 4, the state of Florida has developed a review process by which modeling firms must show that their products meet a set of technical criteria. Insurers submitting modeled rates must do so using a model certified for use in Florida. This chapter discusses the case of the California Earthquake Authority, in which results from catastrophe models formed the basis of a state-organized insurance program. In both Florida and California, the issue of modeling as a basis for rate-setting has become politicized and been subject to criticism by public interest advocates.

Other states have followed their own path. Texas initially disallowed any rates filed on the basis of computer models. However, the Texas Department of Insurance later modified its stance by allowing information developed from models to be included in rate filings. The Department expressed continued concern about differences in results between modeling firms and noted that they would request additional data to determine the reasonableness of these filings (Mah, 2000).

The National Association of Insurance Commissioners (NAIC) has a working group focused on the use of computer models for rate filings. In February 1999, department of insurance representatives from several states in the region surrounding the New Madrid seismic zone requested presentations from the major modeling firms on earthquake loss estimation. Its goal was to gain an understanding of how these tools were being used to develop rates, with particular emphasis on the validation of results for areas with little historical loss experience. One product of this working group is that states can request insurers to submit with their rate filings a form that describes the scientific basis of their model results.

Recognizing that these models involve technical expertise outside their traditional knowledge base, regulators have looked elsewhere in the government for support. For example, the California Geological Survey explored the process of calculating earthquake insurance loss costs with publicly available models (Cao and others, 1999). These results can then become a baseline for comparison with results from private firms.

5.5 Case Study of Rate-Setting: California Earthquake Authority (CEA)

The rate structure of the CEA formed in 1996 was significantly influenced by the application of catastrophe modeling. Prior to the Northridge Earthquake in January 1994, most residential insurers based their earthquake rates on past experience. With very few losses in the prior 20 years (San Fernando earthquake in 1971, Whittier earthquake in 1987 and Loma Prieta earthquake in 1989), average residential rates were approximately $2.00 per $1,000 of coverage for a policy that had a deductible of either 5% or 10%, along with generous limits for contents and loss of use.

5.5.1 Formation of the CEA

The Northridge earthquake resulted in approximately $12.5 billion of insured losses and almost $40 billion of total damage. Total residential losses exceeded the total earthquake premiums collected in the previous 20 years. Fearing insolvency, over 90% of the homeowners' insurers in California either refused to write or severely restricted issuance of new residential policies in order to avoid offering earthquake coverage.

In response, the California State Legislature designed a policy which permitted insurers to offer a basic policy consisting of a 15% deductible plus much reduced contents coverage ($5,000) and living expense ($1,500). Catastrophe modeling indicated that this policy, if it had been offered in place of the standard 10% deductible policy, would have reduced industry losses by half following the Northridge earthquake. However, the industry was still concerned about insolvency and continued to threaten to leave the California market.

In response, the Legislature established the CEA in 1996, creating a unique publicly managed stand-alone residential earthquake insurance company. Catastrophe modeling was used to estimate the loss probabilities to the reinsurance layers, thereby assisting in the largest catastrophe reinsurance placement (over 100 global reinsurers) ever consummated.

SIDEBAR 1: Modeling and solvency regulation in Canada

In Canada, the property and casualty market is more fragmented than in the U.S., with a large number of companies vying for premiums. In the mid- to late 1990's, many of the firms using modeling tools for earthquake portfolio management felt they were being placed at a competitive disadvantage. By being responsible in their surplus accumulations, they were losing business to insurers that were attempting to capture market share with lower rates.

The Office of the Superintendent of Financial Institutions (OSFI) Canada stepped in with guidelines for managing earthquake exposure. OSFI (1998) required companies with exposure in British Columbia or Quebec to report gross and net PMLs based on a computer model. Guidelines were set for PML return periods (250 and 500 years) and treatment of deterministic or probabilistic models. If a company chose not to use a model, they would have to report precompiled damage factors per CRESTA zone (i.e., a bounded geographic area designated by the Catastrophe Risk Evaluation And Standardizing Target Accumulation organization; the aim of the zones is to establish a globally uniform system for the accumulation risk control of natural hazards). These were relatively draconian, having been derived from the highest losses from the major modelers, with an additional factor for conservatism.

5.5.2 Rate-Setting Procedures

The CEA began to write policies in late 1996, with rates determined through the use of a catastrophe model. A rate application was filed in early 1997, and immediately challenged by consumer groups. Under California insurance law, rate applications submitted to the Department of Insurance can be challenged through a formal public hearing process, similar to a civil court trial but with an appointed Administrative Law Judge. (Sidebar 2 indicates which factors the CEA took into account when establishing rates for earthquake insurance.)

The legislature clearly indicated that rates must be risk based, using the best available scientific information, and that the use of a catastrophe risk model to estimate the rates was anticipated. And the risk factors identified in item 1 of Sidebar 2 were specifically incorporated into the model in estimating loss costs at the ZIP code level.

The public rate hearing commenced in May of 1997, with testimony lasting over four months and culminating in over 7,000 pages of testimony (California Department of Insurance, 1998a). This was the most complex and lengthy insurance rate filing case in California, with rates challenged by four

SIDEBAR 2: Rate-Setting Considerations For The California Earthquake Authority

The CEA's legislative creation (Insurance Code 10089.40) was accompanied by a series of considerations for the establishment of rates, as stipulated in the code:

1. Rates established by the Authority shall be actuarially sound so as to not be excessive, inadequate, or unfairly discriminatory. Rates shall be established based on the best available scientific information for assessing the risk of earthquake frequency, severity, and loss. Rates shall be equivalent for equivalent risks. Factors the Board shall consider in adopting rates include, but are not limited to, the following:

    (a) Location of the insured property and its proximity to earthquake faults and to other geological factors that affect the risk of earthquakes or damage from earthquakes.
    (b) The soil type on which the insured dwelling is built
    (c) Construction type and features of the insured dwelling
    (d) Age of the insured dwelling

2. If scientific information (and/or modeling assumptions) is used in setting rates, such information must be consistent with the available geophysical data and the state of the art of knowledge within the scientific community.

3. Scientific information that is used to establish different rates between the most populous rating territories in northern and southern California cannot be used unless that information is analyzed by experts, such as the U.S. Geological Survey or the California Geological Survey, and they conclude that such information shows a higher risk of loss to support those rate differences.

4. The legislature does not intend to mandate a uniform statewide flat rate for residential policies.

5. Rates established shall not be adjusted to provide rates lower than are justified for classifications of high risk of loss or higher than are justified for classifications of low risk of loss.

6. Policyholders who have retrofitted homes to withstand earthquake shake damage shall receive a 5% premium discount, as long as it is determined to be actuarially sound.

consumer organizations, one insurer, plus the California Department of Insurance. The case was separated into actuarial and earthquake modeling sessions to facilitate expert testimony. Because of the statutory language requiring rates to be consistent with the scientific state of the art, the model was held to both actuarial as well as scientific standards.

Actuarial issues focused on aggregate cost allocations, territorial rating plans, and risk classification based pricing. Discussions on modeling issues centered on definitions of what is the best available scientific information on such elements as ground motion and damage estimates. Because of the public perception of a proprietary "black box" model, considerable challenges to model assumptions and outputs were made. Major modeling issues raised in the hearing included a number of items, as discussed below.

Earthquake Recurrence Rates

Since historical earthquake data in California is limited to a maximum of 150 years, determining the long-term rate of earthquakes, especially medium and large events, is critical. Catastrophe model assumptions based on published scientific information were reviewed and challenged, and compared with models produced by the California Division of Mines and Geology (CMDG).[1] It was determined that the model results compared favorably with such state of the art examples as the CDMG's model. One of the most significant issues was that all the models produced earthquake frequencies that were more than twice the historical record. This finding challenged the acceptability of the CEA model's frequency estimates based on past data.

Uncertainty Values in Estimating Time Dependent Probabilities

Certain earthquake faults or fault segments have been studied in sufficient detail to estimate the likelihood of future rupture, based on geological investigations. This time-dependent probability of rupture differs from the conventional assumption that earthquakes are a random process characterized by a Poisson distribution (Stein, 2003).

At issue in the hearing was the use of time-dependency and the uncertainty factor (σ) associated with the recurrence interval between historical events. A smaller value of σ implies a lower level of uncertainty in the historical recurrence pattern, and hence, the greater weight given to a time-dependent recurrence estimate. Conversely, the larger the value of σ, the less weight given to the time dependent estimate. If σ approached a value near 1.0, then the estimate is essentially time independent and it would be the

---

[1] Since the hearings the CDMG has been renamed the California Geological Survey (CGS).

same as a Poisson distribution estimate. Hence, differences in σ would affect both recurrence rates and loss costs.

Since neither the CDMG nor the USGS had produced seismic hazard models that were based on time-dependency, the CEA felt that these models were not state of the art. However, since both the CDMG and USGS have produced working group reports using time-dependency to estimate earthquake probabilities as early as 1988, the Administrative Law Judge ruled that their models were consistent with the state of the art. The Insurance Commissioner noted that this was another area of scientific dispute yet to be resolved.

Damage Estimates

Model-based damage estimates are derived by associating a given level of ground shaking severity at a site with the vulnerability to shaking damage for a specific class of structure defined by age, type of construction, number of stories, etc. Prior to the Northridge Earthquake, earthquake damage curves were based on engineering opinions and judgments published by the Applied Technology Council (ATC). However, the model based its curves on over 50,000 claims from the Northridge quake. It was argued that the ATC-13 curves, which were in the public domain since 1985, should be relied upon as opposed to model-based proprietary curves, which were derived from principally one event. Testimony from representatives of the ATC itself supported the use of claims-based curves as the best available source of information for the link between shaking intensity and damage.

Underinsurance Factor

Model-based damage estimates are expressed as a percent of the building's value. Accordingly, if the value used is less than the replacement cost, damage and loss estimates are understated. In addition, the policy deductible is likely to be understated since it is typically defined as a percent of the policy limit.

Because of inflation and lack of accurate valuation, the insurance to value ratio for most buildings is usually less than 1.0. In other words, most buildings are underinsured. Since the residential insurers in California did not readily have an estimate of the degree of underinsurance, consumer groups challenged the initial model assumptions of 13% derived from surveys of insurance actuaries in the state. They claimed that there was 0% underinsurance and that the properties were fully insured. Ultimately, a 6% underinsurance figure was agreed to and rates were lowered from the initial projections to reflect this compromise.

Demand Surge

Following a major natural disaster, increases in demand for construction material and labor can result in increased claims settlement costs. Settlement costs may also rise from large events such as Hurricane Andrew or the Northridge earthquake due to the demands upon insurers to settle hundreds of thousands of claims in a short time. Based on actuarial principles, it is reasonable to include these additional costs in establishing the appropriate rate. However, determining a demand surge factor is difficult since limited data are available to measure the impact of this phenomenon on claims costs.

The CEA testified that insurers estimated a 20% impact for demand surge following the Northridge earthquake. Since the vulnerability curves were based on Northridge data, the curves used were adjusted and initially reduced by 20% to eliminate the demand surge effect. Then the curves were increased by an adjustable factor, relating demand surge to the size of loss from each stochastic event in the model's probabilistic database. Although interveners argued that demand surge does not exist, the CEA actuarial group's testimony was accepted as reasonable even though little empirical data exists to support this assertion.

Policy Sublimits

Although a catastrophe model was used to establish the loss costs through such risk factors as location, soil conditions, age and type of structure, the model could not determine the contribution to losses from certain CEA policy features such as sublimits on masonry chimney damage, walkways, awnings, etc., because insurance claims data do not identify sources of loss from these categories. Hence, actuaries had to reduce the modeled loss costs to account for the specific CEA policy sublimits which were not reflected in the claims data used in the damage estimates produced by the model.

Rating Plan-Deviation

The statewide loss cost is derived from the sum of loss costs from approximately 1,700 ZIP codes containing residential exposures. From these detailed loss costs by ZIP, the CEA constructed a rating plan consisting of 19 contiguous territories based on modeled loss costs, four housing types (single family, mobile home, condominiums, and rentals), two construction types (wood frame and other) and age (three groups).

Interveners challenged the plan since they claimed it was unfairly discriminatory. According to the insurance code (10089.40(a)), "rates shall be equivalent for equivalent risk," but the CEA capped the rates in two territories because of affordability issues, and spread the capped costs to other territories. One insurer challenged these rates, claiming that they were not actuarially sound, adversely impacting other policyholders. The insurer argued that capped rates did not reflect true costs, with the CEA undercharging in high hazard areas and overcharging in low hazard areas. This had the potential of causing adverse selection problems with only the highest risk individuals purchasing policies at subsidized rates to them. This could leave the CEA as the main insurer in high hazard areas and with few individuals purchasing policies in low hazard areas. In response to the challenge, the commissioner ruled that a rating plan does not have to base premiums on risk in view of the affordability issues, and that the plan was still actuarially sound and not unfairly discriminatory.

Retrofit discount

The CEA statutory language requires a premium discount of at least 5% if policyholders have retrofitted their homes for earthquake shake damage, and the discount is determined to be actuarially sound. The CEA offers discounts for three mitigation measures: bolting the walls to the house foundation, cripple wall bracing, and water heater tie-down (which minimizes fire following risk, which is not covered by the CEA policy). Based on conversations the CEA actuary had with structural engineers, he concluded that losses would be reduced. With no empirical or scientific guidance on the loss reduction, the statutory minimum of 5% was used as the premium discount. Interveners challenged the discount, claiming more studies were needed to actuarially justify the discount. In response, the Commissioner ruled that the discount was appropriate since the actuary had relied on input from engineering experts.

Changing Deductibles and Coverage Limits

Typically, various combinations of deductibles and limits have been used to reduce the amount of earthquake loss to an insurer. In its initial rate filing, the California Earthquake Authority proposed a policy that combined the effects of a relatively high deductible (15% of the coverage amount) with strict limits on the payouts of contents ($5,000) and additional living expense ($1,500). Testimony given during the rate hearing supported the assertion that the insurance cost for the proposed CEA policy was one-half the cost of the previous standard earthquake policy form, which had a 10% deductible, with much higher limits for contents and additional living expense.

Conclusion

The Commissioner (California Department of Insurance, 1998b) ruled in favor of the CEA loss estimates based on catastrophe modeling on almost all major issues. This demonstrates the contribution of catastrophe modeling for rate setting with respect to meeting actuarial standards and legislative requirements. However, many scientific and technical issues still remain.

5.5.3 Future Research Issues

The hearings associated with CEA rate-setting procedures raised a number of questions that require future research. The scientific community and stakeholders utilizing catastrophe models could profitably work together to improve state-of-the-art knowledge for use in policy decisions in the following areas: scientific uncertainty, additional claims data, retrofit discounts, and demand surge.

First, the hearing highlighted the significant disagreement among earth scientists on frequency estimates, maximum magnitudes, and time dependent calculations. Given the high level of seismic research undertaken by academics and researchers in government agencies such as the USGS, and the inherent uncertainty in the estimation process, disagreements are likely to persist. The challenge is to select credible and representative research, and in some cases to include more than one methodology in the catastrophe models.

Additionally, insurance claims data from catastrophic loss events are by nature very limited. Yet, it is the single best source from which to estimate future losses. Insurers need to capture and preserve loss data and portfolio exposures for each loss event. Because of the legal and commercial aspects, release of this data to third parties needs to be carefully managed to protect the insurance companies' interests.

Mitigating future catastrophic losses via structural retrofits, with commensurate insurance premium reductions, is strongly desired by politicians and the public. Models have the ability to quantify the benefits of various wind or earthquake mitigation applications, but are hampered by the lack of detailed loss data, since insurers typically do not distinguish losses by structural component, such as roof, chimney, foundations, or non-load-bearing walls. The states of Florida, California, and Hawaii are encouraging research and studies to assist in estimating such benefits. Results of these efforts will undoubtedly find their way into model analysis in the development of actuarially sound retrofit discount programs.

Finally, increases in settlement costs following a major catastrophe have been noted in Hurricane Andrew, the Northridge Earthquake and Typhoon Mirielle (1991) in Japan. Actuaries estimated a 20% increase in Northridge with similar levels for the hurricane events. Unfortunately, little research has been conducted to identify the sources of these losses and what size events would evidence such behavior.

5.6 Open Issues for Using Catastrophe Models to Determine Rates

In the last five to ten years, the use of catastrophe models for insurance rate making has become common practice in states with the potential for severe catastrophic insured losses. There are still a set of open questions that need to be resolved with respect to their use in rate-making decisions.

Regulatory Acceptance

Proprietary sophisticated models create a problem for regulators, who are unlikely to have the technical expertise to judge the reasonableness of the inputs, assumptions, and outputs. Some states, such as Florida, have created independent commissions consisting of technical experts who certify models for use in insurance rate-setting situations in Florida. However, the State insurance commissioner has publicly criticized all models as biased in favor of the insurers.

In California, the Insurance Commission relied on the rate hearing process with experts provided by the interveners as well as by the Department of Insurance to examine model details and assumptions. However, regulators have a dual responsibility in setting rates. Rates need to be acceptable and affordable to the general public, but also actuarially sound to preserve the financial integrity of the insurers.

Public Acceptance

As expected, public acceptance of the models has been low, principally because their use resulted in substantial increases in wind or earthquake rates. No one likes a rate increase. The problem is that previous rate making approaches based on historical experience fail to capture the potential severity and frequency of these loss events. Rate estimates from models are not precise due to the uncertainty in the science, but they provide considerably more insight than extrapolations based on past loss experience.

Actuarial Acceptance

Rate filings are usually the responsibility of a casualty actuary, who needs to comply with actuarial practice and principles. The catastrophe model is a tool that can be used by an actuary in meeting his/her obligations to determine the fair and equitable rates to charge an insured. Since the models are outside an actuary's usual professional expertise, it is necessary for them to become familiar with the model components.

More recently, the Actuarial Standards Board has published Standard of Practice No. 38 that requires actuaries to (a) determine appropriate reliance on experts, (b) have a basic understanding of the model, (c) evaluate whether the model is appropriate for the intended application, (d) determine that appropriate validation has occurred, and (e) determine the appropriate use of the model (Actuarial Standards Board, 2000).

Model-to-Model Variance

Given the inherent uncertainty in catastrophe loss estimates, significant differences in loss estimates from one model to another do occur. Often models are dismissed for this reason, with claims that models are good only if they agree with each other. However, models are based on inputs from varying scientific data and engineering information, which may differ because of uncertainty in the understanding of hazards. The modeler is required to use one or more sub-models of hazard or severity defined by a reputable scientific researcher, which may result in different loss results. That is the inherent nature of the modeling process. Risk, and uncertainty in estimating the risk of loss, derives not only from the randomness of the event occurrence, but also from the limits in knowledge and different interpretations by experts. It is unlikely that science will provide us all the answers, thus leading to continued differences in model results.

5.7 Summary

Catastrophe models are playing an important role in managing the risk of natural hazards through the establishment of risk-based insurance rates. These rates provide price information and economic incentives to mitigate and manage risks from low probability events that otherwise would be ignored until the disaster has occurred. This chapter has detailed the actuarial principles on which rates are based. It then illustrated how the four components of catastrophe modeling play a role in the rate setting process.

By focusing on an actual hearing in the context of rate setting by the California Earthquake Authority as a case study, the challenges of linking science with policy were highlighted. The chapter concluded by discussing future research issues and open questions related to the use of catastrophe models for rate-setting purposes.

5.8 References

Actuarial Standards Board (1991). Actuarial Standard of Practice (ASOP) No. 9, Documentation and Disclosure in Property and Casualty Insurance Rate making, Loss Reserving, and Valuations, January 1991.

Actuarial Standards Board (2000). Actuarial Standard of Practice No. 38, Using Models Outside the Actuary's Area of Expertise (Property and Casualty), June 2000.

ATC-13 (1985). *Earthquake Damage Evaluation Data for California*, Applied Technology Council, Redwood City, CA.

Bertero, V. (1989). Personal Communication. University of California, Berkeley.

California Department of Insurance (1998a). Administrative Law Bureau, *In the Matter of the Rate Filing of* THE CALIFORNIA EARTHQUAKE AUTHORITY, FILE NO. PA-96-0072-00, Proposed Decision, January 22, 1998.

California Department of Insurance (1998b). Office of the Commissioner, *In the Matter of the Rate Filing of* THE CALIFORNIA EARTHQUAKE AUTHORITY, FILE NO. PA-96-0072-00, Decision, December 3, 1998.

California Earthquake Authority (2001). CEA Project Consulting Team Report, Tillinghast-Towers Perrin lead consultant, July 5, 2001.

Cao, T., Petersen, M., Cramer, C., Toppozada, T., Reichle, M. and Davis, J. (1999). The calculation of expected loss using probabilistic seismic hazard, *Bulletin of the Seismological Society of America*, 89: 867-876.

EQE International QuickLook Report (1989). *The Loma Prieta Earthquake.*

Klein, R.W. (1998). Regulation and Catastrophe Insurance, in Howard Kunreuther and Richard Roth, Sr., eds., *Paying the Price: The Status and Role of Insurance Against Natural Disasters in the United States* (Washington, D.C.: Joseph Henry Press): 171-208.

Kreps, R. (1998). Investment-Equivalent Reinsurance Pricing, Presented At the May 1998 Meeting of the Casualty Actuarial Society.

Mah, C.H. (2000). Use of catastrophe models in ratemaking. Texas Department of Insurance Commissioner's Bulletin B0037-00.
<http://www.tdi.state.tx.us/commish/b-0037000.html>

OSFI (Office of the Superintendent of Financial Institutions Canada) (1998). Earthquake Exposure Sound Practices Guideline, (Appendix 1, P&C, B-9), Ottawa, http://www.osfi-bsif.gc.ca/eng/documents/guidance/docs/b9e.pdf

Stein, R. (2003). "Earthquake Conversations" *Scientific American,* 288: 72-79.

Chapter 6 – Insurance Portfolio Management

Major Contributors:
Weimin Dong
Patricia Grossi

6.1 Introduction

Per standard insurance terminology, a portfolio refers to an ensemble of individual policies. Each policy, in turn, may cover a number of individual assets, for example buildings, which may or may not be spread out geographically. The use of the term portfolio is not restricted to primary insurers; it applies to reinsurers as well. In this chapter, the focus is on how catastrophe modelers can aid primary insurers in managing their book of business, but the approach is also relevant to reinsurers.

Insurers who issue policies to cover catastrophe losses are concerned with the maximum loss they might experience. Hence, the risk of a portfolio is important to understand. It is an aggregation of the risks of the individual policies, which, in turn, are the aggregation of the risks at various locations. However, the aggregation is not simply one of addition or summation. Unlike events, such as fires, where each accident is normally localized and independent of one another, a catastrophe casts a large footprint, which is likely to affect a number of assets covered by a portfolio.

Essential for good portfolio management is a thorough understanding of risk and the instruments that are available to reduce the likelihood and magnitude of catastrophic losses. The combination of new engineering knowledge, advances in loss modeling, and innovations in the insurance and financial industries, have increased the effectiveness in managing catastrophe risk significantly compared to a decade ago. Quantification of the contributing losses and their associated uncertainties is now possible.

After presenting an overview of an insurance portfolio, the chapter describes how portfolio risk can be quantified using catastrophe modeling. This is followed by an illustration of how optimal portfolio risk management can be achieved by better underwriting and risk selection. The chapter concludes with a discussion of the features of the risk quantification process that affect the nature of an insurer's portfolio, such as data quality, uncertainty modeling, and impact of correlation.

6.2 Portfolio Composition and Catastrophe Modeling

6.2.1 Portfolio Composition

Insurance companies who issue coverage for natural hazard events usually have portfolios that consist of many individual policies, either residential, commercial or both. Residential properties and assets that are insured are often physically located in a single location while commercial properties are often distributed across many regions. The insurance policy stipulates how properties located at a group of locations are to be covered.

Most residential policies have a simple insurance structure: one policy for building, contents, and additional living expenses with a deductible and coverage limits. A portfolio of such policies may be in the hundreds of thousands. Most primary insurance companies collect relatively detailed data for each of their policies with the data including building type, year built, street address (or ZIP code) and market values. Some insurers record building-specific features, such as the number of stories, presence of cripple walls, past retrofits, and/or site-specific geologic conditions.

Within a commercial portfolio, an insurance policy may insure a large corporation against losses to its facilities in many locations. Some policies, for example a fast food chain, may cover a number of nearly uniform buildings in different parts of the country. Since the insured value for a commercial building is much greater than a residential structure, detailed information about the property is normally required by the insurer to underwrite these policies. An engineer may inspect construction plans or be sent to the site to examine particularly valuable risks.

In most cases, there will be a location-level deductible and coverage limit for building, contents, and business interruption. There may also be a policy-level deductible and coverage limit to protect against excessive insurance losses for that policy. For example, a policy may cover 100 locations, each with $1 million coverage limit. If there was no aggregate limit on the policy and all locations suffered total damage from an event, the insurer would have to pay $100 million. In order to avoid excessive loss, the insurer may impose a policy coverage limit of $20 million, for example. In that case, if the sum of losses for all 100 locations was greater than $20 million, the loss to the insurer would be capped at $20 million.

The resulting collection of policies constitutes a portfolio. To illustrate, suppose the portfolio depicted in Figure 6.1 contains commercial structures covered by a single insurer. There are a total of m policies, each with its own structure (e.g., deductible and limit level) for different types of coverage (e.g., building and contents). Moreover, for each policy, there are n locations covered. If this were a residential portfolio, there would be m different policies at individual locations, with the number of policies per location allowed to vary.

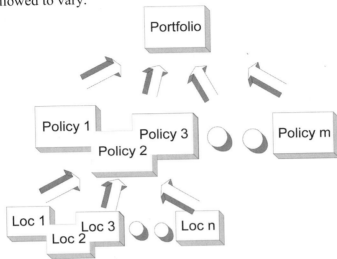

Figure 6.1. Depiction of an insurance portfolio.

6.2.2 Catastrophe Modeling – Bottom-up approach

The development of catastrophe models that can generate a loss exceedance probability curve for a portfolio greatly expands the underwriting options available to insurers. A portfolio manager could use a catastrophe model to calculate the probability that the portfolio loss will exceed a given level (e.g., 1%) or to calculate the probability of experiencing a loss that exceeds the company's survival constraint. The insurer could also examine the effect of changing deductibles and coverage limits on the existing portfolio.

An underwriter's decision to write a new account is based on the magnitude of the risk, its correlation with the existing portfolio, and the highest acceptable price that a client is willing to pay for insurance. In addition, there are factors related to what is being insured (e.g., flammability or fragility of contents, performance of the structure type under wind or earthquake loads), where it is located (e.g., distance from the coast or to active faults, potential for ground failures such as landslides), and how much can be charged (i.e., regulatory constraints and competitive impacts on rates for a given policy form).

122

Suppose a hypothetical insurer has a corporate policy of maintaining sufficient surplus to withstand a 250-year loss corresponding to a survival constraint with an annual probability of exceedance of 0.4% (0.004). This constraint is currently satisfied, but the insurer would like to increase his exposure in a hurricane-prone state without significantly increasing the potential 250-year loss. In order to achieve this objective, the insurer can perform a hurricane analysis and identify and rank tiers of ZIP codes by their contribution to events causing losses in excess of the 250-year value.

New business in the ZIP codes with the largest loss contribution would be eliminated from consideration unless the structure had a sufficiently high enough score on the basis of wind-resistance structural features. In this case, its potential loss from a major disaster in the area would be low enough for it to qualify as a candidate for the portfolio. Other factors, such as the age of the structure or its size, might assume less importance in ranking ZIP codes because they contribute less risk to the portfolio.

Given an event, a catastrophe model is used to calculate a ground-up loss for each location in the portfolio. Stepping through the levels of the model allows one to allocate this ground-up loss to each of the participating parties: insured, insurer, and reinsurer. Since the event is random, an annual rate of occurrence is associated with it and, by extension, with the calculated losses. For all possible events with their occurrence rates, calculations of all losses associated with each event can be completed; an event loss table is compiled as illustrated in Table 6.1.

Table 6.1. Conceptual event loss table.

Event (E_i)	Annual probability of occurrence (p_i)	Loss (L_i)
1	p_1	L_1
2	p_2	L_2
:	:	:
i	p_i	L_i
:	:	:
N	p_N	L_N

From the table, various portfolio risk metrics are computed for any or all of the participants. For example, the average annual loss, AAL, is the expected loss for the portfolio, calculated as the product of loss from an event and its annual rate, summed over all events that cause a loss. Based on cumulative rates of occurrence, an exceedance probability (EP) curve is generated such as the one shown in Figure 6.2. For example, there is a 1% chance that the loss will exceed $50 million.

The bottom-up approach provides the most robust means to quantify portfolio risk. That is, losses are first calculated for insured and insurer at the location level based on deductible and coverage limit. The next step is to aggregate all location losses in a policy to find the gross loss to the insurer for this policy. Finally, losses are aggregated over all policies in the portfolio.

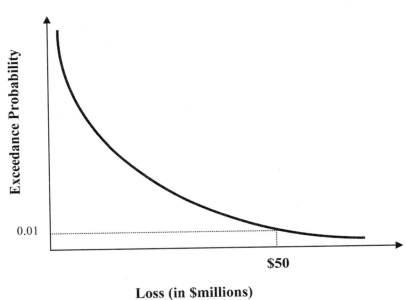

Figure 6.2. Exceedance probability curve for portfolio.

A valuable graphic tool in characterizing the role of insurance in managing portfolio risk is the loss diagram. The loss diagram is a two-dimensional representation of loss that is the backbone of the insurance model (Figure 6.3). The y-axis of a loss diagram measures the loss. Three thresholds are of fundamental importance in loss modeling. They are, in increasing order of magnitude: deductible, coverage limit, and total exposure. The deductible is the first portion of the loss absorbed by the policyholder or insured. The insurer will absorb the loss above the deductible up to the coverage limit. The total exposure refers to the replacement value of the property if it is completely destroyed. If the actual loss is greater than the coverage limit, then the remaining portion will be borne by the insured.

The x-axis runs from 0% to 100%, which corresponds to 0% to 100% proportionality, which is only applicable in the case of reinsurance (See Sidebar 1). Since there is no reinsurance on this portfolio, the insurer assumes the entire loss above the deductible amount and capped at the coverage limits as shown in Figure 6.3. For this sample loss, the insurer covers the entire loss above the deductible.

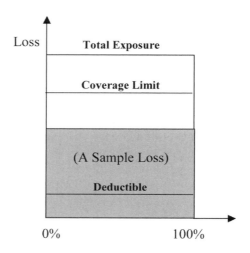

Figure 6.3. Loss diagram.

6.2.3 Portfolio Aggregation

By constructing event loss tables for the different portfolios that comprise the insurer's book of business, it is easy to combine these portfolios to generate the aggregated EP curve. Table 6.2 shows a simple example of how such an aggregation procedure could be performed. It is apparent that the total loss is simply the sum of losses across portfolios for the same event. If one examines the figures for each event across the three portfolios in the table, it is evident that Portfolio 1 and Portfolio 2 are positively correlated with each other and that Portfolio 3 is not. Based on this visual examination, if the insurer needed to reduce its risk, then the obvious candidates to eliminate would be either Portfolio 1 or 2. The aggregate risk will be more highly diversified when either 1 and 3 or 2 and 3 are combined than if 1 and 2 make up the total portfolio.

Table 6.2. Aggregation of Event Loss Tables From Three Portfolios

Event (E_i)	Probability (p_i)	Loss for Portfolio 1	Loss for Portfolio 2	Loss for Portfolio 3	Total Loss
1	p_1	$100,000	$80,000	$0	$180,000
2	p_2	60,000	50,000	10,000	120,000
3	p_3	50,000	40,000	30,000	120,000
..	..	..	..	..	..
i	p_i	30,000	25,000	50,000	105,000
..	..	..	..	..	..
..	..	..	..	..	..
N	p_N	10,000	8,000	120,000	138,000

SIDEBAR 1: Loss Diagram with Reinsurance

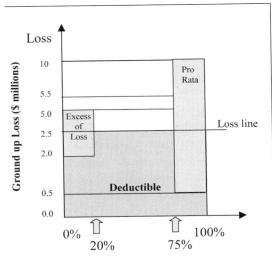

The figure to the right shows a more complex loss diagram with two traditional reinsurance contracts: one pro-rata contract and one excess-of-loss contract (See Chapter 7 for more details). In general, reinsurance contracts have an attachment, a limit and a participation level (in a percentage). In conventional shorthand, this is written % Limit X Attachment. In the case shown here, the insurance policy has deductible of $0.5 million and a coverage limit of $10 million. The excess-of-loss contract is 20% of $3 million excess of $2.0 million (or, in conventional shorthand, 20% 3M X 2.0 M). In other words, the reinsurer pays 20% of the portion of the loss that is between $2 million and $5 million once the deductible is taken into account. The pro-rata contract is 25% of $9.5 million above the deductible, so the reinsurer pays 25% of any loss between $0.5 and $10 million. If the ground-up or economic loss is $2.5 million as shown by the loss line, then the insured loss will be $2 million. In this event, the excess-of-loss amount is 0.2*($2.5 - $2.0) million or $0.1 million and the pro-rata contract covers 0.25*$2 million or $0.5 million.

6.3 Portfolio Management Example

A portfolio manager faces two critical questions with regard to dealing with catastrophic risks: What is the average annual loss (AAL) and what is the likelihood that the company may become insolvent? The first question is linked to the premium rate. A proper rate enables a company to operate smoothly while making reasonable profits for its shareholders. The second question relates to the company's ability to survive and ensure that the risk of insolvency remains acceptable. To address both of these issues, it is critical to adequately model the right hand tail of the EP curve where the loss is large and there is a significant amount of uncertainty.

In broad terms, there are two levels of portfolio risk management: micro and macro. Micromanagement addresses individual policies or even locations, while macro management considers the aggregate portfolio.

6.3.1 Understanding risk

The first step to managing a portfolio is to quantify the risk. Computer-based modeling and loss estimation are important tools in this process. Based on currently available models, a probabilistic risk analysis can identify the key drivers of loss by business unit, by peril, by geographic region, or by account. This can be used to manage the level of risk of a portfolio.

Consider a company that wants to limit its 250-year loss to be less than $100 million; that is, the annual probability of exceeding $100 million should be less than 0.4%. Based on its current book of business, the losses from various events with their annual occurrence rate are calculated and listed in descending order in Table 6.3. For each event, HU indicates a hurricane event and EQ indicates an earthquake event. From the table, it is found that the probability of exceeding $100 million is approximately 0.557%.

Table 6.3. Event Loss Table for an insurer's portfolio

Event (E_i)	Loss (L_i)	Annual probability of occurrence (p_i)	Exceedance probability $(EP(L_i))$
HU_1	$279,707,730	0.0079%	0.008%
...	...	...	...
HU_{20}	$106,945,669	0.0098%	0.232%
EQ_1	105,964,573	0.0586%	0.290%
HU_{21}	105,821,572	0.0127%	0.303%
HU_{22}	103,944,373	0.0068%	0.310%
HU_{23}	103,428,541	0.0079%	0.318%
HU_{24}	102,631,772	0.0267%	0.344%
EQ_2	102,438,481	0.0659%	0.410%
HU_{25}	101,664,120	0.0529%	0.463%
EQ_3	101,056,232	0.0888%	0.552%
HU_{26}	100,329,263	0.0052%	0.557%
HU_{27}	99,526,987	0.0220%	0.579%

Scanning all events whose losses are greater than $100 million in Table 6.3, there are three earthquake events (EQ_1, EQ_2, EQ_3) whose losses barely exceed $100 million. In the aggregate, however, the annual rate of occurrence of these three events is 0.213%, or approximately 38% of 0.557%. As a potential strategy, if the earthquake exposure is reduced such that the aggregate loss for each earthquake scenario is lowered by 6%, then losses from all three earthquake events will be less than $100 million. This will result in a portfolio with the probability of exceedance at 0.344% for a loss threshold of $100 million (Table 6.4).

Table 6.4. Event Loss Table for an insurer's revised portfolio

Event (E_i)	Loss (L_i)	Annual probability of occurrence (p_i)	Exceedance probability (EP(L_i))
HU_1	$279,707,730	0.0079%	0.008%
...	...	...	...
HU_20	$106,945,669	0.0098%	0.232%
HU_21	105,821,572	0.0127%	0.245%
HU_22	103,944,373	0.0068%	0.251%
HU_23	103,428,541	0.0079%	0.259%
HU_24	102,631,772	0.0267%	0.286%
HU_25	101,664,120	0.0529%	0.339%
HU_26	100,329,263	0.0052%	0.344%
EQ_1	99,606,700	0.0586%	0.403%
HU_27	99,526,987	0.0220%	0.425%
EQ_2	96,292,172	0.0659%	0.491%
EQ_3	94,992,858	0.0888%	0.579%

6.3.2 Underwriting and Risk Selection

Catastrophe modeling is also a valuable tool for underwriting and pricing. By quantifying risk, the impact of adding another policy to a portfolio becomes transparent. If the potential loss from adding the policy to the portfolio is too large, then the underwriter can decide not to provide coverage for this risk. Certain types of structures, like unreinforced masonry buildings in earthquake-prone areas, may then not be eligible for coverage. The insurer will also avoid areas with soils that have a high potential for landslide or liquefaction. By estimating potential losses and their variability, catastrophe models provide a means to determine the appropriate actuarial premium for a particular insurance policy. Given the concern with aggregate losses, the insurer can examine the impact on portfolio losses by varying the deductibles as well as coverage limits on insurance contracts.

6.4 Special Issues Regarding Portfolio Risk

There are three important issues that insurers must take into consideration when managing their portfolio risk from natural disasters: data quality, uncertainty modeling, and impact of correlation. While each of these issues has been raised in other parts of this book, they are revisited here due to their unique impact on a portfolio.

6.4.1 Data Quality

Amongst all the data elements that are necessary for input into a catastrophe model, insurers must pay special attention to the inventory component. In defining as accurately as possible the composition for their portfolio, they can reduce the degree of epistemic uncertainty. Specifically, past natural disaster events have shown that the building construction type, the age of the building, the soil data (for earthquake events) and exposure data are important elements for estimating loss. Having this information available on each structure will enable the insurer to estimate the risk of claims exceeding certain amounts more accurately.

The type of construction and the age of a building are two key components in assessing the vulnerability of a structure. While this point may seem evident since different construction types respond to load differently, and older buildings have more wear and tear, the impact of construction type, and age of a building sometimes play out in subtle ways. For example, after the 1989 Loma Prieta earthquake, a portfolio for an insurance company covering industrial facilities had an incurred loss that was much less than the projected loss. An extensive investigation and field inspection of the buildings in the portfolio revealed that a number of the structures had been coded incorrectly as unreinforced masonry buildings.

With each new natural disaster event, the structural engineering community learns more about how different construction types respond to lateral loads. For example, until the 1994 Northridge earthquake in Southern California, steel structures were thought to perform well under earthquake loading. However, inspections following this earthquake revealed that a large number of steel moment-frame buildings experienced fractured or cracked connections.

Earthquakes provide engineers with the opportunity to gradually improve the building design code. In California there were two major revisions to the building code: one after the Long Beach Earthquake in Los Angeles in 1933 and another after the San Fernando Earthquake in 1971. Buildings constructed before 1933 did not consider earthquake resistance and are consequently more vulnerable. The San Fernando earthquake pointed out deficiencies in concrete tilt-up structures built before 1971. They often lacked proper connection between the roof and tilt-up panels. Consequently, the walls of a number of tilt-ups separated from the roof diaphragm and collapsed outward on strong ground shaking. In general, building age can be used to infer the design code used to construct it and therefore to select the appropriate vulnerability function for use in loss prediction.

Besides construction and age of a building, other factors that are important in assessing vulnerability are the geology and geography of the site and the value of the covered policy. Accurate classification of underlying soils for earthquake loss modeling and surrounding surface terrain for hurricane loss modeling can aid an insurer in estimating expected loss. Furthermore, residential policies often use tax assessor data, which are generally outdated and under-valued. As discussed in Chapter 4, under-valued exposure will result in under-estimating potential insurer's loss.

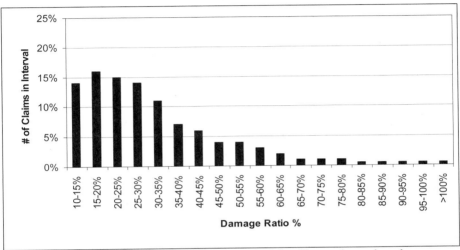

Figure 6.4. Dwelling loss experience for the 1971 San Fernando earthquake.

6.4.2 Uncertainty Modeling

The uncertainty surrounding a loss estimate from a catastrophe model is of paramount importance. One cannot properly allocate losses to different parties simply by using the expected or mean value of the potential ground-up loss. The entire loss distribution needs to be considered in the process. For example, a review of empirical data on building performance reveals that for a given event magnitude, a great deal of variability exists in damage to the same type of structure. Figure 6.4 highlights the variability in building performance for wood frame dwellings, normalized to similar levels of ground motion and soil conditions (Algermissen and Steinbrugge, 1990).

To illustrate the importance of the variability in a loss estimate, suppose the estimated damage to a building has a probability density distribution as depicted in Figure 6.5, with a mean damage ratio (ratio of dollar loss to replacement value of the structure) of 7%. In addition, suppose the deductible on each individual insurance policy is 10% of the structure's value. A loss allocation based on the mean damage can be compared to one based on the damage ratio distribution. In the former, because the mean damage of 7% is less than the deductible (10%), it appears as if the policyholder incurs all of the loss. In the latter, a random damage ratio is sampled from the distribution curve, and the loss is allocated based on the sampled damage and the deductible.

130

All of the sampled losses that are below the deductible must be paid by the policyholder. For sampled losses above the deductible, the first 10% is covered by the policyholder and the excess is paid by the insurer. If all losses are then weighted by the appropriate probability of occurrence, the resulting net mean loss allocations are 5.2% for client, and 1.8% for insurer (Table 6.5). Thus, if only the mean damage is used to estimate loss, the loss allocation to the policyholder and insurer can be inaccurate. In general, deductibles influence the allocation of losses between insurer and insured at the low end and coverage limits affect the allocation of losses at the high end.

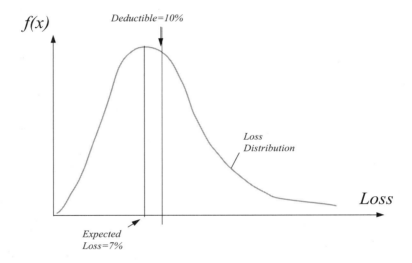

Figure 6.5. Simple example of the difference between expected and distributed loss allocations. (Source: Shah and Dong, 1991)

Table 6.5. Uncertainty in catastrophe modeling.

Allocation Method	Client Loss	Insurer Loss
Point-estimate	7%	0%
Distributed	5.2%	1.8%

6.4.3 Impact of Correlation

An important consideration in portfolio risk management is correlation between losses from different policies. Since most portfolios contain policies at multiple locations and the losses at each location are random variables, the aggregate loss to the portfolio has to incorporate the loss correlation between geographic regions. If losses across regions are independent of one another and the number of locations in a portfolio is large, then the aggregate loss for the portfolio will be highly diversified with a sharp peak at the mean and low variability. On the other hand, if losses across some or all regions are highly correlated, then the aggregate loss for the portfolio will have a large variation and there is a greater chance that claims payments will penetrate the higher levels of loss, thus exceeding the survival constraint.

Currently there are few published studies that investigate the factors influencing loss correlation from a given event. Major factors affecting loss correlation include geographic and site condition concentration, parameter uncertainty in vulnerability modeling, and model uncertainty for hazard attenuation. As discussed in earlier chapters, geographic concentration of a portfolio will normally increase the chances of a large loss from a single disaster. Post-event surveys for both earthquakes and hurricanes have pointed out the existence of local pockets in which all structures suffered more (or less) severe damage as a group than similar buildings in neighboring areas.

For earthquakes, this high correlation is usually due to local conditions that can focus ground motion. Such localized effects are not usually included in general attenuation models. For hurricanes, such effects are observed with the presence of localized tornados within the broad affected area, with affected buildings suffering much higher damage than other structures subject solely to hurricane wind and waves. These localized effects are generally not considered in the general wind field model.

Concentration of locations subject to certain site conditions, such as subsurface geology for ground motion or terrain roughness for wind, will impact loss correlation. If buildings in a portfolio are all located in the vicinity of an area with common geology or terrain, there will be a higher loss correlation within such a portflio. This phenomenon is most important from an earthquake perspective. While a geographically concentrated portfolio could clearly suffer site condition concentration, it is quite possible for a portfolio to have a strong site condition concentration while being geographically distributed.

Finally, if the mean damage ratio for a particular building class is underestimated by the model, then the calculation of losses to all such buildings will be lower than the actual figures, as was the case for wood frame buildings after the Northridge earthquake. If all buildings in a portfolio are located at the same distance from the rupture of an earthquake fault, there is a good chance that all ground motion estimates may be off simultaneously using a particular attenuation model than if the portfolio of buildings were located at a wide range of distances from the rupture. A recent study has tried to quantify the spatial correlation of probabilistic earthquake ground motion and loss (Wesson and Perkins, 2000). This type of risk quantification can improve the portfolio risk management process.

6.5 Summary

An overview of how the insurance sector manages catastrophe risks from natural hazards using a portfolio approach has been presented. A portfolio manager needs to balance pricing with exposure. Pricing is related to the expected annual loss and its uncertainty. Likewise exposure is related to the loss exceedance probability: the likelihood of a crippling loss must be kept at an acceptably low level. The framework based on engineering modeling addresses these and related requirements.

Several points are worth repeating. Adequate portfolio risk quantification involves not only the expected level of loss, but also the associated uncertainty and correlation. Major sources of loss correlation are geographic concentration, site condition, attenuation and vulnerability. In the quantification process, it is also important to recognize that data quality is important; uncertainty or lack of information on the property, site and exposure must be incorporated and accounted for in the risk estimate. The risk modeling framework discussed in the chapter is an essential tool. Reinsurance is an important tool for portfolio risk management and is discussed in the next chapter.

6.6 References

Algermissen, S.T., and Steinbrugge, K.V. (1990). "Earthquake Losses to Single-Family Dwellings: California Experience", USGS Bulletin 1939-A.

Shah, H. and Dong, W.M. (1991). "Treatment of Uncertainty In Seismic Risk Evaluation: The Development of a Distributed Loss Model (DLM)," *Proceedings of the 4th International Conference on Seismic Zonation*, 3: 253-260, Stanford, CA, August 26-29.

Wesson, R. and Perkins, D. (2000). "Spatial Correlation of Probabilistic Earthquake Ground Motion and Loss," USGS, Personal correspondence.

Chapter 7 – Risk Financing

Major Contributor:
David Lalonde

7.1 Introduction

Natural hazard risks are associated with high severity, low frequency events. The significant losses caused by these events can lead to earnings volatility and drain the economic value of organizations. There are many ways of financing these shock losses to alleviate the disruptions they cause.

The focus of this chapter is to discuss alternative methods for dealing with the financial impact associated with natural hazards. Risk assessment deals with understanding a company's current risk profile through the use of catastrophe modeling and the creation of exceedance probability (EP) curves. Once it is determined, for example, that a company's 1-in-100 year loss is unacceptably high, the question becomes: what actions can be taken to address this risk? Risk transfer is one approach to financing risk and deals with techniques to change the shape of the EP curve with the goal of achieving a risk profile consistent with management's objectives and tolerance for risk.

The next section discusses which risks should be financed. Section 7.3 provides an overview of various funding mechanisms and how they respond to losses from natural hazards. Starting with a review of traditional reinsurance products and their evolution to customized products such as triggers, carve-outs and multi-year contracts, a discussion of the emergence of insurance-linked securities as a risk transfer mechanism follows along with an exploration of the key role that catastrophe models play in the crafting of such transactions.

The structure of these instruments is explored in Section 7.4 and techniques are introduced for dealing with the uncertainty introduced by basis risk, a measure of the extent to which the cash flow provided by the financial instrument may not reflect the actual losses experienced by the issuer. The chapter concludes by developing an evaluation framework that companies can use to assess alternative options and make sound strategic risk financing decisions.

7.2 What Risks Should Be Financed?

There is a significant lack of relevant historical experience regarding natural hazard events and other such catastrophes. As a result, companies do not have access to reliable historical loss data to assess their likelihood of sustaining future losses or to assess the effectiveness of various risk financing schemes. In the absence of historical data, catastrophe models that simulate potential catastrophe experience for over thousands of years can be helpful. In addition to modeling random events, the parameters of known historical events can be used to estimate the potential current impact if similar events were to occur today. These models produce exceedance probability (EP) curves that estimate the likelihood that losses will be greater than a given level as shown in Figure 7.1. By using models to look at risk probabilistically the company can appropriately quantify the impact of financing various risks.

A thorough assessment of the current risk profile including the risk from catastrophes combined with the company's tolerance for risk and available resources will determine the level of risk the company is comfortable retaining. As a starting point, the company will want to answer the following questions:

- How will peer companies be affected by similar events? Losing 20% of company surplus is a devastating event; however its impact on the ongoing viability of the company will be much worse if peer companies only lose 5-10% of their surplus.

- What level of retention and limits of loss are rating agencies and regulators concerned about? Historically, both have focused on 100-year hurricanes and 250-year earthquakes.

- What is the single largest loss that could be sustained without leading to financial impairment? After a certain level of loss the company will be facing a rating downgrade that may affect its competitive position. The company can review various rating and regulatory ratios to see how much of a loss would cause concern.

- What is the impact of multiple losses within a short period of time? In addition to a single large loss, the company must also be concerned about the aggregate loss that may arise from smaller catastrophes over the year. Losses from such catastrophes may come from a single peril or a combination of perils.

- What is the appropriate time horizon to consider in determining which risk financing strategy to pursue? The company will need to analyze the impact of catastrophic losses over a period of time – for example, over a five-year period. Similar to the case of accumulation of losses in a single year, the company needs to consider the possibility of multiple years of abnormal levels of catastrophe losses.

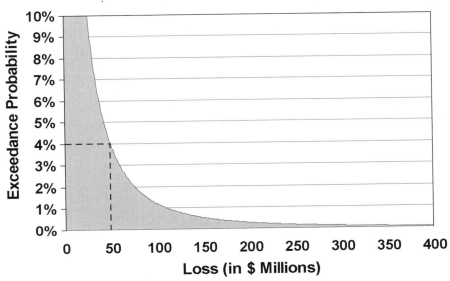

Figure 7.1. Exceedance probability curve.

7.2.1 Level of Risk

The first step in determining an appropriate risk financing strategy is to undertake a risk assessment based on the company's current portfolio. As demonstrated in Part II of the book, catastrophe models provide the probability of exceeding any given level of loss, as well as measures of uncertainty. The goal is to devise strategies to optimize expected return given the company's risk profile and subject to satisfying various constraints. Besides the obvious survival constraint, the company must consider constraints such as the difficulty of changing an existing portfolio, the prevailing conditions and regulatory issues. Figure 7.1, for example, shows a 4% probability per year that gross losses (losses before any risk transfer) will exceed $50 million – a level of risk that the insurer may decide is unacceptable.

One of the constraints faced by the company is that, in order to write business, it must hold an acceptable level of capital. While minimum capital requirements are set by regulation, the true amount required depends on the risk profile of the underlying business. Catastrophe models, which depict the full distribution of potential losses, can be helpful in this regard. There are costs associated with holding capital; higher amounts of capital reduce company leverage. In the example above, consider the strategy of transferring the layer of potential loss between $50 and $100 million to another party, rather than holding surplus to cover the loss directly. These potential losses are represented by the darker shaded area in Figure 7.2. By removing, or

138

ceding, that part of exposure, the company can successfully change the shape of the EP curve and its risk profile.

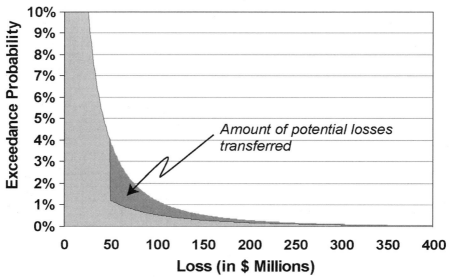

Figure 7.2. The shape of the exceedance probability curve, and therefore the risk profile, is altered by the transfer of risk.

Although the layer discussed above is amenable to risk transfer, in the extreme tail of the EP curve, there is a point at which the cost associated with transferring the risk can be prohibitive. For this layer, the company will be forced to retain the risk. For ease of analysis, the risk profile illustrated by the EP curve above can be segmented into losses that the company can handle through normal operations, losses that require some level of risk transfer/financing and losses that are not economically feasible to finance.

7.2.2 Probable Maximum Loss (PML)

Once the insurer has determined at what point along the EP curve consideration of risk financing options should start, the next question is to determine the amount of financial protection desired. Companies often determine the amount of risk to retain and which risks to finance based on the concept of probable maximum loss (PML). As discussed briefly in Chapter 2, PML is a measure of risk corresponding to the largest loss the entity can reasonably be expected to experience. Often, PML is defined as a return period, which is the inverse of the probability that losses will exceed a dollar threshold.

A 500-year return period loss of $100 million, for example, implies that losses above this amount have a probability of 0.2% of occurring in any given year. Should an insurance company worry about protecting itself against levels of catastrophe loss with a 0.2% probability of occurrence? What about a 1-in-1000 year loss, or 0.1% probability? How large a loss along the EP curve is it economically viable to protect against?

These questions can only be answered in the context of the level of other risks facing the enterprise. For example, if a company purchases reinsurance to protect against a 250-year return period loss (probability 0.4%) and files for bankruptcy after an economic downturn that had a probability of 1%, it has deployed its capital inefficiently. Using catastrophe models to measure the impact of risk financing strategies to alter the EP curve yields the changes in risk. The costs and impact of other company operations must also be considered. These questions are addressed through the evaluation framework discussed at the end of the chapter where catastrophe models are integrated into enterprise risk management. The scenario that maximizes the company's return given their level of risk tolerance will yield the answer as to which risks should be financed.

7.3 Risk Financing Mechanisms

Natural hazard events can lead to concurrent losses on multiple exposures. Continuation of operations depends upon a company's ability to meet its obligations to policyholders and have sufficient resources remaining to pay operating expenses. How a company weathers the event will have an impact on the perception of those in the market and its financial ratings. There is usually an immediate need to pay losses after an event. In fact, quick payment of obligations can have a mitigating effect on total loss. In the following pages, the many financing mechanisms available to pay for catastrophe losses are explored, as well as the implications of employing each. The mechanisms can be classified under two broad categories: generating funds internally or transferring risk.

7.3.1 Generating Funds Internally

When the company chooses to retain risk, it must generate funds internally to pay for losses resulting from a catastrophe. Options available include the following: maintaining funds on hand, borrowing, issuing debt, and issuing equity.

Maintaining Funds on Hand

Funds on hand are usually in the form of physical assets or investments. First, consider funds that can be generated internally by selling physical assets. This can be problematic in that physical assets may not be very liquid and the likelihood exists that the realized value of the assets can be reduced due to the urgency of the liquidation. Additionally, selling assets may impede the company's ongoing operations. On the other hand, the financial benefit of asset liquidation is immediate and there is no lingering debt to affect future earnings.

Funds can also be generated internally by selling investments. An issue of concern here and with the liquidation of physical assets is that the portfolio will have a market gain or loss associated with the sale. If the portfolio has an embedded gain, the catastrophe loss may offset this and reduce the tax burden associated with selling investments that have been profitable. If the portfolio has an embedded loss, the catastrophe will compound the situation, resulting in further impairment of the company.

Funds can also be generated internally by maintaining a catastrophe reserve that finances potential losses in advance over time. In the U.S., this entails the accumulation of after-tax profits into a dedicated account. However, this capital could perhaps be used more advantageously elsewhere, depending upon alternative investment opportunities. The advantage of the reserving approach is that the cost of future events is spread out over time, resulting in more stable earnings.

Borrowing

Companies can choose to borrow funds to cover catastrophic losses. The amount required, however, is likely to be quite large. It will be difficult to arrange for an appropriate level of funds quickly, and because there will be simultaneous demands for funds from other parties, the cost of borrowing can be driven up significantly. Since the cost of borrowing funds to finance losses is unknown until the catastrophe event actually occurs, it is very difficult to plan for this financially. However, options do exist for establishing a line of credit with a preset interest rate spread.

Issuing Debt

The issuance of debt into the market is another form of borrowing. Mutual companies can also issue surplus notes. Again, however, if many parties are trying to place debt simultaneously and the company's financial position is compromised, the rate of return required to attract investors can be artificially high.

Issuing Equity

By issuing equity, the company's current shareholders forfeit some level of ownership and future profitability in exchange for the funds required to finance current obligations. Furthermore, in the immediate aftermath of a catastrophe event, the company's stock price may fall, thus raising the implicit cost of issuing equity.

In general, it is beyond the means of most insurance companies to generate internally the funds necessary to absorb catastrophic losses, though such a strategy may be appropriate for normal operational risk or to absorb small shock losses. In managing catastrophe risk, there is usually a need for some element of risk transfer.

7.3.2 Risk Transfer – Reinsurance

In anticipation of catastrophic events, companies transfer risk by arranging for the right to some level of reimbursement or indemnification when losses actually occur. In all cases, however, the company retains ultimate responsibility for the payment of losses; thus the credit worthiness of the entity to which risk is transferred is an important consideration. Traditionally, risk transfer has been accomplished through reinsurance. In exchange for a premium, the company transfers to a reinsurance company the risk of part of their loss from a given set of exposures. Over the years, the level of sophistication in the reinsurance market has grown as companies have become better able to identify and quantify their risk. The most common form of reinsurance for catastrophes is to protect against losses between a minimum and a maximum amount, with refinements for specific lines of business and geographic regions.

Traditional Reinsurance

The topic of traditional reinsurance is covered in many texts on reinsurance (for example, Carter, 2000). There are two main types: pro rata reinsurance, in which premium and loss are shared on a proportional basis, and excess of loss reinsurance, for which a premium is paid to cover losses above some threshold. Figure 7.3 illustrates how these types of reinsurance contracts relate to the whole of risk transfer. While a certain amount of pro rata reinsurance is used for catastrophe protection, excess of loss reinsurance is the predominant form.

Custom Features in Reinsurance Contracts

The increased sophistication and resolution of models used to analyze catastrophe risk have enabled reinsurers to offer many custom features in their products to meet the growing demands of insurers. Some examples include: carveouts, triggers, multi-year contracts, industry loss warranty, and dual trigger products.

Carving out exposures – Carveouts involve excluding a certain region from the reinsurance program, such as a particularly vulnerable group of counties. Some reinsurers have offered protection at a lower cost when certain areas (where the reinsurer may have already accumulated exposures) are excluded. Carveouts can also apply to particular lines of business or perils. In a carveout arrangement, the insurer retains the riskiest part of the exposure and must find an alternative financing mechanism if it wants to transfer this risk.

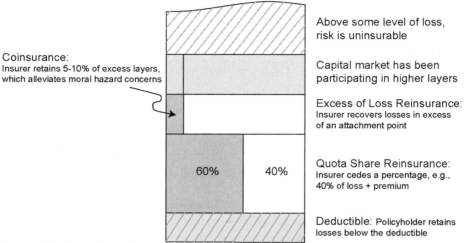

Figure 7.3. Overview of transfer risk: policyholder, insurer, reinsurer, capital market.

Triggers – Reinsurance programs can be activated as the result of triggering events, such as a threshold industry loss, a second catastrophe event, or a threshold loss ratio. An insurer may be able to finance internally a single catastrophe but may need protection should a second or multiple events occur in the same time period. Catastrophe models generate many years of catastrophe activity and can be used to determine the probability of one, two, or more catastrophe losses in a given year. Hence, they can be utilized to design a reinsurance program with a trigger that is most appealing to the primary insurance company.

Multi-year contracts – Companies may want the guarantee of coverage at fixed or indexed variable costs over a longer time horizon. Multi-year reinsurance contracts can be used to achieve these objectives. Most multi-year contracts are two to three year deals and include cancellation provisions.

Industry Loss Warranty – These contracts pay out only if total industry losses arising from the catastrophe event are greater than some specified amount; they do not, therefore, require a detailed analysis of an individual company's exposures. In addition, they do not require a detailed assessment of the company loss once a catastrophe occurs. From a primary company perspective, industry loss warranties carry basis risk. This concept is discussed in more detail later in this chapter.

Dual Trigger Products – Companies may be able to pay catastrophe losses out of their investment portfolio. If interest rates have risen, however, their bond portfolio could contain significant unrealized capital losses.

Realization of these losses at the same time that a catastrophe loss is experienced would be devastating to the financial performance of the company. Buying reinsurance wastes capital because the protection is not needed unless the company faces catastrophe and investment losses simultaneously. This scenario has led to the development of dual trigger reinsurance products that pay only if both a reinsurance retention and an economic trigger have been breached.

Contingent Products – Some innovative products have been developed that provide the right to generate funds if an event happens. These include contingent debt, contingent equity (CatEputs™), and even contingent future reinsurance availability. In the latter, for a premium, the company has the right to purchase reinsurance protection at a prearranged price, if a predefined event occurs.

7.3.3 Risk Transfer – Securitization

Immediately after Hurricane Andrew occurred in 1992, reinsurance rates became expensive and availability was restricted. This event led companies to take a more focused look at determining which risks drive their catastrophe exposure and to restructure traditional reinsurance contracts to address specific areas of concern. Catastrophe models, with their detailed level of output, have been instrumental in the refinement of this market by providing the tools for insurers to structure their contracts and for reinsurers to price and manage them within their broader portfolios of catastrophe exposures.

While the reinsurance market is the traditional venue for risk transfer contracts, insurance-linked securities that transform reinsurance contracts into securities are now being sold in the capital markets. The securitization of catastrophe risk is an increasingly popular route as both insurance and reinsurance companies seek alternative sources of capital.

The capital markets are many times larger than the reinsurance market and experience daily fluctuations in value greater than the largest contemplated catastrophe. In addition, catastrophe risk is potentially attractive to the capital markets due to its demonstrated lack of correlation with other investments. Insurance-linked securities offer a means of diversification in capital market portfolios and thus, theoretically, allow the capital markets to accept catastrophe risk with a lower risk load than reinsurers.

Most reinsurance contracts are indemnity based; that is, they pay losses in accordance with the insured's actual underlying losses. The capital markets have introduced derivatives, whereby payments are tied to an underlying indicator, such as an index of industry losses or the occurrence of a disaster of a given magnitude in a particular location.

The securitization of insurance risk is still evolving as new twists are added to find an effective balance between the needs of the issuers (the insurer) and those of the investors. The issuer desires risk transfer with minimal basis risk so that the amount of the payment from the risk transfer instrument reflects the actual losses for which it has contracted. The issuer would also like broad coverage, competitive pricing, and no counterparty credit risk. Investors want transparency, limited or no moral hazard and maximum yield.

Securitization is more involved than traditional reinsurance in terms of the time and expenses needed to implement each transaction. These costs include underwriting fees plus additional legal, rating agency, and modeling fees. The time commitment on the part of senior management is also significant, as potential investors need to be educated on the assessment of catastrophe risk.

Traditional reinsurance treaties are usually of one-year duration. Through multi-year securitization, the issuer can achieve multi-year risk transfer capacity while avoiding fluctuations in the price of reinsurance and, at the same time, lowering the marginal transaction costs associated with the securitization itself. The process involved in issuing a catastrophe bond can be divided into four basic steps: loss estimation, ratings, prospectus, and investor education.

Loss Estimation

The risk analysis performed by the catastrophe modeler is fundamental to the very structure of the transaction and to its pricing strategy. The underlying risk assessment involves validation and mapping of exposure data and analysis through the catastrophe model. This analysis produces detailed output used to assess the risk and structure the transaction. The key output is the exceedance probability (EP) curve. The attachment point corresponds to the level of loss where the investor will start to lose principal. The exhaustion point is the level of loss at which the investor has lost all of his or her principal. Further analyses of loss probabilities, by peril, line of business, and geography help investors understand how the catastrophe bond may correlate with other securities in their portfolio.

Ratings

Ratings assigned by agencies such as Standard & Poor's, Moody's Investors Service, and Fitch, allow investors to compare the offered insurance-linked security with other corporate bonds with which they are more familiar. Investors do not have the insurance and catastrophe modeling experience and resources of reinsurance companies. They rely, in part, on the research and due diligence performed by the securities rating agencies, which subject the underlying exposure data, the catastrophe models, and the transaction's structure to extensive scrutiny.

The modelers present the results of detailed sensitivity analyses of all major components of the model. Independent experts are also used by the rating agencies to perform stress tests for model robustness. Since catastrophe bonds made their debut in 1996, rating agencies and, to an increasing degree investors, have become quite sophisticated with respect to catastrophe modeling technology.

Prospectus

The prospectus describes the details of the model results. It contains language on the limitations of the analysis and risk factors designed to alert investors of the variability inherent in the catastrophe modeling process. It contains all available information related to the transaction. Over time, disclosure of exposure data and results has become increasingly detailed and the presentation of results is becoming more standardized, allowing investors to better compare transactions.

Investor Education

Investor education has been an important feature in the early development stages of the insurance linked securitization market. Road shows, conference calls, and other investor meetings are required to explain the catastrophe modeling process. There are numerous interactions with investors who require a more careful analysis of the correlation between transactions and real time information on actual events.

7.3.4 Securitization Structures

Figure 7.4 illustrates the typical structure of a catastrophe bond issued in a securitization transaction. The issuing company enters into a reinsurance agreement with a special purpose vehicle (SPV), which transforms insurance risk into investment risk. The issuer pays a premium to the SPV in exchange for loss payments should a covered event occur. The SPV in turn issues securities to finance the coverage. The investors, or noteholders, who purchase the securities are essentially putting up the principal and they receive interest payments equal to a risk free rate, such as LIBOR (London InterBank Offered Rate) and a risk premium. Additionally, they receive the return of their principal investment less any loss payments that may be made.

The funds raised from the issue are deposited into a collateral account and invested in high-grade securities. By entering into a total return swap with a highly rated counterparty, the return on the collateral account is converted to LIBOR and the assets in the collateral account are guaranteed. This feature is used to provide an enhanced return to the collateral account.

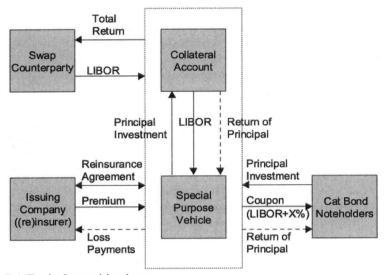

Figure 7.4. Typical securitization structure.

The catastrophe modeling undertaken in support of the transaction reveals the probability that investors will recover their principal in full, in part, or that they will forfeit their principal altogether. The yield on the notes depends on these probabilities, as does their rating. Any default on the notes is triggered by the occurrence of an actual event or events during the period of coverage. The principal, which has been held in trust, is then used to pay the losses of the issuer, or cedant (i.e., the party ceding risk).

The nature of the modeling undertaken to determine these probabilities will depend on the type of transaction, of which there are four principal types that are now discussed (indemnity, index, parametric, and notional portfolio).

Indemnity-based Securitizations

Indemnity-based securitization transactions most closely resemble reinsurance than any type of new financial instrument. Losses from a catastrophe are paid on the basis of actual company losses. The indemnity transaction is suited to situations where certainty of full recovery is critical.

Investors examine individual transactions independently; reinsurers, on the other hand, are familiar with the underwriting process and have long-term relationships and other non-catastrophe business with their clients. The questions and concerns of the investor and the reinsurer will thus differ significantly. A company undertaking a securitization transaction will need to perform a very detailed review of its underwriting processes and data handling.

The quality of the exposure data is critical to the process. In the case of indemnity-based transactions, data should include location, construction type and occupancy; it may also include age, building height, and other information. If more detailed data are available on individual risk characteristics, such as the presence of storm shutters, these can be used in the analysis. Both the purchaser of the bond and the modeler spend considerable effort in evaluating the data and determining whether they meet logical and reasonability tests.

A key concern of the investor is moral hazard, the extent to which the purchaser of the bond is able and willing to control losses. For this reason alone, the investor will want to thoroughly understand the company's motivation for the transaction. This is an area where reinsurers have greater efficiency than investors. In indemnity-based transactions, mechanisms to reduce moral hazard can be built in. Such mechanisms include deductibles, coinsurance, co-participation in the losses or the use of a triggering event, such as restricting recovery to losses from a Category 3 or greater hurricane. The company has no control over these events.

The first truly successful catastrophe bond issues came in 1997. The largest of these was a transaction by which the United Services Automotive Association (USAA) ceded $400 million of hurricane risk to Residential Re, a special purpose vehicle (SPV) set up for the sole purpose of this transaction (Froot, 1999). Funds raised from investors by Residential Re were held in trust for the purpose of paying USAA for claims against it resulting from hurricane losses along the Gulf and East Coasts of the United States. Residential Re has renewed its issue at different amounts every year and in 2002 expanded coverage to include Hawaii hurricanes. Catastrophe modeling was a key component in supporting the transaction and was used to estimate expected losses on USAA's book of business (Figure 7.5).

Figure 7.5 specifies USAA's exposure and policy conditions for insured losses, as well as the detailed output and reports needed for the issue. Insured losses are calculated by applying the specific policy conditions to the total damage estimates. Policy conditions may include deductibles by coverage, site-specific or blanket deductibles, coverage limits and sublimits, coinsurance, attachment points and limits for single or multiple location policies, and policy-specific reinsurance terms. Explicit modeling of uncertainty in both intensity and damage calculations enables a detailed probabilistic calculation of the effects of different policy conditions.

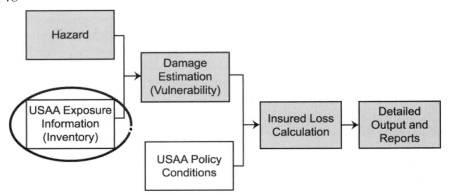

Figure 7.5. Catastrophe modeling components for an indemnity-based transaction.

Probability distributions of losses and their complement, the exceedance probability curve, are estimated for potential levels of annual aggregate and occurrence losses that the insurer may experience given their book of business. The curves also provide the probabilities of attachment for various reinsurance layers and therefore the probabilities that investors will suffer a loss of interest on, or all or part of the principal amount of, the notes.

In the 1997 Residential Re transaction, which was a one-year term, actual losses could be triggered by the occurrence of any single Gulf or East Coast hurricane of Saffir Simpson Category 3 or greater that resulted in losses to USAA in excess of $1 billion. Concern about moral hazard was ameliorated, at least in part, by a 20% coinsurance arrangement by USAA in the securitized reinsurance layer. The structure of that initial issue is shown in Figure 7.6. This structure has remained largely the same in subsequent years, though the size of the issue has varied.

The results of the risk analysis performed for this transaction indicated that the probability that USAA's hurricane losses would exceed $1 billion and that the holders of the notes would suffer a loss was 1%. Further, the probability that it would suffer a complete default was 0.39%. The transaction was the first to be rated by all four rating agencies in existence at the time (Moody's Investors Service, Standard & Poor's, Fitch, and Duff & Phelps).

Index-based Transactions

In index-based transactions, the model estimates losses on estimated industry exposures with the trigger based on actual industry losses resulting from an event. Industry-wide losses are typically used for catastrophe indices. Based on the industry losses from an event, a formula is used to derive payment to the company.

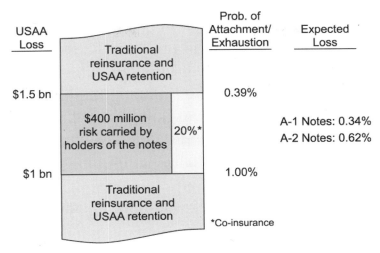

Figure 7.6. 1997 Residential Re (USAA) summary features.

Two issues that need to be addressed to accommodate the increasing use of such derivatives are pricing and basis risk. Specifically, is pricing competitive with that of traditional reinsurance products, including any additional monitoring and educational costs? Is there strong correlation between the underlying variable and the variable being hedged so that there is limited basis risk? A third issue, availability, requires the first two issues to be settled.

Index-based contracts are attractive to investors because they only have to understand and evaluate the index, not underwrite individual companies. In order to minimize basis risk, companies must assess what their loss would be given a particular industry loss. Reviewing market share, as well as correlation with past industry losses can help accomplish this.

From an investor's point of view, index-based transactions are attractive because they reduce moral hazard, since an individual cedant has little control over industry losses. To estimate expected losses on the notes, a catastrophe model is utilized. Modelers have developed, in house, detailed databases of property values. These annually-updated databases include estimates of total property exposures, typically at ZIP code resolution. Data include the number of risks and their values broken down by line of business, by coverage, by occupancy, and by construction type. The modeling process is illustrated in Figure 7.7 on the next page. The hazard components of the model operate in the same manner as for the indemnity-based transaction. The hazard is superimposed on industry exposures and damages are estimated, as before. Insured losses are calculated by applying industry average policy conditions.

150

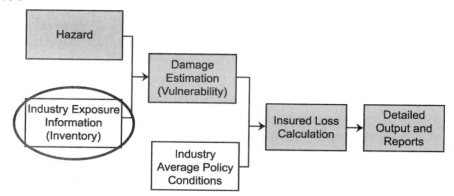

Figure 7.7. Catastrophe modeling components for an industry index-based transaction.

In February 2001, Swiss Re ceded $100 million of earthquake risk to Western Capital, an SPV. Western Capital, in turn, issued $97 million in notes and $3 million in preference shares. Funds raised are held in trust for 23 months to pay claims resulting from industry earthquake losses in California.

This type of transaction is called a transformer, since Swiss Re was ceding the residential risk they underwrote for the California Earthquake Authority (CEA) into the capital markets via an industry loss measure. Swiss Re thus transformed CEA residential losses into industry losses, accepting the basis risk. The reporting agent of industry losses is Property Claim Services (PCS). PCS develops its estimate of industry loss by conducting surveys of insurers after the occurrence of a catastrophe event. The structure of the Western Capital transaction is illustrated in Figure 7.8. If industry losses from an earthquake in California between February of 2001 and January of 2003 were less than $22.5 billion, then investors in this· contract would pay nothing. If these industry losses exceeded $31.5 billion, they would pay $97 million to Swiss Re. No earthquakes of any sizeable magnitude occurred in California during this 23-month period.

One advantage of the index-based transaction from the point of view of the cedant is that there is no need to disclose details of its book of business, since losses to the notes are triggered by industry losses and not the cedant's book. From the investor's point of view, this also alleviates the problem of asymmetry of information; because the investor does not need to understand the details of the issuer's business or its risk profile, the risk inherent in the notes is easier to evaluate. Therefore, concerns about moral hazard, as well as adverse selection, are reduced.

The primary disadvantage associated with an index-based transaction is that the cedant is exposed to basis risk to the extent that its own exposures – and therefore losses – differ in kind and geographical distribution from that of the industry's, or from that of the index used to determine the payoff of the contract. It should be noted, however, that the modeler can help the cedant assess and minimize the basis risk by quantifying the correlation between the potential losses from the cedant's book of business and industry-wide exposures.

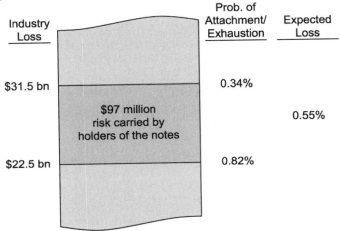

Industry Loss	Prob. of Attachment/ Exhaustion	Expected Loss
$31.5 bn	0.34%	
$97 million risk carried by holders of the notes		0.55%
$22.5 bn	0.82%	

Figure 7.8. 2001 Western Capital summary features.

Another disadvantage is that the index of industry losses may require a long time to develop. Preliminary surveys are conducted in the immediate aftermath of an event, but results are revised as actual claims data come in. This may take months, particularly in the case of earthquakes. In order to alleviate this issue, if a triggering event or events occur during the covered period, the maturity date on the notes can be extended so that a more accurate value of the index can be determined. In this case, however, investors must be compensated with a higher return for the potential delay in receiving their payment.

Parametric Indices
This type of transaction uses a catastrophe model to estimate the likelihood that an event of or above a given intensity will occur in a given location during the covered period. Any payment to the cedant is triggered not by a loss amount, but rather by the physical parameters of the actual event, should one occur. More specifically, parametric index involves measuring an intensity measure at multiple locations in proximity to the portfolio risk sites, and weighting each recording by the values at risk and the vulnerabilities of each insured risk.

Payment depends on the intensity of an event as measured by an independent and objective third party, such as earthquake magnitude as measured by the United States Geological Survey (USGS) or a category hurricane issued by the National Oceanic and Atmospheric Association (NOAA). The basis risk from this type of contract depends on the correlation between the parameters of an event and the level of loss. The basis risk will be high if a large event produces limited damage or a mild event causes severe losses.

From the point of view of the investor, losses on the notes are no longer connected to the cedant's losses, thus obviating any need for the investor to understand details of the cedant's business – or of the industry's, for that matter. From the investor's point of view, only the hazard probability needs to be assessed and the catastrophe modeling process undertaken in support of the transaction only works with the hazard component of the model.

This is misleading, however. It is true that once the transaction has been structured and priced, the potential investor need only be concerned with gauging the modeler's expertise in estimating event frequencies and intensities, rather than in their ability to determine the vulnerability of structures and estimate probable losses on some book of business. From a cedant's point of view, however, the modeler must determine the most appropriate trigger – one that mitigates, as much as possible, basis risk. That determination will very likely involve a catastrophe loss analysis of the cedant's exposures. In the end, however, some degree of basis risk will remain, which can be quantified by the modeler.

Again, from the investor's viewpoint, both adverse selection and moral hazard are no longer issues, and risk on the notes is independent of the quality of exposure data. In January 2000, PRIME Capital issued two separate security offerings of $306 million based on parametric indices. Funds raised are held for three years to cover claims against Munich Re resulting from earthquakes in California, hurricanes in the Miami and New York City areas of the eastern seaboard, and European windstorm. The three-year deal protects Munich Re from fluctuations in the price of reinsurance and the parametric nature of the transaction provides transparency to the investor.

The epicenter of a triggering earthquake, for example, must be located within one of eight boxes, or seismic source zones, four around the San Francisco area (as shown in Figure 7.9) and four around Los Angeles. The reporting agent of epicentral location is the USGS. The moment magnitude (M_w) of a covered earthquake must be equal to or greater than certain defined magnitudes for each source zone for Munich Re to receive payments from the notes.

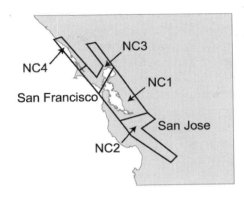

Figure 7.9. 2000 PRIME Capital (Munich Re).

Losses to the notes stemming from the occurrence of hurricanes are triggered by central pressure within certain defined landfall zones. The reporting agency here is the National Hurricane Center. For European windstorms, losses to the notes are triggered by a weighted parametric index calculated from wind speeds measured at stations across Western Europe, as reported by various governmental meteorological organizations. These transactions can be quite complex in structure.

In the case of parametric transactions, scrutiny by rating agencies and investors is focused on the hazard components of the catastrophe model. Here the scientific, rather than engineering, expertise of the modeler's professional staff of seismologists, meteorologists and climate scientists is of paramount importance.

Notional portfolio

Utilization of a notional portfolio is another form of indexing in which payments are based on loss to a fixed hypothetical, or notional, portfolio. This reference portfolio typically stays fixed during the period of coverage. The trigger is based on modeled losses on the notional portfolio.

A notional portfolio can be structured to closely resemble the issuing company's portfolio, minimizing basis risk. By virtue of a fixed portfolio, the investor is protected from changes in or differences from the underlying actual portfolio of an indemnity transaction.

Insurance-linked securities based on losses to a notional portfolio are among the more interesting transactions. They also put the highest demand on the catastrophe modeler for, in this case, not only does the modeler quantify the risk inherent in the notes, but is also the reporting agent in determining losses to the notes after the occurrence of a covered event. That is, the trigger is based not on actual realized losses, but rather on modeled losses.

154

The risks that comprise the notional portfolio are typically on the books of the cedant, though, theoretically, a notional portfolio could be an entirely synthetic construct. To minimize basis risk, it is structured to be representative of the cedant's exposures at risk from the covered peril(s). The model estimates expected losses by superimposing local intensity on the notional portfolio' exposures, damage functions are applied and estimates of insured loss are calculated by applying the policy conditions of the notional portfolio (Figure 7.10).

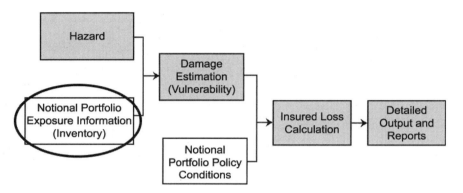

Figure 7.10. Catastrophe model for a notional portfolio.

The model and the notional portfolio then go into escrow for the duration of the covered period. If a qualifying event occurs, the model is pulled out of escrow and losses on the notional portfolio are estimated by inputting the actual physical parameters of the event into the model. Results will indicate whether the attachment point has been reached and what losses, if any, noteholders will experience.

From the point of view of the investor, the risk of moral hazard and the risk of portfolio growth are eliminated, since the notional portfolio stays fixed during the period of coverage. Uncertainty regarding data quality, vulnerability of the exposures and other variables is also eliminated in both the prospective risk assessment and the post-event loss determination. The cedant need not disclose as much information about its business as in the case of an indemnity-based transaction, but does face more basis risk because payments are based on modeled rather than actual losses.

Another issue with this type of transaction is the potentially complex nature of the loss calculation that takes place in the aftermath of an event. In order that it is as transparent as possible to all concerned parties, the catastrophe modeler must develop, in writing, a step-by-step post-event calculation procedure, also held in escrow. The parameters used as input into the model are named, as are the reporting agencies, and alternatives to those parameters are listed in order of priority if the preferred parameter is not readily available. The exact lines of computer code used to run the model are specified. The cedant, placement agency, and modeler work closely together to develop the procedure so that the post-event calculation will go as quickly and as seamlessly as possible (Figure 7.11).

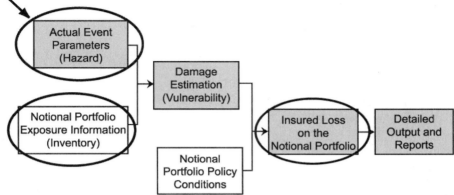

Figure 7.11. Catastrophe model for a notional portfolio after the occurrence of a trigger event.

In July 2001, Trinom Ltd. issued $200 million in notes and preference shares with a three-year maturity to provide protection for Zurich Re against hurricane, earthquake, and windstorm losses. A risk analysis was performed using catastrophe modeling on three separate notional portfolios structured by Zurich Re to match specific books of its European windstorm, California earthquake, and U.S. East Coast hurricane exposures. Figure 7.12 illustrates one small part of this multi-faceted transaction: Class A-1 Notes covering European windstorm.

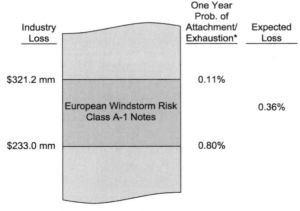

*assumes no prior loss

Figure 7.12. 2001 Trinom Ltd. (Zurich Re) summary features.

7.3.5 Dealing with Basis Risk

Basis risk arises in derivative products as a result of uncertainty associated with ability of the cash flows of the hedging instrument to exactly offset the cash flows from the instrument being hedged. Although there are several factors that may be present which lead to basis risk, the main concern for insurance companies using an industry-based index to hedge the company's catastrophe losses is the cross basis risk.

This arises when the company's losses will not be perfectly correlated with industry losses. This correlation will vary depending on the layer of loss and the region being examined. It is necessary, therefore, to ensure that correlation is being calculated between similar variables, e.g. losses within a specific layer. Examining the correlation of a company's past loss experience with industry losses may not be a good indicator of future correlation. Catastrophe models can provide estimates of both company and industry losses so one has the ability to examine correlation under a wide range of potential scenarios.

Table 7.1. Determining Basis Risk for the Layer $50M Excess of $100M

Event ID	Company Loss	Recovery with Reinsurance	Industry Loss Based Index	Index-based Recovery	Basis Risk
1	8	0	75	0	0
2	42	0	101	1	-1
3	153	50	140	40	10
4	156	50	139	39	11
5	200	50	250	50	0
6	133	33	130	30	3
⋮	⋮	⋮	⋮	⋮	⋮
10000	141	41	150	50	-9

The value of derivative transactions depends on how well the company's losses are correlated with the relevant index-based recovery. Catastrophe models are used to derive both the company loss and the underlying index. For the example in Table 7.1, the company wants to recover losses over $100 million up to a limit of $150 million. A reference contract is defined here as traditional reinsurance for $50 million excess of $100 million. Under this reference contract, the company will achieve full recovery (ignoring co-insurance). The index is defined as some function of industry losses. A hedge contract is set up to pay $1 million for every point the index reaches above 100, with a cap of 150. Company losses are not perfectly correlated with industry losses due to differences in geographic distribution and mix of business. Therefore index-based recoveries under the hedge contract will not exactly match the full recovery under the reference contract. The difference between the full or reference recovery and the index-based recovery is known as basis risk.

As seen in Table 7.1, the basis risk can be positive or negative, reflecting over- and under-recovery. The graph in Figure 7.13 illustrates the recovery under each scenario where the reference and hedge are defined above.

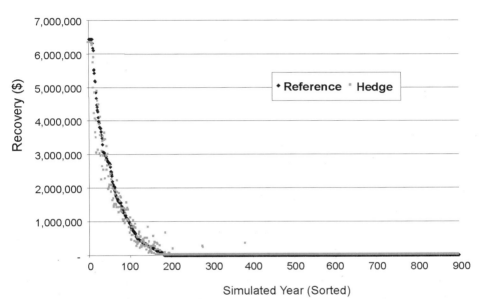

Figure 7.13. Recovery under reference and hedge scenarios.

Figure 7.14 compares basis risk in the above hedge contract with the losses to insurers using a traditional reinsurance product with 20% co-insurance. Insurers have always been exposed to some losses from coinsurance, which in some cases may be greater than the basis risk in index-based products. Some level of basis risk may be acceptable; the company's goal is not to eliminate basis risk, but to maximize expected return for a given level of risk.

Once management has made the decision to consider derivatives, they must determine what to buy. There is not a unique solution to this question and management will need to impose constraints and have tools available to address the goals of maximizing expected return and minimizing basis risk.

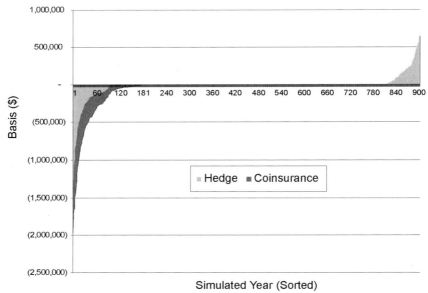

Figure 7.14. Basis risk vs. coinsurance.

7.4 The Costs of Risk Transfer

Decisions regarding how much risk to transfer and which form of risk transfer to use involve pricing the various strategies and checking availability. Securitization transactions to date have typically provided protection above traditional catastrophe reinsurance layers, attaching at probabilities around 0.4 to 1.25%. Pricing will consider the true underlying cost, as well as availability capacity and other market conditions; market prices will be a function of supply and demand. The first step involves using the catastrophe model to assess the underlying theoretical cost of each option.

The theoretical cost of risk transfer consists of three components: the expected losses, expenses associated with the transaction, and a risk load. The differences in market pricing between the reinsurance and capital markets are based on expenses and risk load. Models help quantify the risk load, but the uncertainty in the models used to evaluate the risk needs to be considered. To the extent risk can be quantified, it can be priced commensurately.

The pricing of securities involves detailed analysis of the cash flows and contingencies and is driven by the underlying catastrophe loss distribution as determined by the model. Investors often look for comparable securities to gauge price adequacy. Although there are no direct comparison products in the financial markets, the prices can be compared to prices for traditional reinsurance. Use of the reinsurance markets, which often participate in the transactions, provides important price validation for investors.

The usual operational efficiency of the capital markets, which also could reduce the cost of transferring catastrophe risk, has not as yet materialized due to high legal costs and costs of educating the investors about these transactions. This will surely change as investors become more sophisticated in assessing catastrophe risk and understanding the models that support these transactions. In the meantime, multi-year deals are gaining popularity because they allow the amortization of certain costs over a longer time period, thereby reducing the annualized cost.

There are many more issues to be addressed for management to pursue a derivative strategy. Even after the issue of basis risk has been addressed, there remains the issue of index estimation error, overhead costs, timing of premium payments, loss recoveries, and reinstatement options.

7.5 Evaluation of Risk Financing Schemes

Catastrophe risk dominates the risk profile of most property casualty insurance and reinsurance companies. While the level of sophistication of traditional catastrophe models has been evolving, so too has the industry's view of the risks they face when writing insurance exposures. Questions no longer focus exclusively on the magnitude of a potential loss from a natural disaster, but more broadly on what is the overall financial impact of such a loss on earnings. For example, aside from the direct property loss, what are the ancillary types of losses that may affect the corporation? What other lines may be affected? Is stock market performance really uncorrelated with cataclysms, events that strain worldwide insurance and reinsurance industry reserves (Cutler and Zeckhauser, 1999)? Enterprise Risk Management (ERM) can help answer these and other questions relating specifically to catastrophe risk.

Integrating catastrophe models with ERM models provides a robust context for managing the entire enterprise risk profile in general, and for evaluating risk transfer options and other management questions regarding pricing and underwriting guidelines in particular. Today, companies are using ERM to assess the impact of a catastrophe treaty not only on the catastrophe loss curve, but also on overall financial results. Just as catastrophe models derive the risk profile in terms of an exceedance probability curve, ERM models are producing full probabilistic distributions of the enterprise-wide risk profile.

The way companies view risk is changing. The tragic events of 9/11 opened the eyes of many companies as to the nature of the risks to which they are exposed. Just as Hurricane Andrew was a wake-up call to the industry in terms of managing accumulations of property exposures, the terrorist attacks of 9/11 have companies concerned about the potential combination of losses across multiple lines of business (see Chapter 10). Insurers and reinsurers are taking a much broader view of catastrophe risk, realizing they have not adequately addressed the financial exposure faced by companies writing business across multiple lines, companies, and regions. The insurance industry is revisiting existing processes with the goal of improving knowledge of accumulated exposures and potential enterprise-wide financial losses that could result.

To evaluate properly all alternatives, a framework is needed to put them into the same context and integrate the natural hazard risk into an ERM strategy. Only then can a systematic comparison be made and incorporated into a risk management decision. Such a framework will encompass the steps outlined next.

7.5.1 Analyze Current Risk Profile

Natural hazard risks should not be considered in isolation of the total enterprise risk profile. There are many other sources of risk that may offset or compound the company's overall risk profile. This first step integrates the EP curve from catastrophe risk with other company risks from other lines of business, investment risk, and operational risk to develop an enterprise-wide EP curve. The level of risk tolerance should not depend on the source of risk. A company is not rationally managing its risk if it manages the risk of a 1-in-100 year catastrophe without contemplating the risk of a 1-in-100 year investment return or expense ratio. Catastrophe models are evolving to address the issue of extreme event risk in general.

7.5.2 Customize Decision Model

The decision models should incorporate the current risk profile and how the components of risk interact under multiple economic, business, and catastrophe scenarios. ERM provides a way of integrating all sources of risk so that the interaction of risks can be evaluated. Catastrophe models or their output are being integrated into ERM and the interaction with other risks such as liquidity can be measured. These models also allow for a better understanding of how the risk from various lines of business may react to a catastrophe.

7.5.3 Establish Performance Measures, Constraints, Critical Function

For any type of risk management, the company needs to determine the key measures of performance. These may include profitability, growth, and operating ratios. Consideration must be given to time horizons as well. Qualitative measures are used to set the framework, but in order to effectively evaluate the impact of various risk transfer alternatives, they must be put into quantitative terms. Constraints, such as the ability to significantly change a book of business, need to be considered. A critical function is a measure of risk associated with the quantification of those items of most concern to the company. These may include a rating downgrade, loss of x percent of surplus, and minimum profitability levels. By establishing a risk-return framework the company can answer questions in the same context and be able to systematically evaluate the effect of potential strategies.

7.5.4 Develop Risk Management Alternatives

Each alternative will have benefits, drawbacks, and varied impacts on return as well as on the corporate risk profile. Some alternatives may work better for high layers and others are useful for filling gaps in coverage. A review of the company's risk management alternatives involves not just a simple evaluation of each; instead, the company needs to consider the interaction of various combinations. The bases of selecting the best alternate will be cost, availability, and the monitoring requirements of each component. In addition to the EP curve, catastrophe models can also provide detailed loss data by geography and line of business. From this information, the company can explore the areas that drive their risk and obtain customized transfer mechanisms to address these risks specifically. This can also ensure they are not purchasing unneeded protection.

7.5.5 Evaluate Alternative Strategies

Evaluating alternative strategies involves establishing a measurement of risk and reward, and evaluating the tradeoffs relative to the company's tolerance for risk. For each alternative under consideration, the impact of the risk/reward tradeoff on the company's enterprise-wide risk profile must be compared.

The various alternatives for financing the natural hazard risk will, of course, have associated costs and differing impacts on the risk profile. The risk appetite of the company will determine the optimal shape of the company's risk profile. The company must employ a systematic evaluation of the countless combinations of available alternatives to move toward the target balance between risk and return. Catastrophe models are used to measure the costs and risk in each of the alternatives. To evaluate the alternatives, the results can be plotted on a risk-return graph, such as in Figure 7.15.

In Figure 7.15, each point represents one potential alternative for risk financing, with Alternative A representing no risk financing. Returns may be high year after year until there is a large catastrophe, which would result in significant losses. This variability in return is one measure of risk that can easily be assessed within a catastrophe model. Purchasing reinsurance, such as the $50 million excess of $100 million coverage in the earlier example, would decrease risk. At the same time the cost of the reinsurance would lower return (this is reflected in Alternative B). Alternative C reduces both risk and return significantly. It is clearly sub-optimal to Alternative D which reduces risk the same amount but at a lower cost. The points on the line reflect the

162

efficient frontier along which the company will strive to balance risk and return (a so-called efficient frontier of risk management strategies); points below the line are sub-optimal.

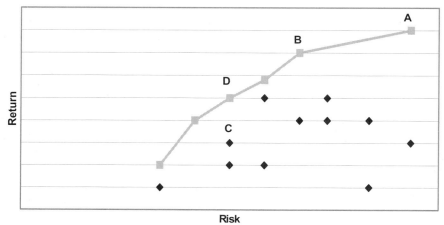

Figure 7.15. Risk vs. Return.

Because many risk-financing alternatives have been developed to address specific issues and to have different impacts on the risk profile, the company can create a highly tailored solution to its risk-financing program. By evaluating the alternatives in a risk versus return context, the company will be able to eliminate many sub-optimal structures. The scenario that maximizes the company's return for its given level of risk tolerance will yield the best strategy.

7.5.6 Select, Implement, and Monitor Strategy

Once a strategy is selected based on the company's risk/return preference, the risk management program needs to be implemented. The capacity and costs assumed in the evaluation must be confirmed and deviations from the strategy can be fed into the evaluation framework to ensure the selected strategy is still optimal. Over time, the strategy is monitored and rebalanced as assumptions are realized or altered. Catastrophe models have become an integral part of insurance company operations, as they continuously monitor natural hazard risk and test new strategies.

7.6 Summary

Catastrophe models generate the full EP curve reflecting natural hazard risk. This information is used to evaluate risk transfer and financing schemes in the context of an overall risk versus return evaluation. As new approaches arise, the modeling framework produces the information to price and manage the risk without the direct need for details of the insurance market.

A catastrophe model plays a critical role in the issuance of insurance-linked securities. The risk analysis performed is fundamental to the very structure of the transaction and to its pricing strategy. The modeler must perform a detailed analysis of loss probabilities by peril, line of business, and geography up front and, in the case of notional portfolio transactions, a post-event calculation after a triggering event has occurred. In multi-year deals involving loss triggers, the modeler must perform an annual reset of attachment and exhaustion amounts to maintain a constant probability of expected loss. They can also assist the cedant in understanding and even reducing their basis risk.

Originally used for gauging an insurance company's likely maximum loss from natural hazards, catastrophe modeling is now a critical tool for the development of finely crafted pricing, underwriting, and risk-transfer strategies, leading to overall portfolio optimization and integrated risk management.

7.7 References

Carter, R.L. (2000). *Reinsurance: The Industry Standard Textbook*, Fourth Edition, London: Reactions Publishing Group.

Cutler, D.M. and Zeckhauser, R.J. (1999). "Reinsurance for Catastrophes and Cataclysms", in K.A. Froot (ed.) *The Financing of Catastrophe Risk*, Chicago, University of Chicago Press.

Froot, K.A. (1999). "The Evolving Market for Catastrophic Event Risk", National Bureau of Economic Research, NBER Working Paper No. 7287, August 1999.

PART IV

RISK MANAGEMENT STRATEGIES USING CATASTROPHE MODELS

Part IV examines risk management strategies for three model cities completed at the Wharton School under the guidance of three leading catastrophe loss modeling firms: AIR Worldwide, EQECAT, and Risk Management Solutions (RMS). The three cities are Oakland, California (subject to earthquakes), Long Beach, California (subject to earthquakes), and Miami/Dade County, Florida (subject to hurricanes). The analysis illustrates how an insurer can more effectively manage catastrophe risk. Chapter 8 analyzes how residential mitigation measures in high hazard areas can reduce losses to property owners and insurers. Chapter 9 then considers the impact of reinsurance and catastrophe bonds, in conjunction with mitigation measures, on an insurer's profitability and solvency. Chapter 10 examines the challenges of using catastrophe models for terrorism risk.

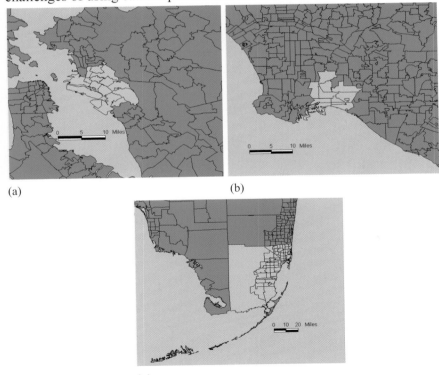

(a)   (b)

(c)

Model Cities: (a) Oakland; (b) Long Beach (c) Miami/Dade County

Chapter 8 – The Impact of Mitigation on Homeowners and Insurers: An Analysis of Model Cities

Major Contributors:
Paul Kleindorfer
Patricia Grossi
Howard Kunreuther

8.1 Introduction

This chapter focuses on the evaluation of the economic impact of specific loss reduction measures to property owners and insurers in the event of a natural disaster. After discussing the impact of such measures on insurers offering coverage to residential property owners, the tradeoffs that property owners face in deciding whether or not to invest in mitigation are examined. The results presented here include the impact of mitigation measures on damage to residential structures in three model cities: Oakland, California (subject to earthquakes), Long Beach, California (subject to earthquakes), and Miami/Dade County, Florida (subject to hurricanes). The analysis also shows how uncertainty in catastrophe risk impacts the effectiveness of different mitigation measures. The primary focus of the chapter is to examine the potential benefits of mitigation to property owners in the form of reduced losses and lower insurance rates. The chapter also includes a discussion of the interaction of mitigation and policy design, underwriting strategies, profitability, and solvency of insurers that provide coverage for catastrophe risk.

The discussion begins with the study of the impact of mitigation on the losses to the homeowner and the insurer using exceedance probability (EP) curves. If a mitigation measure is to be effective, it should produce sufficient expected benefits in the form of reduced losses to the property owner so that investing in the measure makes financial sense.

Sharing these benefits between the property owner and the insurer is, however, a more complex matter. Benefits from a particular mitigation measure affect different parts of an insurer's EP curve (low-end, mid-range, or right hand tail), as shown in Figure 8.1. The precise location of these effects will determine the impact of deductible levels, coverage limits, and premium structures on the insurer's retained risks, profitability, and solvency. In addition, the net benefits to the insurer of mitigation measures will depend on the cost of the various risk bearing and risk transfer methods the insurer uses for each part of the EP curve.

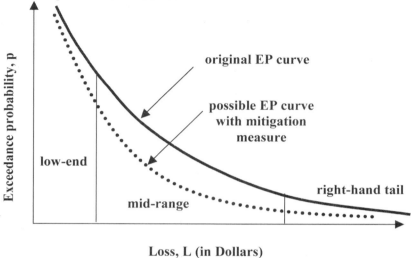

Figure 8.1. An insurer's exceedance probability curve.

The following interdependent issues arise from these observations. First, it is not a foregone conclusion that policyholders will adopt mitigation measures even when they are shown to be effective and properly priced by the insurer. Second, determining the proper pricing of insurance to ensure that all aspects of the cost of risk are properly accounted for requires a detailed assessment of the impact of each mitigation measure on the insurer's entire exceedance probability curve. This impact is dependent on the full characteristics of the insurer's book of business, its strategies for risk bearing and risk transfer, as well as the number of policyholders who adopt the measure.

To keep matters relatively simple, two issues are discussed here: (1) the decision by a property owner to invest in a mitigation measure, and (2) the interaction of mitigation, premium setting, and deductible levels on profitability and solvency of an insurer assuming the insurer retains all the risk. Both issues are presented within a framework of uncertainty regarding the mitigation measure's effectiveness over time. The more complex scenario including the additional impact of risk transfer and the use of reinsurance and catastrophe bonds is considered in the next chapter.

8.2 Framework of Analysis

Figure 8.2 depicts a framework for analyzing the themes discussed earlier. It builds on concepts developed in a report by the Heinz Center (1999) and by Kleindorfer and Kunreuther (1999), and is analogous to the framework depicted in Chapter 2. Using a catastrophe model and taking into account the decision processes of insurers and homeowners, the performance of insurance and other risk transfer mechanisms on future losses, with and without mitigation measures in place, can be evaluated. The discussion here is focused on building structural damage and the related losses. Any disruption of infrastructure, such as loss of the water supply or electric power that can cause indirect losses to residents, is not considered here.

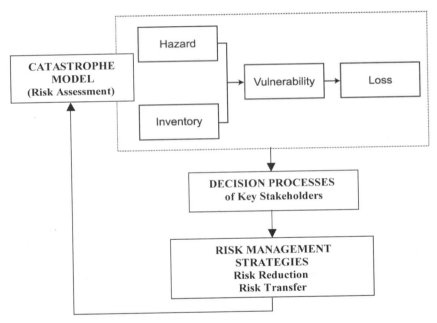

Figure 8.2. Framework for analysis.

As discussed in more detail in earlier chapters, the main ingredients for evaluating the vulnerability of an insurer's book of business to catastrophes are the nature of the hazard and the inventory of buildings at risk. The probability of events of different intensities occurring within a certain proximity of the building inventory specifies the nature of the hazard. Such features as location, construction class, occupancy class, and year of construction characterize the building inventory. An EP curve describes the resulting loss curve for the insurer's book of business.

The key link between the risk assessment process as described above, and the risk management process, is the stakeholders' decision processes. What impacts the homeowner's decision as to whether or not to retrofit his home to reduce his future losses from a severe earthquake or hurricane? What information does he need on the natural hazard and the potential damage with and without a mitigation measure? What type of decision rule(s) does the property owner utilize in determining whether or not to invest in this mitigation measure? What type of data and decision rules do insurers utilize in evaluating the effectiveness of different mitigation measures? In order to get support for specific risk reduction programs, the nature of the decision processes of these interested parties must be understood. Sidebar 1 presents information on how corporate risk mitigation measures reduced disaster losses.

SIDEBAR 1: Corporate "wins" from mitigation

Cost-benefit analysis of risks from natural disasters and potential benefits from mitigation may prompt a company to reduce these risks through mitigation measures. Two FEMA publications, 294 and 331, describe case studies of corporations, utilities, and homeowners that have taken this route to protect themselves against catastrophic losses (FEMA, 1997; 1998). Discussed below are examples of several businesses that experienced catastrophic events after mitigation measures were put into place and thus could compare actual versus potential losses:

o *Anheuser-Busch brewery (Los Angeles, California).* Seismic reinforcement to buildings and critical equipment saved the company an estimated $300 million in direct and business interruption losses from the 1994 Northridge earthquake.

o *Warner Brothers Studio (Burbank, California.)* Nonstructural mitigation such as bracing of building contents prevented an estimated $1 million in damages from the 1994 Northridge earthquake.

o *Andritz, Inc. (Muncy, Pennsylvania).* Losses from two similar levels of hurricane-related flooding dropped from $3.4 million in 1972 to $0.23 million in 1975 following flood-proofing measures implemented between the two events (1979 dollars).

Based on an understanding of the vulnerability of the book of business and the decision processes of the key interested parties, strategies can be developed and evaluated for reducing losses and providing financial protection to those subject to risk. As expected, these measures will differ across regions within the United States and between countries, depending on the current institutional arrangements, the science and engineering infrastructure available, and existing legislation and laws.

8.3 Construction of Model Cities

This section sets the stage for evaluating the impact of mitigation on the property losses in the three model cities. For modeling purposes, two broad assumptions are made. The first assumption is that the homeowner is willing to implement mitigation measures. The second assumption is that all residents desire some form of hazard insurance and have the financial ability to purchase coverage. With respect to the second assumption, it should be noted that although all homeowners desire coverage, if an insurance company is concerned with the possibility of insolvency, the amount of coverage it provides may be limited so some property owners may be unprotected.

8.3.1 General Model Structure

The general structure of the analysis is as follows. First, scenario variables that describe the set of hazard events and their associated probabilities are set. Next, the Model City is specified according to the number and types of residential structures characteristic of the region, the type of mitigation measures applicable to these structures, and the types of residential insurance policies offered. The set of hazard events and residential structure characteristics for Oakland (referred to hereafter as Model City 1 or MC1) was provided by Risk Management Solutions, the Long Beach (referred to as MC2) data was provided by EQECAT and the Miami/Dade County (referred to as MC3) data was provided by AIR Worldwide.

The variables that describe the nature of the hazard and characteristics of the buildings at risk are used in conjunction with a catastrophe model to generate an EP curve for the insurer's book of business. For an individual residential property owner, the EP curve is a function of the set of natural hazard events that are used in the model, the impact of mitigation (risk reduction) and the amount and structure of the residential insurance purchased (risk transfer). For a given insurance company, the EP curve is a function of the amount and nature of insurance sold, the number and types of properties insured, overall adoption of mitigation measures, and the natural hazard events that are used to generate loss exposures. For the modeling exercise, all these parameters and decisions must be specified. The EP curves for the residential property owners and the insurance companies provide the foundation for evaluating expected and worst-case consequences of a set of scenarios, as well as the shares of the losses borne by each stakeholder. Each of these elements is now considered in more detail.

172

8.3.2 Mitigation Measures

Each model city was evaluated to determine the appropriate residential mitigation measure to consider. Based on feedback from structural engineers in California, the mitigation measure used in MC1 and MC2 was bracing a wood-frame structure's cripple wall (the wall/crawl space between the structure's foundation and its first-floor diaphragm) and securing the structure to its foundation with additional anchor bolts. This only applies to wood-frame structures built before or immediately after World War II in California, since a large portion of these were built without adequate cripple wall bracing (due to the sparse supply of plywood). The mitigation measure used in MC3 was partial roof mitigation, which leads to better uplift resistance and an improved ability to withstand lateral loads in a hurricane. This can be accomplished without removing the roof covering, which is assumed to be wind resistant and in good condition. Partial roof mitigation includes bracing roof trusses and gable end walls, applying wood adhesive where the roof decking and roof supports meet, installing hurricane straps or clips where the roof framing meets the top of the studs, and anchoring the walls to the foundation.

The proportion of structures in each model city that adopted a mitigation measure was assumed to vary from 0% to 100%. For illustration purposes, the extreme points 0% and 100% are considered here. Full adoption of mitigation (100%) assumes that all eligible structures in the model city utilize the mitigation measure. In MC1 and MC2, the mitigation costs are based on a data survey undertaken by Grossi (2000), which revealed that the estimated average cost of bracing a wood-frame structure's cripple wall was approximately $5,000 (1998 dollars). In MC3, for a typical single-family dwelling in the Miami metropolitan area, the estimated average mitigation cost was assumed to be $3,000 (1998 dollars) based on an estimate provided by AIR Worldwide.

8.3.3 Books of Business for the Insurance Companies

For each Model City, 5,000 residential structures were randomly selected to represent the maximum exposures that an insurance company could write. Companies could insure fewer than 5,000 structures to maintain an acceptable probability of insolvency (1%).

It is assumed that all structures in MC1 and MC2 are wood frame, single-family residences. The distribution of structures is given in Table 8.1. In MC1, the structures were picked randomly from over 62,000 wood frame, single-family residences in the model city and all pre-1940 structures were considered eligible for mitigation. Structures whose age was unknown are assumed to fall into the pre-1940 or post-1940 category with the same likelihood as the known structures. Based on the ratio of pre-1940 homes in the group of homes with known ages, it was assumed that 172 of the 259 structures with unknown age were constructed prior to 1940. Thus, 3,263 homes or 65.3% of the structures were eligible for mitigation in MC1. In MC2, only the low-rise homes built prior to 1949 with unbraced cripple walls are considered eligible for mitigation. Thus, only 409 homes or 8.2% of the structures, were eligible in the analysis.

Table 8.1. Composition of books of business in the model cities

MC1 (Oakland) Structure by Year of Construction	
Unknown	259
Pre-1940	3,091
Post-1940	1,650
Total	**5,000**
MC2 (Long Beach) Structure by Type and Year of Construction	
Low Rise Average	704
Low Rise pre-1949 braced cripple walls	1448
Low Rise 1949-78 braced cripple walls	1616
Low Rise post-1979 braced cripple walls	823
Low Rise pre-1949 unbraced cripple walls	409
Total	**5,000**
MC3 (Miami/Dade County) Structure by Type	
Wood Frame	496
Masonry Veneer	1,005
Masonry	3,117
Semi-Wind Resistive	260
Wind Resistive	122
Total	**5,000**

The properties selected in MC3 are also single-family residences that reflect the general distribution of structures in the entire model city. All homes were considered eligible for roof mitigation. It was assumed that the five structure types listed in Table 8.1 had similar expected mean damage reduction ratios if mitigation measures were undertaken.

8.3.4 Insurance Company Premium and Asset Levels

Table 8.2 specifies the parameters for the insurance companies in each Model City. Full insurance coverage against damage from the disaster is available, with a deductible of 10% in MC1 and MC2 and 1% in MC3.

Since insurers are concerned with insolvency, they focus on worst-case scenarios in determining the portfolio of risks to which they offer coverage. For this analysis, a Worst-Case Loss (WCL) is defined as a loss corresponding to a target ruin probability (TRP) of 1%. This implies they would like to limit their book of business such that they have at least a 99% chance of avoiding insolvency (see Table 8.2). The asset levels for each company are set such that each firm's insolvency probability is roughly 1 percent when mitigation is present.

Table 8.2. Base case insurance company parameters

Parameter	MC1 Company	MC2 Company	MC3 Company
Assets	$57 million	$20 million	$24 million
Deductible	10%	10%	1%
Target Ruin Probability (TRP)	1%	1%	1%

8.3.5 Incorporating Uncertainty into Analysis

For each of the model cities, the analysis uses mean estimates for all of the hazard parameters. In order to incorporate uncertainty into the study, two parameters are varied from each mean estimate and the sensitivity of the resulting losses to these changes is presented. For the earthquake hazard, the annual frequency of seismic events, F_E, and the vulnerability of the building inventory, V_E, are subjected to variation. For hurricane hazard, the filling rate, F_H, and the structural vulnerability, V_H, are varied. Specifically, high and low estimates of these parameters are determined such that they encompass a 90% confidence interval for each parameter in question. In other words, these high and low estimates are selected such that they cover the true estimates of the model parameters with a probability of 90%. The high estimate (95th percentile) is conservative since it produces a parameter estimate that will be exceeded only 5% of the time. The low estimate (5th percentile) is optimistic in that it produces a parameter estimate that will be exceeded 95% of the time.

Furthermore, based on the assumption that (a) the two curves for the F and V parameters are on the high side, and (b) the two curves for the F and V parameters are on the low side, two more 90% confidence intervals using the joint distribution for these parameters were generated. The values for the F and V parameters based on the joint distribution, assuming they are independently distributed, are less extreme than the earlier ones to yield the joint confidence interval[1]. These joint curves are the ones utilized in this chapter.

8.4 Insurer Decision Processes

Literature in economics in recent years suggests that insurers and other firms are risk-averse due to their concern with the consequences of financial distress. Hence, they pay particular attention to non-diversifiable risks such as catastrophic losses from disasters (Mayers and Smith, 1982). Insurers are also likely to be averse to ambiguity in their risk. The term "ambiguity averse" denotes an insurer's reluctance to make decisions based on imprecise probabilities of loss occurrence. Both actuaries and underwriters utilize decision-making processes that reflect an aversion to excessive risk and ambiguity (Kunreuther, Hogarth, and Meszaros, 1993).

The actuarial premium is based on the value of expected annual loss loaded for uncertainty and fixed costs. A commonly used formula for determining premium is:

$$z = (1+\lambda_I)E[L]$$

where $E[L]$ = expected loss and λ_I = an insurance "loading" factor. The loading factor reflects administrative costs as well as an additional provision to reflect uncertainty in loss estimates. The loading factor used here is 1.0.

8.4.1 Impact of Mitigation on Losses and Insurer Behavior

First, the effects of mitigation and uncertainty on total losses to the insurer are considered. The statistics presented here are the insurer's expected loss, worst-case loss, and probability of insolvency. These results are shown assuming coverage was offered to all 5,000 residential property owners for each of the three books of business in Table 8.1. The expected and worst-case losses to the insurer are determined using the full book of business for levels of mitigation of 0% and 100%. The mean values of these losses are displayed in Table 8.3 (mean) along with the bounds, denoted as low (5th percentile) and high (95th percentile).

The mean expected loss, $E[L]$, is the loss borne by the insurer after the deductible is applied to each policy. In MC1 and MC2, this deductible level is 10%; in MC3, there is a 1% deductible level. The worst-case loss, WCL, is the loss at the 1% probability of exceedance level. Finally, the

---

[1] It is assumed that the joint probability of both parameters being at their designated confidence levels is the product of their marginal probabilities. For example, at the 5th percentile, $P\{F < f_{5\%}$ and $V < v_{5\%}\} = P\{F < f_{5\%}\} \times P\{V < _{5\%}\} = 5\%$. There are an infinite number of ways to pick $f_{5\%}$ and $v_{5\%}$ to make this equality true. Arbitrarily, $f_{5\%}$ and $v_{5\%}$ are chosen so that $P\{F < f_{5\%}\} = P\{V < v_{5\%}\} = 22.36\%$. (For more information, see Grossi, et al., 1999.)

Probability of Insolvency is the likelihood that the insurer's losses will exceed the sum of its premiums and assets. Two other statistics are shown in Table 8.3: the percentage of Properties Insured and the Expected Profits of the insurer. Properties Insured is the percent of the full book of business that each insurer can cover without having its probability of insolvency exceed 1%; expected profits are equal to the sum of the premiums minus the losses and administrative costs.

Table 8.3. Effects of mitigation on insurer ($ in $1000s)

MC1	0% Mitigation			100% Mitigation		
(Oakland)	Low	Mean	High	Low	Mean	High
E[L]	$770	$1,700	$3,140	$460	$1,000	$1,740
WCL	$40,020	$92,940	$141,580	$25,080	$58,660	$85,460
Probability of Insolvency (%)	0.74%	1.35%	1.84%	0.70%	1.00%	1.57%
Properties Insured (%)	100%	66.1%	42.8%	100 %	100%	70.9%
Expected Profits	$2,590	$1,100	$90	$1,510	$1,000	$160
MC2	**0% Mitigation**			**100% Mitigation**		
(Long Beach)	Low	Mean	High	Low	Mean	High
E[L]	$230	$760	$2,230	$230	$730	$2,150
WCL	$6,720	$22,220	$59,840	$6,560	$21,430	$57,970
Probability of Insolvency (%)	0.44%	1.03%	2.94%	0.43%	0.99%	2.86%
Properties Insured (%)	100%	98.0%	34.5%	100%	100%	35.6%
Expected Profits	$1,280	$740	-$250	$1,240	$730	-$250
MC3	**0% Mitigation**			**100% Mitigation**		
(Miami/Dade)	Low	Mean	High	Low	Mean	High
E[L]	$1,570	$1,920	$2,300	$1,060	$1,300	$1,550
WCL	$34,030	$42,490	$51,430	$22,360	$27,620	$33,530
Probability of Insolvency (%)	1.33%	1.84%	2.29%	0.77%	1.04%	1.38%
Properties Insured (%)	80.3%	62.6%	50.7%	100.00%	97.1%	78.3%
Expected Profits	$1820	$1,200	$780	$1,530	$1,260	$820

As expected, the analysis shows that mitigation reduces losses to the insurer in each of the three model cities - with a more pronounced impact on worst-case loss than expected loss. For MC1 and MC3, the reduction in annual expected loss is $700,000 or 41% and $620,000 or 32%, respectively. In comparison, for MC2, mitigation is not as significant in reducing losses and the reduction in expected annual loss is only $30,000 or 4%. This is primarily due to the extremely small number of homes eligible for mitigation in MC2 (approximately 8%).

A principal reason for investigating the impact of mitigation on the worst-case loss is to understand how mitigation reduces the probability of insolvency. Based on Table 8.3, one can see that for MC3, for the mean scenario, the probability of insolvency is reduced significantly from 1.84% to 1.04% with mitigation. For MC1, the corresponding reduction is from 1.35% to 1.00%.

Since mitigation shifts the EP curve downward (as illustrated in Figure 8.1), it will also increase the percentage of structures for which the insurer can provide coverage and still maintain an annual probability of insolvency of 1%. In other words, insurers can provide coverage to more homes if each homeowner is required to adopt mitigation as a condition for insurance. Consider the mean scenario in Table 8.3. When no mitigation is adopted, the insurance company in MC1 will only be able to provide coverage for 66% of those property owners who would like to buy a policy. As the percentage of homes adopting mitigation increases, so does the percentage of homes for which the insurer can provide coverage. When all of the homes have adopted the mitigation measure, the insurer is willing to provide coverage to all of the structures, a significant increase over the percentage covered when no mitigation is in place. Similarly, in MC3, the percentage of homes that the insurance company is willing to cover increases from approximately 63% to 97% with mitigation.

A good representation of the findings for the mean loss estimates and changes in insolvency probability with mitigation is shown via the exceedance probability curve for the insurer in MC3 (Figure 8.3). As one can see, the EP curve shifts downward when all homes are mitigated and the insurer's losses are reduced significantly. In particular, at the 1% probability of exceedance, the loss to the insurer shifts from $42.5 million to $27.6 million.

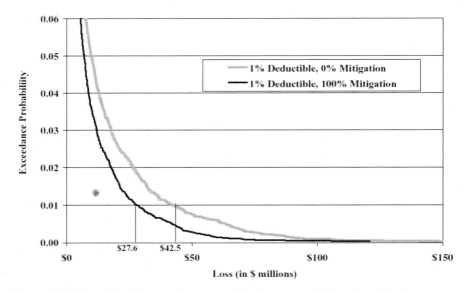

Figure 8.3. Example of exceedance probability curve shift with mitigation in MC3 (Miami/Dade).

8.5 Homeowner Decision Processes

Studies suggest that individuals are not willing to invest funds for mitigation even if they are residing in highly hazard-prone areas (Mileti, 1999). Simple steps, such as strapping a water heater with plumbers' tape, can normally be done by residents at a cost of under $5 in materials and one hour of their own time (Levenson, 1992). This measure can reduce damage from gas leaks and fire by preventing the heater from toppling during an earthquake. Yet residents in earthquake-prone areas are not adopting such simple and other loss-reduction measures unless they are required to do so. This section provides a more detailed analysis of the factors that influence the decision to adopt protective measures and an illustration of how the adoption of mitigation measures can reduce the cost of insurance for homes in the three model cities.

8.5.1 Factors Influencing Mitigation Adoption Decisions

Basically there are four principal reasons why homeowners do not want to invest in mitigation measures: myopia, desire for a quick return on investment, budget constraints, and lack of perception of added economic value. Individuals want to recoup their investment in a mitigation measure, in general, on a relatively short time horizon. Even if the expected life of the house is 25 or 30 years, the person may only consider the potential benefits from the mitigation measure over the next 3 to 5 years. This may be based on their expected length of stay in the current residence. A related reason why mitigation is often unattractive is that individuals expect a quick return on their investment. Financially this is consistent with using a high discount rate for evaluating potential future payoffs.

Third, many individuals perceive the probability of a disaster causing damage to their property as being so low that an investment in protective measures is deemed unnecessary. Even if there is some concern with the potential of a hazard, budget constraints lead homeowners to place mitigation as a low priority item. In fact, many residents in hazard-prone areas feel they simply cannot afford these measures. It is not unusual for one to hear the phrase "We live from payday to payday" when asked why a household has not invested in protective measures (Kunreuther, et al., 1978).

Finally, individuals may have little interest in investing in protective measures if they believe that the measures will provide limited added economic value to them. For example, homeowners may not consider an investment to be cost effective if they believe it will not increase the resale value of their property. If they are financially responsible for only a small portion of their losses should a disaster occur, the measure would be even less attractive. In addition, if they have limited assets at stake, they may feel they can walk away from their destroyed property without much financial harm. Similarly, if residents anticipate liberal government disaster relief, they have even less reason to invest in a mitigation measure.

In analyzing a homeowner's decision to mitigate or not to mitigate, the fixed mitigation costs are converted to an annual expenditure based on a time horizon of 30 years. This allows a comparison of these costs to annual insurance premiums and expected annual losses to the homeowner. In this way, the robustness of the mitigation measure can be viewed in terms of an average homeowner's decision process.

The results are presented in Table 8.4 for the homeowners in the three model cities when no insurance is purchased. The expected loss is the annual mean loss to the average property owner. The cost of mitigation is the annual average cost discounted at a 7% rate over a 30-year time horizon, applicable only to those homeowners who mitigate. This corresponds to 3,263 homeowners in MC1, 409 homeowners in MC2, and 5,000 homeowners in MC3. The worst-case loss is the average homeowners' loss at the 1% probability of exceedance level.

From Table 8.4, it can be seen that mitigation reduces losses in each of the model cities. But, it is not cost-effective in most cases. More specifically, when one adds the annualized cost of mitigation to the expected loss with mitigation, this total is larger than the expected loss without mitigation. One exception is the high case in MC1. For this one case, the potential loss to the homeowner is $1,550 without mitigation. With mitigation, including the cost of mitigation, the total potential cost is lower and equal to $1,480. These results imply that for most scenarios, for the eligible structures in the three model cities, the disaster risk is not serious enough to justify investing in mitigation based solely on the mean potential loss and the costs of the measure combined.

A basic point to recognize from these results is that whether particular mitigation measures will be viewed as worth adopting by a homeowner is not a foregone conclusion, but requires a detailed assessment of the costs and benefits under various hazard scenarios. It is important to note as well that only the direct property losses are evaluated in this analysis. Mitigation could have additional real and perceived benefits for homeowners in reducing the risk of fatalities, stress and interruption of home life. These are not considered here, but are discussed in more detail in the Heinz Center report (1999).

If the homeowner's worst-case loss (WCL) is examined, a different picture emerges. In MC1 and MC3, there is a significant decrease in the WCL when homes are mitigated. If a homeowner is concerned with a potential catastrophic loss, these results suggest that the homeowner has an incentive to invest in mitigation. Furthermore, to the extent that insurers are risk averse and concerned with reducing their probability of insolvency, they will require mitigation measures to be implemented for structures that they insure.

Table 8.4. Effects of mitigation on average homeowner (No Insurance)

MC1 (Oakland)	0% Mitigation			100% Mitigation		
	Low	Mean	High	Low	Mean	High
Expected Loss	$430	$910	$1,550	$310	$640	$1,070
Mitigation Cost	--	--	--	$410	$410	$410
Total	$430	$910	$1,550	$720	$1,050	$1,480
Worst-Case Loss	$14,850	$30,100	$40,700	$11,280	$20,390	$27,170

MC2 (Long Beach)	0% Mitigation			100% Mitigation		
	Low	Mean	High	Low	Mean	High
Expected Loss	$110	$280	$640	$110	$270	$630
Mitigation Cost	--	--	--	$410	$410	$410
Total	$110	$280	$640	$520	$680	$1,040
Worst-Case Loss	$3,340	$8,370	$17,600	$3,300	$8,260	$17,290

MC3 (Miami/Dade)	0% Mitigation			100% Mitigation		
	Low	Mean	High	Low	Mean	High
Expected Loss	$360	$440	$520	$250	$300	$360
Mitigation Cost	--	--	--	$240	$240	$240
Total	$360	$440	$520	$490	$540	$600
Worst-Case Loss	$7,560	$9,230	$11,080	$5,120	$6,230	$7,400

8.5.2 The Interaction of Mitigation Decisions and Insurance Decisions

Turning to the relationship between insurance and mitigation, some interesting findings emerge from recent surveys undertaken by Risa Palm and her colleagues. Palm and Carroll (1998) report that individuals who adopt mitigation measures were also more likely to buy earthquake insurance. This raises the question as to whether certain types of individuals want protection for reasons that have less to do with their perception of the risk than their intrinsic worries and concerns.

In analyzing a homeowner's decision to purchase insurance or adopt a mitigation measure in the three model cities, the time horizon is once again set at 30 years with a discount rate of 7%. Total expected loss and worst-case loss for insured homeowners are computed for the property owners under the assumption that the insurer is providing coverage to the full book of business. In this case, the homeowner expected loss corresponds to the average deductible loss. Worst-case loss is the loss borne by the homeowner at the 1% exceedance probability level, and costs of mitigation are the same as those noted in Table 8.4.

The results of this analysis are presented in Table 8.5. They suggest that when insurance is purchased, the earthquake mitigation measure is cost-effective for both the mean and high scenarios in MC1. By lowering the cost of insurance, mitigation becomes a financially feasible option even for the mean scenario. In MC1, the total mean annual costs are $1,240 and $1,250 with and without mitigation, respectively.

For the average homeowner in MC2, the results suggest mitigation is not cost-effective under any scenario. However, when insurance is purchased, the WCL is $3,930 for the mean scenario compared to $8,370 when the homeowner is uninsured (See Table 8.4). These findings suggest that if a homeowner is risk averse and is concerned with the impact of a catastrophic loss, purchasing insurance makes sense.

8.6 Implications for Workable Public-Private Partnerships

Suppose homeowners were to voluntarily adopt mitigation measures and insurers were to set premiums that reflected the reduction in losses resulting from the mitigation. Under these ideal conditions, there would be a reduction in losses to residents as well as a reduction in the probability of insolvency for the insurers.

Table 8.5. Effects of mitigation on average homeowner (with Insurance)

MC1 (10% Deductible) (Oakland)	0% Mitigation			100% Mitigation		
	Low	Mean	High	Low	Mean	High
Expected Deductible Loss	$280	$580	$920	$220	$440	$720
Insurance Premiums	$670	$670	$670	$390	$390	$390
Cost of Mitigation	--	--	--	$410	$410	$410
Total	$950	$1,250	$1,590	$1,020	$1,240	$1,520
Worst-Case Loss	$6,850	$11,510	$12,390	$6,630	$8,660	$10,080
MC2 (10% Deductible) (Long Beach)	**0% Mitigation**			**100% Mitigation**		
	Low	Mean	High	Low	Mean	High
Expected Deductible Loss	$70	$130	$190	$60	$120	$190
Insurance Premiums	$300	$300	$300	$290	$290	$290
Cost of Mitigation	--	--	--	$410	$410	$410
Total	$370	$430	$490	$760	$820	$890
Worst-Case Loss	$2,000	$3,980	$5,690	$1,990	$3,930	$5,630
MC3 (1% Deductible) (Miami/Dade)	**0% Mitigation**			**100% Mitigation**		
	Low	Mean	High	Low	Mean	High
Expected Deductible Loss	$50	$55	$60	$40	$45	$50
Insurance Premiums	$770	$770	$770	$520	$520	$520
Cost of Mitigation	--	--	--	$240	$240	$240
Total	$820	$825	$830	$800	$805	$810
Worst-Case Loss	$760	$730	$790	$640	$705	$700

In reality, as pointed out above, most property owners have limited interest in investing in these measures. Furthermore, insurers have little reason to encourage mitigation in hazard-prone areas if they are not forced to provide coverage and the rates they are allowed to charge are inadequate. In this case, insurers would want to do everything they could to reduce their exposure and encourage the policyholder to seek coverage from another insurer. Insurers may have an interest in mitigation if they have no choice in providing coverage to individuals in hazard-prone areas. If rates in these hazard-prone areas were risk-based, insurers would want to encourage mitigation, reduce overall losses, and charge lower premiums for those who adopted the measures. If, on the other hand, they are forced to charge the same maximum premium for all the risks, they have no incentive to charge lower premiums for homeowners that mitigate. This would enable them to collect as much premium as possible.

In the following subsections, three types of public-private partnership programs that can encourage mitigation are explored: (1) building codes and other legislation, (2) premium reductions linked with long-term loans for mitigation, and (3) insurers offering lower deductibles for those investing in mitigation. In evaluating these programs, it is assumed that there has already been an attempt to use market-based mechanisms to encourage the different interested parties to take action[2].

8.6.1 Role of Building Codes

Building codes require property owners to meet standards on newly built structures. Often such codes are necessary, particularly when property owners are not inclined to adopt mitigation measures on their own. One way to encourage the adoption of mitigation measures is for banks and financial institutions to provide a seal of approval to each structure that meets or exceeds building code standards. Under the Institute for Business and Home Safety's (IBHS) "Fortified for Safer Living" program, structures that meet predefined criteria receive a certificate of disaster resistance. Upon receipt of that certificate, there are a set of incentives provided by banks (e.g., lower mortgage rates), contractors, and insurers. The success of such a program requires the support of the building industry and a cadre of qualified inspectors to provide accurate information as to whether existing codes and standards are being met. Such a certification program can be very useful to insurers who may choose to provide coverage only to those structures that are given a certificate of disaster resistance.

Cohen and Noll (1981) provide an additional rationale for building codes. When a building collapses, it may create externalities in the form of economic dislocations and other social costs that are beyond the economic loss suffered by the owners. These may not be taken into account when the owners evaluate the importance of adopting a specific mitigation measure. For example, if a building topples off its foundation after an earthquake, it could break a pipeline and cause a major fire that would damage other homes not structurally damaged by the earthquake in the first place. Additionally, if a family is forced to vacate its property because of damage that would have been prevented had a building code been in place, then avoiding relocation costs is an additional benefit of mitigation.

The latest in the battle to encourage individuals to adopt mitigation measures is the Earthquake Loss Reduction Act of 2001. If the U.S. Congress passes this Act[3], the government would offer incentives for commercial and residential property owners to adopt mitigation measures. Residential property

---

[2] See the report issued by the Earthquake Engineering Research Institute (1998), which indicates the challenges facing property owners in improving the seismic performance of their structures and suggests ways to encourage cost-effective investments.

[3] This legislation is still under review in the Senate finance committee as of May 2004.

owners would receive a 50% tax credit for a qualified seismic retrofit expense (limited to $6,000 per year). Further, businesses will be allowed to depreciate expenses associated with earthquake mitigation over a period of five years.

8.6.2 Long-Term Mitigation Loans

If homeowners are reluctant to incur the upfront cost of mitigation due to budget constraints, then a long-term loan may provide a financial incentive for adopting cost-effective measures. The bank holding the mortgage on the property could provide funds for this purpose through a home improvement loan with a payback period identical to the life of the mortgage. For example, a $1,500 loan with a 20-year term at an annual interest rate of 10% would result in payments of $145 per year. If the annual insurance premium reduction due to the adoption of the mitigation measure is greater than $145 per year, the insured homeowner would have lower total payments by investing in mitigation (Kunreuther, 1997).

One additional factor to consider is that many poorly constructed homes are owned by low-income families who cannot afford the costs of mitigation measures or the costs of reconstruction should their house suffer significant damage from a natural disaster. Social considerations suggest providing this group with low interest loans and grants for the purpose of adopting mitigation measures or to relocate them to a safer area. Such subsidies can be justified from an economic perspective as well since low-income victims are more likely to receive federal assistance after a disaster.

8.6.3 Lower Deductibles Tied to Mitigation

An alternative way to encourage consumers to mitigate is to change the nature of their insurance coverage. More specifically, the insurer could offer a lower deductible to those who adopt mitigation. Such a program is likely to be very attractive given the empirical and experimental evidence that suggests that consumers appear to dislike high deductibles even though they offer considerable savings in premiums. (See Braun and Muermann, in press, for a summary of the empirical evidence on preference for low deductibles).

Table 8.6 examines the impact of lowering the deductible on insurance policies for earthquake and hurricane protection if the property owner adopted a mitigation measure on his property. This table compares the total expected costs to the homeowner (labeled HO in Table 8.6) who mitigated with those who did not mitigate for two different levels of deductibles: 0% and 10% for those in MC1 and MC2 and 0% and 1% for those in MC3.

Table 8.6. Effects of mitigation on homeowner losses and insurer insolvency probabilities

MC1 (10% Deductible)	0% Mitigation			100% Mitigation		
	Low	Mean	High	Low	Mean	High
HO Deductible Loss	$280	$580	$920	$220	$440	$720
Insurance Premium	$670	$670	$670	$390	$390	$390
Cost of Mitigation	--	--	--	$410	$410	$410
Probability of Insolvency	0.74%	1.35%	1.84%	0.70%	1.00%	1.57%

MC1 (0% Deductible)	0% Mitigation			100% Mitigation		
	Low	Mean	High	Low	Mean	High
Insurance Premium	$1820	$1820	$1820	$1270	$1270	$1270
Cost of Mitigation	--	--	--	$410	$410	$410
Probability of Insolvency	1.06%	1.75%	2.58%	0.91%	1.47%	1.97%

MC2 (10% Deductible)	0% Mitigation			100% Mitigation		
	Low	Mean	High	Low	Mean	High
HO Deductible Loss	$70	$130	$190	$60	$120	$190
Insurance Premium	$300	$300	$300	$290	$290	$290
Cost of Mitigation	--	--	--	$410	$410	$410
Probability of Insolvency	0.44%	1.03%	2.94%	0.43%	0.99%	2.86%

MC2 (0% Deductible)	0% Mitigation			100% Mitigation		
	Low	Mean	High	Low	Mean	High
Insurance Premium	$560	$560	$560	$540	$540	$540
Cost of Mitigation	--	--	--	$410	$410	$410
Probability of Insolvency	0.74%	1.82%	3.87%	0.73%	1.80%	3.85%

MC3 (1% Deductible)	0% Mitigation			100% Mitigation		
	Low	Mean	High	Low	Mean	High
HO Deductible Loss	$50	$55	$60	$40	$45	$50
Insurance Premium	$770	$770	$770	$520	$520	$520
Cost of Mitigation	--	--	--	$240	$240	$240
Probability of Insolvency	1.33%	1.84%	2.29%	0.77%	1.04%	1.38%

MC3 (0% Deductible)	0% Mitigation			100% Mitigation		
	Low	Mean	High	Low	Mean	High
Insurance Premium	$880	$880	$880	$600	$600	$600
Cost of Mitigation	--	--	--	$240	$240	$240
Probability of Insolvency	1.62%	2.19%	2.51%	0.90%	1.23%	1.64%

The results are interesting in two ways. First, insurers tend to be better off when homeowners mitigate than when they fail to adopt mitigation measures. In MC1, at the same deductible level, insurer insolvency probability fell measurably with mitigation in place. There was further reduction with the higher deductible in place and, in fact, it moved from an unacceptable level of 1.75% when the homeowners did not mitigate and had a 0% deductible level to an acceptable 1.00% when mitigation was in place and the homeowners were subject to a 10% deductible. Similar results apply to the companies in MC2 and MC3. In general, the effects of mitigation are sufficiently positive in these three model cities so that insurers, looking for ways of decreasing the chances of insolvency, can profit from mitigation.

Second, homeowners are better off in terms of their insurance premiums after they invest in mitigation. Thus, residents in MC1 who bought insurance would have their premiums reduced from $670 to $390. This result is not surprising since insurance premiums would benefit from a reduction in claims costs as well the associated loading costs. As pointed out above, however, it may be difficult to convince property owners of the merit of the higher deductible since they may focus on their out-of-pocket expenses following a disaster when they buy coverage. As would be expected, those who undertake mitigation have considerably lower worst-case loss than those who do not invest in loss reduction measures. In summary, homeowners, who are risk averse and hence concerned with the consequences of a catastrophic loss, are likely to have an interest in these measures.

8.7 Conclusions

Scientific and modeling uncertainties play an important role in accurately assessing natural hazard risk. If one focuses solely on reductions in property damage, mitigation measures may not be cost-effective for a homeowner in earthquake and hurricane-prone areas. However, if one includes indirect benefits of protective measures such as reduction in injuries and fatalities as well as avoiding the costs and stress of having to relocate after a disaster, then mitigation may be viewed as an attractive option. As seen in the sensitivity analysis, mitigation measures can be cost-effective. While the risk perceptions of homeowners often lead them to overlook these strategies, mitigation and insurance are effective tools in reducing worst-case losses to homeowners. Building codes, premium reductions linked to long term mitigation loans, and lower deductibles tied to the adoption of mitigation are several strategies that could be pursued to encourage homeowners to adopt these measures.

8.8 References

Braun, M. and Muermann, A. (in press). "The Impact of Regret on the Demand for Insurance," *Journal of Risk and Insurance*.

Cohen, L. and Noll, R. (1981). "The Economics of Building Codes to Resist Seismic Structures," *Public Policy*, Winter 1-29.

Earthquake Engineering Research Institute (1998). *Incentives and Impediments to Improving the Seismic Performance of Buildings,* Oakland, CA: Earthquake Engineering Research Institute.

FEMA (1997). *Report on Costs and Benefits of Natural Hazard Mitigation.* FEMA Publication 294. FEMA: Washington, DC. 57pp.

FEMA (1998). *Protecting Business Operations: Second Report on Costs and Benefits of Natural Hazard Mitigation.* FEMA Publication 331. FEMA: Washington, DC. 50pp.

Grossi, P., Kleindorfer, P., and Kunreuther, H. (1999). "The Impact of Uncertainty in Managing Seismic Risk: The Case of Earthquake Frequency and Structural Vulnerability," *Working Paper 99-03-26*, Risk Management and Decision Processes Center, The Wharton School, Philadelphia, PA.

Grossi, P. (2000). *Quantifying the Uncertainty in Seismic Risk and Loss Estimation.* Doctoral Dissertation, University of Pennsylvania.

Heinz Center for Science, Economics, and the Environment (1999). The Hidden Costs of Coastal Hazards: Implications for Risk Assessment and Mitigation, Washington, D.C., Island Press.

Kleindorfer, P. and Kunreuther, H. (1999). "The Complementary Roles of Mitigation and Insurance in Managing Catastrophic Risks," *Risk Analysis*, 19(4): 727-738.

Kunreuther, H. et al. (1978). *Disaster Insurance Protection: Public Policy Lessons.* New York: John Wiley and Sons.

Kunreuther, H., Hogarth, R. and Meszaros, J. (1993). "Insurer Ambiguity and Market Failure" *Journal of Risk and Uncertainty*, 7: 71-88.

Kunreuther, H. (1997). "Rethinking Society's Management of Catastrophic Risks," *The Geneva Papers on Risk and Insurance*, 83: 151-176.

Levenson, L. (1992). "Residential Water Heater Damage and Fires Following the Loma Prieta and Big Bear Lake Earthquakes," *Earthquake Spectra*, 8: 595-604.

Mayers, D., and Smith, C. (1982). On corporate demand for insurance: *Journal of Business*, 55: 281-296.

Mileti, D. (1999). Disasters by Design: A Reassessment of Natural Hazards in the United States. Washington, D.C., Joseph Henry Press.

Palm, R. and Carroll, J. (1998). *Illusions of Safety: Cultural and Earthquake Hazard Response in California and Japan,* Boulder, Colorado: Westview Press.

Stone, J. (1973). "A Theory of Capacity and the Insurance of Catastrophe Risks: Part I and Part II," *Journal of Risk and Insurance*, 40: 231-243 (Part I) and 339-355 (Part II).

Chapter 9 – The Impact of Risk Transfer Instruments: An Analysis of Model Cities

Major Contributors:
Howard Kunreuther
Paul Kleindorfer
Patricia Grossi

9.1 Introduction

This chapter builds on the analyses completed in Chapter 8 and focuses on the impact that risk transfer instruments, such as reinsurance and catastrophe bonds, have on the performance of insurers. As it is throughout the book, the exceedance probability (EP) curve is utilized in structuring the analysis. A typical insurance company's goal is to operate under two somewhat conflicting constraints: a safety first constraint and a return on assets constraint. The first relates to both a target ruin probability level and a target insolvency level; the second is to satisfy the firm's shareholders and investors.

Of particular interest is how the homeowners' adoption of mitigation measures impacts the need for risk transfer instruments by insurers. This chapter should thus be viewed as a supplement to the analyses on mitigation and residential property insurance undertaken in Chapter 8. After characterizing the types of strategies that an insurance company can pursue to meet its profit maximization goal while still satisfying a number of constraints, an example using the model city of Oakland illustrates how an insurer makes its portfolio decisions. The chapter concludes by exploring the potential impact of multiple region catastrophe bonds for increasing the profitability of an insurer while meeting a solvency constraint.

9.2 Framework for Evaluating Alternative Strategies

The framework for analysis used here is similar to Chapter 8 (Figure 8.2), but the focus is on how reinsurance and other financial instruments can play a role in meeting an insurer's objectives. The insurance company's principal goal is to maximize expected profits, denoted $E(\pi)$, but it must also take into account the needs of its shareholders who require a positive minimum Return On Assets (ROA), defined as the ratio of expected profits to assets, in any given year.

As indicated in Chapter 8, an insurer sets a Target Ruin Probability (TRP) based on its appetite for risk and uncertainty. The safety first constraint reduces the company's expected profits from what they could have been had it been risk neutral. More specifically, if a firm cannot meet a predetermined level of insolvency risk with a given strategy, then it must take steps to reduce the amount of risk in its portfolio. This is likely to lower the firm's ROA since the insurer will typically either hold additional funds to maintain an acceptable level of claims-paying capacity (increasing the denominator of ROA) or purchase reinsurance or catastrophe bonds at prices exceeding the expected value of the risk transferred (thus decreasing the numerator of ROA). Alternatively, the company may need to limit its insurance exposure by insuring only a fraction of the available book of business.

In some cases, it may be impossible for the insurer to meet its TRP and desired ROA even when risk transfer instruments are utilized. For example, purchasing a catastrophe bond can reduce an insurer's insolvency probability to its target level, but it may be so costly that it results in an ROA below the level desired by the insurance company's shareholders. A risk would be considered uninsurable if there is no feasible strategy to meet the two relevant constraints. For an insurer, strategies to achieve both sets of objectives involve a combination of the following different options: (1) charging a higher premium, (2) varying deductibles and coverage levels, (3) employing underwriting strategies which limit the insurer's book of business in hazard-prone areas, (4) utilizing risk transfer instruments, or (5) requiring that the homeowner adopt specific mitigation measures as a condition for insurance.

The insurer's model can be expressed mathematically as follows. Given j different risk management strategies associated with the use of the above factors:

Maximize $E(\pi_j) = (1+\lambda_l)E(L_j) - E(L_j) + E(B_j) - E(C_j)$
Subject to:
$$Pr\{ WCL_j > CPC_j \} \leq TRP \quad \text{(Safety First Constraint)}$$
$$ROA_j \geq ROA^* \quad \text{(Return on Assets Constraint)}$$

$E(L_j)$ and $E(\pi_j)$ are the expected loss and expected profits under strategy j, where loss L_j is a function of mitigation and underwriting elements of strategy j. $E(B_j)$ and $E(C_j)$ are the expected benefits and costs of risk transfer instruments under strategy j; and λ_l is the insurance loading factor for determining the premiums to charge homeowners. The insurance loading factor, as discussed in Chapter 8, reflects the administrative costs, profits, and costs of accumulating and maintaining capital in liquid form to pay for large losses.

In the first constraint, CPC_j is the available Claims Paying Capacity under strategy j to cover losses incurred and WCL_j is the associated Worst-Case Loss, which depends on the TRP. The claims paying capacity, CPC_j, is defined as the insurer's initial assets, A_j, plus premium revenues (both of which may generate interest income, although neglected here) minus the sum of ultimate losses incurred, the net payouts of any risk transfer instruments and administrative costs, C_j, and profits, B_j. In the notation of the above model:

$$CPC_j = A_j + (1+\lambda_I) E(L_j) - L_j + B_j - C_j$$

In the second constraint, ROA_j [i.e., $E(\pi_j)/A_j$)] is the expected return to the firm on initial assets for strategy j. ROA^* is the minimum ROA required by insurance company shareholders. The values of ROA depend on the nature of the risk involved and degree of uncertainty associated with it.

9.3 Evaluating Different Strategies for the Insurer

Suppose an insurance company is considering whether to provide earthquake coverage to homes in Oakland, California and has to determine what level of initial assets (A) are necessary to meet the target ruin probability of 1% and investor's minimum return on assets, ROA*, while still earning a positive expected profit based on an insurance loading factor of $\lambda_I = 1$.

One way to meet this goal is to impose a 10% deductible on all insurance policies and to use underwriting standards that assure that all eligible homes in the insurer's book of business have been appropriately mitigated. This implies all pre-1940 wood-frame homes are required to adopt mitigation as a condition for insurance.

Suppose the asset level A_1 associated with Strategy 1 is set so that the safety first constraint is exactly satisfied. Figure 9.1 shows the EP curve based on the portfolio of homes this company insures in the Oakland region. Based on the curve, WCL_1 is approximately $59 million. For Strategy 1, A_1 equals $57 million, the expected profits, $E(\pi_1)$, are approximately $1 million and the return on assets, ROA_1, is approximately 1.75% (See Table 9.1). If the insurer utilized other strategies, such as lowering its deductible levels and/or not requiring mandatory mitigation measures, the company would need a higher level of assets to meet the target ruin probability of 1%. On the other hand, the expected profits would increase due to the collection of more premiums. The ROA could either increase or decrease depending on the change in profits relative to the required level of assets.

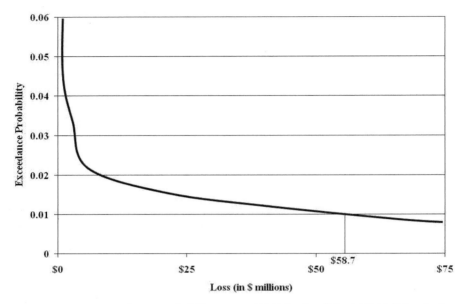

Figure 9.1. Loss exceedance probability curve (10% Deductible, 100% Mitigation)

In order to evaluate Strategy 1, the insurer can investigate the effects of varying deductibles and mitigation levels on E(π) while still meeting the TRP of 1%. Three other strategies are considered here. Strategies 1 and 2 assume all applicable homes undertake mitigation measures and Strategies 3 and 4 assume no residential homeowners mitigate. The deductible levels can be one of two levels: 10% (Strategies 1 and 3) or 0% (Strategies 2 and 4) of the value of the structure. In each case, the level of assets A_j is set at the minimum required to meet the safety first constraint at TRP of 1%. Table 9.1 shows A_j, E(π_j), and ROA_j for these four strategies.

Table 9.1. Performance of strategies to meet safety-first constraint

Strategy j (Deductible, Mitigation)	Asset (A_j) (in $1000s)	E(Profits) E(Π_j) (in $1000s)	Return on Assets (ROA_j)
1 (10%, 100%)	$57,000	$1,000	1.75%
2 (0%, 100%)	96,000	3,350	3.50%
3 (10%, 0%)	89,000	1,700	1.91%
4 (0%, 0%)	135,000	4,720	3.50%

From Table 9.1, it is clear that there are tradeoffs between these strategies with respect to the insurer's objectives. Strategy 1, with the highest deductible and required mitigation, necessitates considerably fewer assets for the insurer to meets its TRP than Strategy 4, which has no deductible and no required mitigation. On the other hand, expected profits and ROA levels are highest for insurance policies with the lowest deductible levels and no mitigation requirements. This is because the insurer collects considerably more in premiums and is compensated for the additional risk it assumes.

9.4 Impact of Indemnity Contracts on Insurer Performance

One of the principal ways for an insurer to reduce the asset level required to meet a prescribed value of TRP is through the use of risk transfer mechanisms. In this section, the role of reinsurance and its impact on the insurer's expected profits and ROA is explored. The typical reinsurance contract is an excess-of-loss policy that provides coverage against unforeseen or extraordinary losses. A typical excess-of-loss reinsurance contract requires the primary insurer to retain a specified level of risk with the reinsurer covering all losses between an attachment point, L_A, and exhaustion point, L_E on the EP curve (See Figure 9.2). In the analysis of the insurer's strategy in this section, it is assumed that the exhaustion point, L_E, corresponds to the worst-case loss, WCL and is defined by the target ruin probability (TRP) of 1%. The layer of reinsurance, $L_E - L_A$, is denoted as Δ.

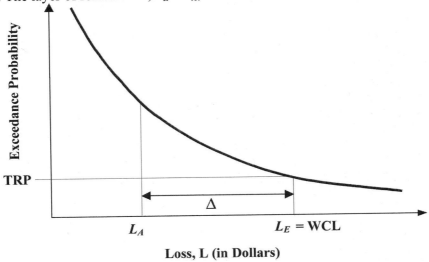

Figure 9.2. Excess-of-loss reinsurance contract

Excess-of-loss reinsurance contracts have the following features: the reinsurer pays all losses in the interval L_A to L_E with a maximum payment to the insurer of Δ. In return for this protection, the insurer pays the reinsurer a premium that reflects the expected loss, as well as a loading factor, λ_R. Thus, if $E(\Delta)$ = the expected losses for Δ units of reinsurance, and the loading factor is λ_R, then the insurer pays a premium to the reinsurer of $E(\Delta)(1+ \lambda_R)$. In practice, of course, the reinsurance loading factor λ_R will vary as the attachment points of the reinsurance contract vary. For simplicity, λ_R is held constant here.

Prior to utilizing reinsurance as a strategy, the insurer needs to know how Δ and λ_R impact TRP, $E(\pi)$ and ROA. In the analysis that follows, it is assumed that there is sufficient capacity in the reinsurance market to provide the amount of excess-of-loss protection that the insurer desires.

9.4.1 Excess-of-Loss Reinsurance Using Strategy 1

Suppose that the company follows Strategy 1 in Table 9.1 and wants to explore the impact of an excess-of-loss reinsurance contract on TRP, $E(\pi)$ and ROA. As expected, the level of assets required to meet a TRP of 1% decreases as the reinsurance layer, Δ, increases as shown in Table 9.2 since the reinsurer absorbs more of the risk. Thus, for a reinsurance loading factor of $\lambda_R =1$, the required asset level (A_1) decreases from \$57 million with no excess-of-loss reinsurance in place to approximately \$18 million with a reinsurance layer of \$40 million. Table 9.2 also shows that the impact on A_1 is negligible for all values of Δ as λ_R increases, since this change only impacts the premium that the insurer pays to the reinsurer. This is a small dollar figure relative to potential losses from earthquakes.

Table 9.2. Required asset level (A) to meet safety first constraint (TRP = 1%) for Strategy 1 (in \$1000s)

Reinsurance Layer	Reinsurance Loading Factor (λ_R)			
Δ	1	1.5	2	2.5
\$ 0 million	\$ 57,000	\$ 57,000	\$ 57,000	\$ 57,000
\$ 10 million	46,900	46,900	47,000	47,000
\$ 20 million	37,100	37,100	37,200	37,300
\$ 30 million	27,300	27,500	27,600	27,700
\$ 40 million	17,700	17,900	18,100	18,300

The picture changes considerably when one looks at the impact that changes in Δ and λ_R have on expected profits earned by the insurer. Table 9.3 shows the values of $E(\pi)$ for the same values of Δ and λ_R shown in Table 9.2 under the assumption that assets are set as in Table 9.2 to just satisfy the required solvency constraint. Expected profits decrease significantly when one changes Δ due to the smaller amount of premiums collected by the insurer. As λ_R increases, the expected profits decrease even further because the insurer is required to pay the reinsurer more for protection. In fact, when $\lambda_R = 2.5$ and the maximum reinsurance layer is $40 million, the company experiences an approximate loss of $40,000.

Table 9.3. Expected profits [E(π)] while meeting safety first constraint (TRP = 1%) for Strategy 1(in $1000s)

Reinsurance Layer	Reinsurance Loading Factor (λ_R)			
Δ	1	1.5	2	2.5
$ 0 million	$ 1,000	$ 1,000	$ 1,000	$ 1,000
$ 10 million	950	920	900	870
$ 20 million	860	790	720	650
$ 30 million	740	600	470	340
$ 40 million	580	370	170	-40

Finally, the data from Tables 9.2 and 9.3 enable one to determine how changes in the amount of reinsurance affect the return on assets to the insurer. Table 9.4 considers the same sets of policies as previously considered. One sees that if the loading factor is sufficiently low, then the insurer obtains a higher ROA as it increases the size of its reinsurance layer. To illustrate, if $\lambda_R = 1$, then the ROA increases from 1.75% without any reinsurance to 3.29% if the reinsurance layer is $40 million. On the other hand, if $\lambda_R = 2.5$, the ROA is at its highest level when reinsurance is $10 million and decreases monotonically as the reinsurance layer increases. As a result, the insurer experiences negative expected profits, and hence a negative ROA, when the reinsurance layer is $40 million.

Table 9.4. Return on assets (ROA) given safety first constraint (TRP = 1%) for Strategy 1

Reinsurance Layer	Reinsurance Loading Factor (λ_R)			
Δ	1	1.5	2	2.5
$ 0 million	1.75%	1.75%	1.75%	1.75%
$ 10 million	2.02%	1.96%	1.91%	1.85%
$ 20 million	2.32%	2.13%	1.94%	1.75%
$ 30 million	2.69%	2.20%	1.72%	1.24%
$ 40 million	3.29%	2.09%	0.92%	-0.23%

The above analysis clearly shows that there are tradeoffs associated with any decision that the insurer makes regarding its choice of a reinsurance contract. The larger the reinsurance layer, the fewer the assets required to satisfy a predetermined safety first constraint. On the other hand, expected profits may decrease as the reinsurance layer increases, particularly if λ_R is relatively high. If the safety constraint is satisfied, then it is natural for the insurer to focus attention primarily on ROA. As discussed next, every aspect of the insurer's strategy, from mitigation and underwriting criteria, to choice of reinsurance contract terms, becomes important in attempting to maximize ROA.

9.4.2 Comparison of Performance Across Insurer's Strategies

Consider an insurance company that can purchase reinsurance with a loading factor $\lambda_R = 1$. It wishes to compare the impact that different values of the reinsurance layer Δ would have on its performance for Strategies 1 through 4. More specifically, the insurer is interested in the optimal level of reinsurance to purchase when the deductible levels and mitigation requirements change. Tables 9.5 through 9.7 compare the required asset level, the expected profits and the ROA for the four different strategies that the insurer is considering.

Table 9.5. Required asset level (A) to meet safety first constraint (TRP= 1%) with Reinsurance Loading Factor ($\lambda_R = 1$) (in $1000s)

Δ	Strategies (Deductible, Mitigation)			
	1 (10%, 100%)	2 (0%, 100%)	3 (10%, 0%)	4 (0%, 0%)
$ 0 Million	$ 57,000	$ 96,000	$ 89,000	$ 135,000
$ 10 Million	47,000	86,000	79,000	126,000
$ 20 Million	37,000	76,000	69,000	112,000
$ 30 Million	27,000	66,000	59,000	105,000
$ 40 Million	18,000	56,000	49,000	96,000

Table 9.6. Expected Profits [E(π)] to Meet Safety First Constraint (TRP= 1%) with reinsurance loading factor ($\lambda_R = 1$)

Δ	Strategies (Deductible, Mitigation) Expected Profits E(Π) in $1,000's			
	1 (10%, 100%)	2 (0%, 100%)	3 (10%, 0%)	4 (0%, 0%)
$ 0 Million	$ 1,000	$ 3,350	$ 1,700	$ 4,720
$ 10 Million	950	3,300	1,640	4,660
$ 20 Million	860	3,220	1,560	4,580
$ 30 Million	740	3,120	1,460	4,490
$ 40 Million	580	2,990	1,330	4,380

Table 9.7. Return on assets (ROA) to meet safety first constraint (TRP= 1%) with reinsurance loading factor ($\lambda_R = 1$)

Δ	Strategies (Deductible, Mitigation)			
	1 (10%, 100%)	**2** (0%, 100%)	**3** (10%, 0%)	**4** (0%, 0%)
$ 0 Million	1.75%	3.50%	1.91%	3.50%
$ 10 Million	2.02%	3.85%	2.08%	3.72%
$ 20 Million	2.32%	4.25%	2.26%	3.98%
$ 30 Million	2.69%	4.72%	2.46%	4.26%
$ 40 Million	3.29%	5.31%	2.70%	4.58%

In comparing the four strategies, two principal conclusions can be drawn regarding the role of reinsurance in satisfying the company's objectives. First, it is possible to reduce the required assets to a relatively small figure if one requires mitigation as a condition for insurance and incorporates a deductible in the policy. As shown in Table 9.5, Strategy 1 (10% deductible; 100% mitigation) requires $27 million in assets to achieve the safety first constraint if the insurer has a $30 million layer of reinsurance. This is approximately one-fourth of the assets required by the insurer when utilizing Strategy 4 (0% deductible; 0% mitigation).

As shown in Table 9.6, $E(\pi)$ is highest when there is no mitigation and no deductible (Strategy 4). However, the required assets to support this strategy range from $135 million when there is no reinsurance to $96 million when the reinsurance layer is $40 million. Consistent with the inherent risk, the capital requirements and the ROA (Table 9.7) for this strategy are significantly higher. However, this strategy would only be feasible if the insurer could raise the required capital at reasonable interest rates.

9.5 Catastrophe Bonds As Additional Sources of Funding

To avoid the possibility of insolvency or a significant loss of claims-paying capacity, insurers have traditionally utilized reinsurance contracts as a source of protection. While the reinsurance market is a critical source of funding for primary insurers, the magnitude of catastrophic losses makes it implausible for them to adequately finance a mega-catastrophe. Cummins, Doherty and Lo (2002) have undertaken a series of analyses that indicate that the U.S. property-liability insurance and reinsurance industry could withstand a loss of $40 billion in practice with minimal disruption of insurance markets. According to their model, a $100 billion loss would create major problems by causing 60 insolvencies and leading to significant premium increases and supply side shortages.

The losses from Hurricane Andrew and the Northridge earthquake were signals to the insurance industry that they could face major problems from a future catastrophic disaster. It stimulated financial institutions to market new types of insurance-linked securities known as catastrophe bonds for providing protection against large-scale disasters. This solution looks promising given the fact that the $26.1 trillion U.S. capital market is more than 75 times larger than the property/casualty industry (Insurance Services Office, 1999). Thus the capital markets clearly have the potential to enhance the risk-bearing capacity of the insurance industry and allow them to spread risks more efficiently on a broader level.

Though the market for risk-linked securities is still in its early stages, insurers and reinsurers have over $4.3 billion in catastrophe bonds outstanding at the end of 2003, an increase in more than 50% over 2002. The total amount of risk-linked securities since its inception in 1996 is over $9.5 billion (Swiss Re, 2004). This section illustrates the performance of a catastrophe bond in interaction with other policy variables. Only the simplest type of catastrophe bond is treated here, where the trigger and payouts are anchored on aggregate losses of the insurer issuing the bond. This type of bond is useful for illustrative purposes and it is similar to the first hurricane-related catastrophe bond issued by USAA in June 1997.

Other catastrophe bonds being issued today are tied to an industry or parametric index as discussed in Chapter 7. These bonds cover damage from a certain natural peril based on insurance industry losses or the physical parameters of the actual event (e.g. hurricane wind speed, earthquake magnitude) within a specified region rather than to the insurer's actual losses.[1] Since these parameters are normally independent of the firm's actual losses, payments can be made to the firm immediately after the disaster occurs rather than being subject to the time delay necessary to compute actual losses, as in the case of the catastrophe bond considered in this section. Hence indexed catastrophe bonds reduce the amount of moral hazard in loss estimation. On the other hand, such an indexed catastrophe bond creates basis risk. Basis risk refers to the imperfect correlation between the actual losses suffered by the firm and the payments received from the bond. In contrast, excess-of-loss reinsurance has very little basis risk because there is a direct relationship between the loss and the payment delivered by the reinsurance instrument.

9.5.1 Structure of Catastrophe Bond for Oakland

Suppose that the insurer who is providing coverage against 5,000 homes in Oakland is considering issuing a catastrophe bond to reduce its chances of insolvency. Naturally, those investing in the bond would require an

---

[1] For more details on the challenges in marketing catastrophe bonds, see U.S. General Accounting Office (2003).

appropriate return (greater than the risk-free rate of interest) to assume the additional risk of loss of principal and interest which might occur should a disaster trigger payouts from the bond.

The specific pricing model is as follows. An insurer issues a catastrophe bond that pays investors an interest differential in exchange for guaranteed funds based on the occurrence of a disaster. For this analysis, the bond is priced assuming that investors demand a Sharpe Ratio of 0.6. The Sharpe Ratio measures the amount of excess return required by investors for an additional unit of risk. In other words, the Sharpe Ratio $= (r - r_f)/\sigma$, where r is the return on the catastrophe bond, r_f is the risk free return (in this case assumed to be 5.5%) and σ is the standard deviation of bond returns. The Sharpe Ratio of 0.6 represents the average historical Sharpe Ratio for catastrophe bonds issued prior to 1999 (Bantwal and Kunreuther, 2000) and approximates the Sharpe ratio for more recent cat bonds.[2] It should be noted that in practice, a bond is not priced solely on the basis of a Sharpe Ratio. Investors often think about many other metrics, including spread as a multiple of expected loss.

Suppose a catastrophe bond is issued with face value, B, of $10 million. The payout, PO, from the bond to the insurer is calculated as follows:

$$PO(\alpha, L, T, K) = \text{Minimum} \left[\alpha (L - T)^+, K \right]$$

where α is a fraction between 0 and 1 representing the co-payment rate borne by the bondholders (the fraction of losses paid by the bond holders in excess of the trigger T). The co-payment rate α is usually less than 1 to provide incentives to the insurer to accurately estimate claims even when these are in the range covered by catastrophe bond payouts. L represents the random variable of losses in the region in question, T is the trigger point for the catastrophe bond, and K is the maximum payout from the catastrophe bond, with $K \leq B$. Finally, $(L - T)^+$ is defined as the maximum of either $(L - T)$ or zero.

To illustrate, suppose the trigger, T, is $20 million, $\alpha = 0.9$ and the maximum payout, K, is $10 million. Then the payouts to the insurer, PO(0.9, L, $20, $10), from the catastrophe bond are 90% of losses in excess of the trigger level of $20 million, until the maximum payout of $10 million

---

[2] The average Sharpe ratio for a sample of six recent cat bonds analyzed by Swiss Re was 0.64 (Swiss Re, 2003, p. 19).

has been reached at a loss of L = \$31.11 million.[3]

The actual dollar payout from the catastrophe bond to the bondholder or investor, PB, at the end of the period (assumed here to be a year) is defined as:

$$PB(\alpha, L, T, K, B) = B - PO(\alpha, L, T, K)$$

The structure of the catastrophe bond is as follows: at the beginning of the year, investors would provide the insurer an amount of capital, $B/(1+r)$, where r is the promised rate of return on the zero-coupon catastrophe bond. The investors are then paid $PB(\alpha, L, T, K, B)$, as given above, at the end of the year. Sidebar 1 details the formulae for calculating the rate of return to investors from this catastrophe bond. This involves considering the ratio of the payout, $PB(\alpha, L, T, K, B)$, to what investors provide at the beginning of the year.

The insurer's actual profits at the end of the year are defined as:

$$\pi = (1+\lambda_I)E(L) - L - [rB - PO(\alpha, L, T, K)]$$

where, as in the earlier model, λ_I is the insurer's loading factor, so that $(1+ \lambda_I)*E(L)$ represents premiums collected, L represents the loss, and $[rB - PO(\alpha, L, T, K)]$ represents the payouts to the bondholders net of any triggered payments to the insurer from the bond. The insurer's basic performance measure, expected ROA, is computed as $E(\pi)/A$, where A represents the assets needed to achieve the desired solvency level, as measured by the TRP.

The above valuation process was used to evaluate various catastrophe bonds from the perspective of a primary insurer. As with reinsurance, the insurer pays investors for the potential protection from the catastrophe bond whether or not the insurer actually collects from it. The rates demanded by investors for catastrophe bonds marketed to date have suggested that investors perceive these bonds to be very risky implying very high rates of return for the bonds. Similar to reinsurance, the key question is whether the high price the insurer has to pay to sell these bonds is compensated for by their ability to substitute investor capital for insurer's capital for a desired level of solvency. The price of the catastrophe bond clearly reduces the insurer's expected profits, but it also reduces the insurer's own capital requirements to achieve a desired level of solvency.

---

[3] For this simple example, the maximum payout of \$10 million occurs at a loss of \$31 million because the investor is only responsible for losses if they exceed T = \$20 million and the insurer absorbs 10% of any loss above this amount since $\alpha = 0.9$. Therefore, at L = \$31.11 million, the insurer absorbs \$1.11 million of the loss above \$20 million and the investor pays \$10 million.

9.5.2 Impact on Insurer's Performance in Oakland

Now, consider the performance of catastrophe bond for the 5,000 Oakland region homes analyzed earlier. The following bond parameters are fixed across all scenarios: $\alpha = 0.8$; the face value, B, is $20 million; T is set so that the probability of the bond triggering a payout to the insurer is 2% corresponding to a trigger of approximately $10 million for all the scenarios considered. The maximum payout level, K, from the bond to the insurer is set at various levels, as shown in Tables 9.8 – 9.10. As expected, the results show that as K increases, the level of assets required decrease since more of the risk is transferred to the bond holders. As with reinsurance, assets levels correspond to a target ruin probability of 1%.

Using the same four strategies by the insurer as for the case of reinsurance, the required assets are shown in Table 9.8, the net expected profits of the bond payments are presented in Table 9.9, and the corresponding ROA is depicted in Table 9.10. These tables are comparable to Tables 9.5 through 9.7 for the reinsurance case. The reader should note, however, that a straightforward comparison between reinsurance and catastrophe bonds is not possible, since a reinsurance loading factor of $\lambda_R = 1$ is assumed in Tables 9.5 - 9.7 and a Sharpe ratio of 0.6 is assumed in Tables 9.8 - 9.10. The answer to the question of which of these instruments, reinsurance or catastrophe bonds, or both, is preferable will depend on their relative pricing in the market (as represented by the reinsurance loading factor and the Sharpe ratio), and in practice would require a thorough analysis of actual reinsurance rates and investor preferences. As expected, the first row of Tables 9.8 through 9.10 reproduces the corresponding row of Tables 9.5 through 9.7, since the case of $K = 0$ represents no effective coverage.

Table 9.8. Assets (to the nearest $1000s)

K	Strategies (Deductible, Mitigation)			
	1 (10%, 100%)	**2** (0%, 100%)	**3** (10%, 0%)	**4** (0%, 0%)
$ 0 million	$57,000	$96,000	$89,000	$135,000
$ 10 million	47,000	86,000	85,000	132,000
$ 20 million	37,000	76,000	75,000	122,000

Table 9.9. Expected Profits (in $1,000s)

K	Strategies (Deductible, Mitigation)			
	1 (10%, 100%)	**2** (0%, 100%)	**3** (10%, 0%)	**4** (0%, 0%)
$ 0 million	$1,000	$3,350	$1,700	$4,720
$ 10 million	-1,410	1,150	-706	2,500
$ 20 million	-2,300	150	-2,190	1,280

Table 9.10. Return on Assets

K	Strategies (Deductible, Mitigation)			
	1 (10%, 100%)	**2** (0%, 100%)	**3** (10%, 0%)	**4** (0%, 0%)
$ 0 million	1.75%	3.50%	1.91%	3.50%
$ 10 million	-2.98%	1.33%	-0. 83%	1.89%
$ 20 million	-6.15%	0.20%	-2.93%	1.05%

As seen in Tables 9.8 through 9.10, based on the parameters assumed in the model, catastrophe bonds are not a good option for an insurer providing coverage for homes in Oakland alone. The only strategies for which ROA is positive are for Strategies 2 and 4 where there are no deductibles. In these situations, the insurer experiences higher expected losses and the insurer is able to make positive returns even with the expense associated with the bond.

Of course, if different levels of solvency (TRP) were chosen or if higher premiums were charged in Oakland (for example, $\lambda_I = 1.5$ or 2.0, rather than the level used earlier of 1.0), then the insurer might have a positive ROA even with a 10% deductible. Similarly, if investors in the catastrophe bond were less risk averse than assumed here (Sharpe Ratio lower than 0.6), they would require a lower interest rate and insurers could find these instruments to be more attractive.

9.5.3 Performance of Catastrophe Bonds Across Different Regions

For comparison purposes, the previous exercise is repeated for MC2 (Long Beach) and MC3 (Miami). The catastrophe bonds considered for these regions have the same features as the bond considered for Oakland: $\alpha = 0.8$; B = $20 million and T is set so that the probability of the bond triggering a payout to the insurer is 2%; target ruin probability (TRP) is set at 1%; Sharpe Ratio is 0.6; and two different loading factors $\lambda_I = 1.0$ and $\lambda_I = 2.0$ are used.

Only Strategy 3 is analyzed (with 10% deductible and 0% mitigation). The values of ROA for different face values of catastrophe bonds issued for the three different regions are compared. Table 9.11 shows the results for $\lambda_I = 1.0$. With this loading factor, the bond is not attractive in any of the three model cities. Even with relatively low coverage, the price of the bond is too high for the insurer to make positive profits if they issue it.

Table 9.12 shows the results for $\lambda_I = 2.0$. Even with this relatively high loading factor, a catastrophe bond is not attractive for either Oakland or Long Beach. For Miami, the issuance of a catastrophe bond yields a positive ROA when K = $5 million. This analysis reinforces a point that insurers have made in recent years: single region catastrophe bonds are generally priced too high for them to be an attractive option.

Table 9.11. ROA for catastrophe bonds in Oakland, Long Beach and Miami/Dade for Strategy 3 ($\lambda_I = 1.0$ and K as shown)

K	Region		
	Oakland	Long Beach	Miami/Dade
$ 0 million	1.91%	1.81%	7.59%
$ 5 million	-0.08%	-6.37%	-7.92%
$ 10 million	-0.83%	-16.25%	-32.09%

Table 9.12. ROA for catastrophe bonds in Oakland, Long Beach and Miami/Dade for Strategy 3 ($\lambda_I = 2.0$ and K as shown)

K	Region		
	Oakland	**Long Beach**	**Miami/Dade**
$ 0 million	3.86%	3.68%	16.44%
$ 5 million	1.86%	-0.97%	4.57%
$ 10 million	1.21%	-9.49%	-5.65%

9.5.4 Multi-Region Catastrophe Bonds

By constructing a catastrophe bond that combines several uncorrelated hazards, the risk is diversified resulting in lower required investor interest rates due to diversification of risk. Insurers can clearly profit from improved exposure management which geographical diversification brings. Investors in catastrophe bonds are willing to accept a lower interest rate since they have a smaller chance of losing a given amount of principal if the maximum amount that the bond pays out is now spread across the uncorrelated risks in different regions, or across different types of hazards. A multi-regional catastrophe bond should cost less due to lower variance, increased ROA, and expected profits for a given target ruin probability TRP and investor sharpe ratio.

Recently, there have been several such parameterized catastrophe bonds issued. SCOR, the French reinsurer, issued a three year multi-peril bond that covers earthquakes and fires following an earthquake in Japan, earthquakes in the U.S. and windstorms in seven different European countries (Standard & Poor's, 2000). In June 2002 Swiss Re issued a four-year bond (PIONEER) that covers three types of perils in different parts of the world — hurricanes in the North Atlantic, windstorms in Europe and earthquakes in California, the central US and Japan --- based on five parametric indices tied to each of these natural perils using physical trigger mechanisms. There is also a multi-peril tranche that is linked to all five of these perils (Swiss Re, 2003).

To illustrate the impact of multi-region catastrophe bonds, consider the scenario in which a single insurer owns all three books of business in Oakland, Long Beach and Miami. Table 9.13 compares the ROA for the three single-region catastrophe bond in Table 9.11 with a multi-region bond for the entire portfolio of all three books of regional business for various levels of K. The same bond parameters as before are used with an insurance loading factor of $\lambda_I = 1.0$. Assets are specified so as to achieve a TRP = 1%.

From these results, two observations are made. One is the overall pooling effect of placing the three books of business together in one company. The superior returns to the Miami portfolio and the normal diversification effect allow a significantly higher ROA on the combined portfolio than on the average of the separate portfolios. Additionally, the multi-region catastrophe bond provides a mechanism for risk transfer for all three portfolios and can improve the performance of the ROA over that of all three of the separate regional portfolios, as in the case of K = $5 million. In 2003, many catastrophe bonds are actually priced below similarly rated corporate bonds as there has been a significant widening of spreads in the bond market (due to deteriorating credit quality) while catastrophe bond spreads have remained fairly steady. Note, however, that these bonds continue to be a poor investment in risk transfer by the insurer relative to reinsurance, given the rates of return assumed to be required by investors (namely those implied by a Sharpe ratio of 0.6).

Table 9.13. ROA for Single-Region and Multi-Region Catastrophe Bonds for $\alpha = 0.8$; B = $20 million; TRP = 1%; Sharpe Ratio = 0.6; $\lambda_1 = 1.0$

	Region Covered by Catastrophe Bond			
K	**Oakland**	**Long Beach**	**Miami/Dade**	**Multi-region**
$ 0 million	1.91%	1.81%	7.59%	4.19%
$ 5 million	-0.08%	-6.37%	-7.92%	1.58%
$ 10 million	-0.83%	-16.25%	-32.09%	-0.29%

9.6 Extensions of the Analysis

The framework presented in this chapter can be applied to many different hazards and many types of firms in different situations. The Oakland insurer example presented illustrates a firm concerned with the impact of a catastrophe on its ability to operate. However, it is important to keep in mind that these results for a single model city may themselves have idiosyncratic characteristics. For example, the effect of different risk management strategies may yield rather different payoffs than the Oakland results presented here if one changes the assumptions in the catastrophe model utilized for analysis.

The above analysis does indicate the importance for insurers to integrate risk transfer strategies with risk bearing strategies, underwriting strategies, and mitigation strategies. Each of these strategies has rather different impacts on the EP curve and on the associated profitability and insolvency levels. For some insurers and some books of business, mitigation measures will suffice to satisfy the safety first constraint and yield an attractive return on assets while maintaining demand for the product. Other insurers will require reinsurance and/or catastrophe bonds to deal with their constraints.

Insurance companies issuing policies in a given region may also have to selectively choose the risks they include in their books of business. In another area where catastrophe risks are not as prevalent, an insurer might choose to be stricter in setting the target probability of insolvency. This could be done without incurring huge capital costs associated with assuring sufficient reserves to satisfy their safety first constraint. In a city like Oakland, the problem is significantly more difficult due to the highly correlated risks associated with earthquake losses for the homes in the insurer's portfolio.

It is also worth noting that for certain risks, there are no market solutions, in spite of the existence of reinsurance and cat bonds as risk transfer mechanisms. For these situations, there is a role for the public sector to play in providing financial protection against large losses. California earthquakes are one such example. As described in Chapter 5, the reluctance of the insurance industry to cover losses from earthquakes in California led to the formation of the California Earthquake Authority which is a limited liability state-run insurance company funded by the insurance and reinsurance industry.

9.7 Conclusions

This and the previous chapter explored the relevance of mitigation – with and without the aid of reinsurance and catastrophe bonds – for homeowners and insurers interested in managing catastrophic risk. Two broad themes emerge from the analyses. First from a homeowner's perspective the need to mitigate is not clear-cut. In many cases the long-term benefits of mitigation may not justify the upfront cost of mitigating the structure. In addition, the expected profits for an insurer are higher when mitigation measures are not adopted due to the larger premiums required to cover the higher losses and the associated administrative costs. Hence, if an insurance company is solely interested in maximizing expected profits, it may not be inclined to encourage homeowners to adopt mitigation measures. On the other hand, mitigation measures can significantly reduce the required amount of assets an insurer needs in order to maintain a desired level of solvency. This increases the ROA and limits the downside risk.

Second, when one considers either reinsurance and/or catastrophe bonds as ways to transfer risk – whether or not mitigation is utilized - a more complex story emerges. If insurers have difficulty raising capital at reasonable interest rates, then a strategy requiring mitigation of homes would be a desirable one on their part in combination with some type of risk transfer instrument. These risk transfer instruments increase insurers' return on assets but at the expense of profits.

The two risk transfer instruments considered in this chapter are reinsurance and catastrophe bonds. The relative cost of these two instruments varies according to the insurance underwriting cycle with prices of reinsurance rising after a major disaster when industry capital is in short supply and falling when there is excess supply in the industry (Swiss Re, 2003).

Catastrophe bonds at relatively high interest rates reduce both an insurer's expected profits and ROA. One way to make these instruments more attractive and reduce the interest rates demanded is by issuing a multi-region catastrophe bond that has lower risk than a single-region bond. The yield required by investors in these bonds should be lower due to lower variance of returns associate with them.   If the catastrophe bond is a multi-year instrument, insurers can rely on a fixed price in setting premiums and coverage limits that presents more challenge when they protect themselves against catastrophic losses with traditional single-year reinsurance policies. The challenge is to explain the statistical properties of these instruments so that investors understand the nature of the financial risks they face. The recent offering of the multi-year multi-hazard catastrophe bond, PIONEER, suggests that investors are beginning to appreciate the benefits of diversifying their portfolios in this way.

208

9.8 References

Bantwal, V. and Kunreuther, H (2000). "A CAT Bond Premium Puzzle?" *Journal of Psychology and Financial Markets,* 1: 76-91.

Cummins, J. D., Doherty, M., and Lo, A. (2002). "Can Insurers Pay for the 'Big One?' Measuring the Capacity of an Insurance Market to Respond to Catastrophic Losses." *Journal of Banking and Finance,* 26: 557-583.

Insurance Services Office (1999). *Financing Catastrophe Risk: Capital Market Solutions* New York, N.Y.: Insurance Services Office.

Roy, A.D. (1952). "Safety-First and the Holding of Assets," *Econometrica,* 20: 431-449.

Standard & Poors (2000). *Sector Report: Securitization,* June.

Stone, J. (1973). "A theory of capacity and the insurance of catastrophe risks: Part I and Part II," *Journal of Risk and Insurance* 40: 231-243 (Part I) and 40: 339-355 (Part II).

Swiss Re (2003). *Insurance-linked Securities* (New York: Swiss Re Capital Markets Corporation).

Swiss Re (2004). *Insurance-linked securities quarterly* (New York: Swiss Re Capital Markets Corporation) January.

U.S. General Accounting Office (2003). *Catastrophe Insurance Risks. Status of Efforts to Securitize Natural Catastrophe and Terrorism Risk.* GAO-03-1033. Washington, D.C.: September 24.

Chapter 10 – Extending Catastrophe Modeling To Terrorism

Major Contributors:
Howard Kunreuther
Erwann Michel-Kerjan
Beverly Porter

10.1 Introduction

Since the idea for this book was first conceived, the insurance industry and world were rocked by the events of September 11, 2001. While previous chapters have focused on the risk associated with natural disasters, at the core of this book is a more general problem: how to assess and manage risk associated with extreme events. This final chapter examines the unique challenges of extending catastrophe modeling to these types of risks by focusing on terrorism as well as the new challenges faced by the U.S for providing terrorism risk coverage after 9/11.

Section 10.2 discusses the impact of the 9/11 attacks on the insurance industry and the uncertainty regarding future terrorist activities. After discussing the nature of terrorism coverage in Section 10.3 and the differences between terrorism and natural disaster risk in Section 10.4, Section 10.5 turns to the passage of the U.S. Terrorism Risk Insurance Act of 2002 (TRIA). Section 10.6 discusses recent developments in terrorism modeling that can aid insurers and reinsurers in assessing insurance premiums and coverage limits, including a discussion of how models are used to establish insurance rates nationwide. Section 10.7 analyzes why the current demand for terrorism coverage has been at a low level since TRIA was passed. The chapter concludes with directions for future research for dealing with terrorism and other extreme events.

10.2 September 11, 2001: Impacts on Terrorism Insurance

Prior to the 9/11 attacks, terrorism coverage in the United States was included in most standard commercial policy packages without considering the risk associated with these events. The private insurance market had functioned effectively in the U.S. because losses from terrorism had historically been small and, to a large degree, uncorrelated. Attacks of a domestic origin were isolated and carried out by groups or individuals with disparate agendas.

None of these events created major economic disruption nor produced many casualties. The 1993 bombing of the World Trade Center (WTC) killed 6 people and caused $725 million of insured damages (Swiss Re, 2002). The Oklahoma City bombing of 1995, which killed 168 people, had been the most damaging terrorist attack on domestic soil, but the largest losses were to federal property and employees that were covered by the government. As a result, insurers and reinsurers did not have to pay close attention to their potential losses from terrorism in the United States prior to 9/11.

The terrorist attacks that day on the World Trade Center resulted in the death of nearly 3,000 people and inflicted damage estimated at nearly $80 billion. Approximately 40% of this amount was insured, resulting in the most costly event in the history of insurance (Lehman, 2004). The insurance industry was now confronted with an entirely new loss dimension. Reinsurers, who were liable for the lion's share of the claims, were for the most part unwilling to renew coverage and the few who did charged extremely high rates for very limited protection. Insurers unable to obtain reinsurance, or to raise sufficient capital either internally or from the capital markets, began to offer policies that explicitly excluded terrorism coverage.

The lack of available terrorism coverage had an immediate impact by delaying or preventing certain projects from going forward. For example, the U.S. General Accounting Office (GAO) noted a construction project that could not be started because the firms could not find affordable terrorism coverage (U.S. GAO, 2002). Several years after the event, the larger question being debated is whether terrorism is an insurable risk. That is, can insurers offer coverage at an affordable premium to potential insureds? If so, how does one go about determining how much to charge? Can one estimate the chances of another terrorist event occurring and the severity of insured losses?

Spectacular as were the 9/11 losses to the WTC and the Pentagon, do they represent a worst-case scenario? If some predictions concerning a possible chemical or biological attack become a reality, the answer is probably "no." Since March 2003, the U.S. government has issued clear warnings that additional terrorist attacks are likely, and indeed several have occurred including the deadly explosion at a nightclub in Bali that killed close to 200 people in October 2002 and the large-scale attacks on trains in Madrid, Spain on March 11, 2004 that killed more than 200 people and injured more than 1,500 others (Kunreuther and Michel-Kerjan, in press).

10.3 The Nature of Terrorism Coverage

Another key question triggered by the events of 9/11 is the appropriate role of the private and public sectors in reducing losses and offering insurance protection against the impacts of terrorism (Kunreuther, Michel-Kerjan, and Porter, 2003). In Congressional testimony five months after the 9/11 attacks, Richard J. Hillman of the U.S. General Accounting Office indicated "both insurers and reinsurers have determined that terrorism is not an insurable risk at this time" (U.S. General Accounting Office, 2002).

The following scenario (with fictitious names) illustrates the challenges confronting private industrial companies in obtaining terrorism coverage prior to the passage of the Terrorism Risk Insurance Act (TRIA) in November 2002[1]:

> Over the past 10 years, the AllRisk (AR) Insurance Company has provided $500 million in coverage to Big Business (BB) Inc. against risks to its building, including those due to terrorism at a total premium of $13 million. AR covers $100 million itself and has purchased an excess-of-loss reinsurance contract from Reinsurance Enterprise (RE) to cover the remaining $400 million. Given the events of 9/11, RE has decided that terrorism will no longer be included in its coverage because of the uncertainties associated with the risk. BB needs terrorism coverage since the bank that holds its mortgage requires this as a condition for the loan. AR must decide whether or not to continue providing BB with the same type of insurance as it has had previously and, if so, how much coverage it is willing to offer and at what price.

This scenario raises the following questions regarding terrorism coverage:

- What factors determine whether the risk is insurable?
- How much capital will AR require in order to provide protection against terrorism?

---

[1] This scenario and the analysis of insurability issues associated with terrorism insurance are based on Kunreuther (2002).

10.3.1 Insurability Issues

As discussed in Chapter 2, insurers would be willing to provide insurance coverage if two conditions are met. First, they must be able to identify and quantify, or estimate at least partially, the risk (e.g., probability of an event occurring and the associated losses). Second, they must be able to set premiums for different classes of customers so the risk of insolvency is deemed acceptable.

In quantifying the risk from terrorist attacks, insurers can utilize an exceedance probability (EP) curve. However, it is considerably harder to construct an EP curve for terrorist activities than it is for natural disasters due to the difficulty in determining the likelihood of a terrorist attack. A potential target that may appear to have a high likelihood of attack, such as a trophy building, may also have a high level of protection and security which makes it less likely to be chosen by terrorists (Woo, 2002). So rather than trying to construct an EP curve, insurers normally turn to a scenario-based approach, by considering a range of terrorist-related events and estimating the likelihood of their occurrence and the resulting losses. Section 10.6 illustrates how catastrophe modeling can be utilized for constructing such scenarios.

10.3.2 Expanding Capacity Through Catastrophe Bonds

For insurers to provide their clients with the level of coverage offered prior to 9/11, they need to find new sources of capital. If the cost of this capital is high, the insurance premium will be prohibitively expensive and demand for coverage will dry up. To illustrate this point, it is useful to consider the scenario involving the AR Insurance Company providing terrorism coverage to BB Inc.

Now that RE has decided to eliminate terrorism coverage in its reinsurance treaties, AR has to determine how much protection it can offer BB and what price to charge for this coverage. The first concern of the underwriters at AR is to keep the firm's chance of insolvency below an acceptable risk level; profit maximization is of secondary interest. For AR to offer BB $500 million in coverage, it now has to raise an additional $400 million in capital.

One possibility would be for an investment bank to issue AR a $400 million catastrophe bond to cover the losses from a potential terrorist attack. As discussed in Chapter 7, a catastrophe bond requires the investor to provide upfront money that will be used by AR if a prespecified event, such as a terrorist attack, occurs. In exchange for a higher return than normal, the investor faces the possibility of losing either some or the entire principal invested in the catastrophe bond.

The amount paid out to AR depends on the design of the catastrophe bond. If investors are concerned with the ambiguity associated with terrorism risk, they will require a much larger than average return on their investment in order to compensate them for the possibility of losing their principal. To determine the costs to AR of a cat bond one needs to specify the annual return on investment (ROI) required by investors of a catastrophe bond and compare it with the normal annual return on AR investments, which for illustrative purposes will be assumed to be 8%. The annual cost, C, to AR of obtaining $400 million through issuing a catastrophe bond would then be:

$$C = (ROI - 0.08)\$400$$

Suppose AR believes that the expected annual loss for providing $500 million of coverage is $1 million. Assuming a loading factor of $\lambda_{AR} = 0.5$, AR would have to charge an annual premium (in millions) of P = ($1 + C) (1.5). Table 10.1 shows how C and P are affected by different required ROIs of investors.

Table 10.1. Changes in return on investment (ROI) on catastrophe bond cost (C) and insurance premiums (P) (in millions)

ROI	Catastrophe Bond Cost (C)	Premium (P)
10%	$8	$13.5
12%	$16	$25.5
14%	$24	$37.5
16%	$32	$49.5
18%	$40	$61.5
20%	$48	$73.5

In the above example, it should be noted that the high premium is principally due to the cost (C) of borrowing money from the bond investors. During the fall of 2001, it was not unusual for an ROI to be as high as 20% on capital provided to insurers and reinsurers. The ROI has since declined, but even if it were only 12%, insurers would have to charge $25.5 million to BB for $500 million in terrorism coverage. This is almost twice the $13 million that BB was paying prior to 9/11.

10.3.3 Potential Role of Catastrophe Bonds

It is interesting to speculate as to why with the exception of a few issuances a market for catastrophe bonds to cover losses from terrorist attacks has not emerged since 9/11. Consider the case where an investment banker was issuing a one-year catastrophe bond for covering terrorism losses. Let p represent a conservative estimate of the probability of a terrorist attack during a given year that would destroy BB's building, in which case the investor would lose the principal invested in a cat bond. If the normal annual rate of return is 8%, a risk neutral investor who committed $Y to a catastrophe bond would require a ROI such that:

$$(1-p)(ROI)Y - pY = 0.08Y$$

Let p_i be the annual probability of a terrorist attack where an investor is indifferent between receiving an annual ROI = i % on a catastrophe bond knowing it would lose its entire investment should the attack occur. Substituting i for ROI and p_i for p in the above equation and rearranging terms, p_i becomes:

$$p_i = \frac{(i - 0.08)}{(1 + i)}$$

Thus, if i = 10%= 0.10, then $p_{0.10}$ = 0.02/1.10 = 0.018 or 1.8%. If a risk neutral investor believes the annual probability of a terrorist attack is less than .018, an ROI of 10% would be an attractive investment. If i = 20%= 0.20, then $p_{0.20}$ = 0.12/1.20 = 0.10 or 10%. This implies that if $p <$ .10, a risk neutral investor would invest in a catastrophe bond if it returned 20% in the case of no terrorist attack. These indifference probabilities would be slightly lower if the investor were risk averse. Yet it is still hard to comprehend why the investment community has not viewed catastrophe bonds as a viable option for dealing with terrorism, particularly if the bond comprised only a small portion of the investor's portfolio.

In a recent paper, Bantwal and Kunreuther (2000) specified a set of factors that might account for the relatively thin market in catastrophe bonds in the context of natural hazard risks. They point out that spreads in this market are too high to be explained by standard financial theory, suggesting that they are not just a consequence of investor unfamiliarity with a new asset, but signal some deeper issues that need to be resolved before the catastrophe bond market can fully develop. In particular, the authors suggest that ambiguity aversion, myopic loss aversion, and fixed costs of education might explain the reluctance of institutional investors to enter this market.

Four additional factors may help explain the lack of interest in catastrophe bonds covering terrorism risk. There may be a moral hazard problem associated with issuing such bonds if terrorist groups are connected with financial institutions having an interest in the U.S. In addition, investment managers may fear the repercussions on their reputation of losing money by investing in an unusual and newly developed asset. Unlike investments in traditional high yield debt, money invested in a terrorist catastrophe bond can disappear almost instantly and with little warning. Those marketing these new financial instruments may be concerned that if they suffer a large loss on the catastrophe bond, they will receive a lower annual bonus from their firm and have a harder time generating business in the future. The short-term incentives facing investment managers differ from the long-term incentives facing their employers.

A third reason why there has been no market for these catastrophe bonds is the reluctance of reinsurers to provide protection against this risk following the 9/11 attacks. When investors learned that the reinsurance industry required high premiums to provide protection against terrorism, they were only willing to provide funds to cover losses from this risk if they received a sufficiently high interest rate.

Finally, most investors and rating agencies consider terrorism models to be too new and untested to price a catastrophe bond. Reinsurers view terrorism models as not very reliable in predicting the frequency of terrorist attacks, although they provide useful information on the potential severity of the attacks under a wide range of scenarios. Furthermore, one of the major rating firms noted that the estimates derived from the models developed by AIR Worldwide, EQECAT and Risk Management Solutions could vary by 200% or more. Without the acceptance of these models by major rating agencies, the development of a large market for terrorist catastrophe bonds is unlikely (U.S. General Accounting Office, 2003).

10.4 Comparison of Terrorism Risk with Natural Disaster Risk

Although both terrorist activities and natural disasters have the potential to create catastrophic losses, there are some significant differences between these two risks. Two features of terrorism – information sharing and dynamic uncertainty – make it difficult for the private sector to provide insurance protection without some type of partnership with the public sector.

The sharing of information on the terrorism risk is clearly different than the sharing of information regarding natural hazard risk. In the latter case, new scientific studies normally are common knowledge so that insurers, individuals or businesses at risk, as well as public sector agencies, all have access to these findings. With respect to terrorism, information on possible attacks or current threats is kept secret by government agencies for national security reasons. One justification for government intervention in insurance markets relates to the asymmetry of information between buyers and sellers and the problems this may cause, such as adverse selection. In the case of terrorism, there is symmetry of non-information on the risk between those insured and insurers where government is the most informed party.

A principal terrorist goal is to destabilize a region or country by attacking certain targets that disrupt normal activities and create fear. Since terrorists will adapt their strategy as a function of available resources and their knowledge of the vulnerability of the entity they are attacking, the nature of the risk changes over time, leading to *dynamic uncertainty* (Michel-Kerjan, 2003b). This feature, which translates into considerable ambiguity of risk, reflects an important difference from estimating natural hazards risks. Damage due to a future large-scale earthquake in Los Angeles can be reduced through adoption of mitigation measures; however, it is currently not possible to influence the occurrence of the earthquake itself. On the other hand, the likelihood of specific terrorist attacks will change over time as a function of the constellation of protective measures adopted by those at risk and actions taken by the government to enhance general security.

These characteristics of terrorism, along with the difficulty for insurers in finding new capital for covering this risk, raise the question as to how the government and the insurance industry can work together in providing protection and reducing future losses from these risks. The need for public-private partnerships was actually recognized in November 2002 when the Terrorism Risk Insurance Act of 2002 (TRIA) was passed.

10.5 Terrorism Risk Insurance Act of 2002

In the aftermath of the 9/11 attacks, many insurers warned that another event of comparable magnitude could do irreparable damage to the industry. By early 2002, 45 states permitted insurance companies to exclude terrorism from their policies, except for workers' compensation insurance policies that cover occupational injuries without regard to the peril that caused the injury. On the one-year anniversary of the 9/11 attacks, the U.S. remained largely uncovered (Hale, 2002). The President and the U.S. Congress viewed such a situation as unsustainable. If the country suffered future attacks, it would inflict severe financial consequences on affected businesses deprived of coverage. As a result, the U.S. Congress passed the Terrorism Risk Insurance Act of 2002 (TRIA).

10.5.1 Public-Private Risk Sharing under TRIA

While the passage of TRIA may have been welcome news for the business community, it was a mixed blessing for insurers who were obligated to offer coverage against terrorism to all their clients. The commercial establishments have the choice of either purchasing this coverage or declining it. Insured losses from property and contents damage and business interruption are covered under TRIA under the following conditions: 1) if the event is certified by the U.S. Treasury Secretary as an "act of terrorism" carried out by foreign persons or interests and 2) results in aggregate losses greater than $5 million.

Under TRIA's three-year term (ending December 31, 2005), there is a specific risk-sharing arrangement between the federal government and insurers[2] that operates in the following manner. First, the federal government is responsible for paying 90% of each insurer's primary property-casualty losses during a given year above the applicable insurer deductible (ID), up to a maximum of $100 billion. The insurer's deductible is determined as a percentage of the insurer's direct commercial property and casualty earned premiums for the preceding year. This percentage varies over the three-year operation of TRIA as follows: 7% in 2003, 10% in 2004, and 15% in 2005. The federal government does not receive any premium for providing this coverage.

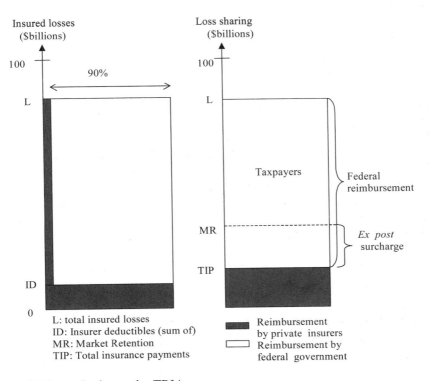

Figure 10.1. Loss sharing under TRIA.

Second, if the insurance industry suffers losses that require the government to cover part of the claims payments, then these outlays shall be partially recouped *ex post* through a mandatory policy surcharge. This

---

[2] Reinsurers are not part of TRIA but can provide coverage to insurers against their losses from terrorist attacks.

surcharge is applied on all property and casualty insurance policies whether or not the insured has purchased terrorism coverage, with a maximum of 3% of the premium charged under a policy. The federal government will pay for insured losses above a specific insurance marketplace retention amount (MR), as depicted in Figure 10.1. That amount evolves as follows: $10 billion in 2003, $12.5 billion for 2004, and $15 billion for 2005.

10.5.2 Challenge for Insurers and Firms: Quantifying the Residual Risk

Under TRIA, insurers were given 90 days after the legislation was enacted on November 26, 2002 to develop and disclose to policyholders new premiums and coverage terms. Many insurance companies found themselves in the situation of having to set a price for a risk they would rather not write. Although their exposure to terrorism risk is much reduced through the public-private partnership created by TRIA, it is still significant. Over the course of these 90 days, insurance companies followed a variety of strategies. Some determined that their exposures were not in high-risk locations and chose to leave existing premiums unchanged. Others with portfolio concentrations in major metropolitan areas deemed at high risk, such as New York, Washington, D.C., Chicago, and San Francisco, set very high premiums. In this situation, many businesses chose not to insure (Hsu, 2003; Treaster, 2003).

At the same time, many insurers and reinsurers have taken advantage of newly available tools designed to help them estimate their potential losses and therefore make rational and informed pricing decisions. Catastrophe modelers, leveraging their considerable experience and expertise in modeling natural hazard events, released the first generation of models to provide insurers with estimates of loss across multiple lines from terrorist attacks. The value of such models is in their ability to reduce uncertainty in risk estimates. One effect of that reduced uncertainty should be a lowering of premiums for terrorism insurance.

10.6 Catastrophe Models for Terrorism Risk

Insurance markets function best when losses are relatively small, random and uncorrelated, and when there is an abundance of historical loss data to which statistical techniques can be applied to predict future losses. As has been discussed throughout this book, when it comes to natural catastrophes, losses can be of catastrophic proportion and are often highly correlated. Furthermore, because such events occur infrequently, loss data are relatively scarce, making reliance on traditional actuarial techniques dubious at best.

As limited as the data is for nature catastrophes, there is much less information available on terrorist attacks for risk estimation purposes. To the extent that historical data do exist and are available from such sources as the Federal Bureau of Investigation (FBI), the U.S. Department of State, the Center for Defense and International Security Studies (CDISS), and the Central Intelligence Agency (CIA), they may not be representative of current threats.

To explore the alternative approaches that modelers have used to overcome the challenges of quantifying terrorism risk, it is useful to begin with the simple modeling framework introduced in Chapter 2 and reproduced here as Figure 10.2.

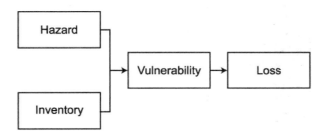

Figure 10.2. Catastrophe model components.

10.6.1 Terrorism Hazard

A terrorism model must first address three basic issues regarding the hazard itself: frequency of occurrence, the most likely locations of future terrorist attacks, and their severity in terms of insured loss. In undertaking this analysis, the different potential targets plus the interdependencies among networks and systems must be taken into account (Pate-Cornell and Guikema, 2002). For example, the loss of electric power or contamination of the water supply could create long-term business interruption risks and require residents in the affected areas to relocate.

The management of international terrorism risks has traditionally relied upon the experience and judgment of a specialist underwriter. For certain individual risks, recourse might be made on the advice of security professionals. For a portfolio, maximum loss would be carefully capped, but the overall risk assessment procedure would remain essentially qualitative and subjective. The most basic terrorism risk model is thus one encoded within the working experience of an underwriter and dependent on his personal expert judgment.

To cover rare catastrophic acts of terrorism, beyond the experience of even the most seasoned underwriter, the judgment of external terrorism experts might be invoked. Terrorism risk management would still be judgment-based, but the underwriter would be supported by the greater knowledge of terrorism experts. Recognizing that experts' risk estimates are based on their own set of assumptions and may reflect a set of biases, the challenge is to evaluate these figures carefully in modeling terrorism risk. Terrorism models incorporate the judgment of teams of experts familiar both with available data and current trends. These experts have operational experience in counterterrorism at the highest national and international levels, with many specializing in terrorism threat assessment. Because each expert is privy to his own sources of intelligence and has his own security clearances, there is no common database of information upon which all experts can form their judgments. In fact, much of the crucial information is confidential.

Determining Likelihood of Attacks

To elicit expert opinion on the likelihood of attacks, several different approaches have been utilized. Some modeling firms employ the Delphi Method; others convene a conference of experts to capture and statistically combine various opinions into a useful and cohesive form that can be used to generate probabilities. For complex problems not governed by scientific laws, the judgment and intuition of experts in their field is not only an appropriate ingredient in any model, but a critical one.

The Delphi Method is a well-known and accepted approach developed by the RAND Corporation at the start of the Cold War. Among its first applications was the forecasting of inter-continental warfare and technological change. The Delphi Method comprises a series of repeated interrogations, usually administered by questionnaire, where the responses are anonymous. Direct interaction between the participants is precluded to eliminate the natural bias of following the leader. After an initial round of interrogation, individuals are encouraged to reconsider and, when appropriate, to change their views in light of the replies of all the others that are shared with everyone in the group (Adler and Ziglio, 1996). While the methodology is highly structured, the final estimates by each participant still only represent opinions, informed by other members of the group.

Experts are asked to weigh in on several aspects of event frequency and intensity: the number of attacks per year, the type of target, the attack mode or weapon type, and finally the specific target of each potential attack. Each of these issues depends in part on the nature of the terrorist organization originating the attack. Critical to the results is the team's operational understanding of the likely terrorist actions in the context of the current state of security countermeasures. Targets and attack methods that were once undefended may now be more vigorously protected by federal homeland security, state and local policy, and private security resources.

An alternative to the Delphi Method is using a conference of experts where participants can exchange views. The agenda is usually topics, such as the kind of weapons a specific terrorist group is more likely to use or what areas/countries are more susceptible to attack. When some experts are unable to attend the conference, their judgment can be elicited separately and fed back to others using the Delphi Method.

The lack of historical data makes the use of experts the only way for modelers to determine the likelihood of new attacks. However, experts have their own limitations in forecasting future behavior, as each of them has specialized knowledge. Some are much more focused on a given terrorist group and disregard dangers from others. Others are specialized on a given type of weapon or on a very specific kind of biological or chemical agent. In other words, each expert can be accurate within his or her small window of expertise, but the whole group of experts can be wrong about the reality of the global threats -- a kind of illusory expertise (Linstone and Turoff, 1975).

Another pitfall is the possible optimism/pessimism bias of experts. For instance, if a terrorist attack recently occurred, a natural trend would be to overestimate the likelihood of new attacks in the short run. Conversely, if a governmental agency arrested leaders of a terrorist group, a natural bias could be to concentrate only on that group and overlook other terrorists, resulting in misconceptions of the likelihood of other attacks.

Identifying Likely Targets and Attack Modes

Obviously target types vary depending on the nature and goals of the individual terrorist groups or organizations, not only because of differences in the resources at this group's disposal, but because of its different political agenda.

Once the target types are identified, databases of individual potential targets are developed. In the case of terrorism, targets within the U.S. might include high profile skyscrapers, government buildings, airports, chemical plants, nuclear power plants, dams, major tunnels and bridges, large sports stadiums, major corporate headquarters, and marine terminals. Trophy targets normally represent a higher value to the terrorists due to the publicity associated with them, and they therefore have a higher probability of attack, other things being equal. Target databases can comprise tens of thousands or even hundreds of thousands of structures.

In the simulations developed by modelers, the terrorist group receives value or utility from the damage inflicted on its adversaries. The expected loss is determined by the probability of success in carrying out the attack and the economic and psychological value of the target. In turn, the probability of success is determined not only by the amount of resources the terrorist group allocates to the attack, but also by the resources its opponent allocates to detecting terrorist activity and defending the target. Both parties are constrained by the funds and people-power at their disposal and the "model" becomes one of strategic decisions as to how to deploy those resources, i.e. which targets to attack and with what weapons, and which to defend. Game theory can thus be used to analyze likely targets and attack modes.

The severity of the attack is a function of the weapon type. Modeled weapon types include so-called conventional weapons, such as package, car and truck bombs, as well as aviation crash. In light of Al Qaeda's clearly expressed interest in acquiring and deploying weapons of mass destruction, models also account for the possibility of non-conventional weapon attacks including chemical, biological, radiological, and nuclear (CBRN) weapons (Central Intelligence Agency, 2003).

10.6.2 Inventory

The 9/11 attacks revealed that not only are the terrorist targets themselves at risk, but so are the surrounding buildings. Nevertheless, the effects of terrorist attacks with conventional weapons are likely to be highly localized compared to natural disasters such as hurricanes and earthquakes. The resulting damage depends on such things as the kind of explosive material used, the amount of material, and the density and verticality of the surrounding buildings. For non-conventional weapons, the spatial extent of damage depends on the delivery mechanism and on external factors such as wind speed and wind direction.

Terrorism models can estimate total losses as well as aggregate insured or insurable losses for individual buildings, insurance company portfolios, and/or the entire insurance industry. While the large losses resulting from natural catastrophes have historically been to property, terrorist attacks can affect multiple insurance lines that include life, liability, workers' compensation, accident, and health, as was the case on 9/11. They can also result in severe stress on the psyche of a nation under siege.

The databases that are utilized in natural catastrophe models are also relevant for terrorism models. Modelers have developed industry databases of employees by building occupancy and construction type at the ZIP code level. These can be supplemented with state payroll and benefit information, generally available to insurance companies, to create an inventory at risk. Since 9/11, modelers are emphasizing to insurers the importance of gathering detailed data on the buildings they insure and the employees who work in them (Insurance Accounting, 2003).

10.6.3 Vulnerability

Research on the impact of explosives on structures has been ongoing since the 1950s. The Department of Defense and the Department of State have examined blast loading in the course of developing anti-terrorism designs for U.S. embassies. In addition, research activity has surged since the bombing of the Alfred P. Murrah Federal Office Building in Oklahoma City (1995) and the U.S. military housing facilities in Dhahran, Saudi Arabia (1996) (Olatidoye et al., 1998).

Modelers have developed damage functions that incorporate historical data from actual events combined with the results of experimental and analytical studies of how different building types respond to such attacks. In the case of a terrorist attack using conventional and nuclear weapons, buildings sustain damage as a result of a variety of assaults on their structural integrity and their non-structural components. In the case of non-conventional weapons, the structure of the building is likely to be unaffected, but the resulting contamination may render it unusable for long periods and result in extensive cleanup costs. In either case, the damage functions determine loss to building, contents, and loss of use.

Conventional Weapons

In terrorism modeling, damage is a function of the attack type and building type. The type of attack, whether package, car or truck bomb, can be expressed as a TNT-equivalent. The size of this charge can be thought of as the intensity of the event. Damage to the target building results from the shock wave, the subsequent pressure wave, and fire.

The target building may sustain total damage from the point of view of insured loss even if it remains standing. If the building collapses, however, it would increase the number of fatalities. Furthermore, different modes of collapse, such as an overturn versus a pancake collapse, will affect the degree of damage to surrounding buildings and thus the total area affected by the event. The buildings surrounding the target building are also likely to be damaged by the resulting shock and pressure waves and/or by falling or flying debris.

Non-conventional Weapons

The effects of nuclear weapons on both structures and populations have been the subject of extensive research for decades (Glasstone and Dolan, 1977). Chemical, biological and radiological (CBR) attacks are more problematical and only a few accidental releases of chemical agents, such as the one that occurred at the Union Carbide chemical plant in Bhopal, India (1984) have been analyzed. Other events include the 1995 sarin attack in the Tokyo subway and the more recent distribution of anthrax through the mail in autumn 2001 in the U.S. (U.S. Department of State, 2003). These examples provide data for empirical analysis and research. Fortunately, those attacks have been extremely rare so there is limited historical data.

Some modelers have developed relationships between the use of non-conventional weapons and potential damage; others employ models developed for various government agencies that follow what is known as a source/transport/effects approach. The "source" refers to how a hazard agent originates, including the type, yield, effectiveness, and other properties of the agent. Various attack types are simulated, including chemical agents such as

224

sarin, VX, tabun, biological agents such as anthrax and smallpox. Nuclear and radiological agents such as cesium, cobalt and plutonium are also simulated (Central Intelligence Agency, 2003).

"Transport" refers to the means by which the agent disperses or moves from the source to the people or facilities presumed to be the targets. A full range of mechanisms is considered ranging from mail-borne dispersal to wide area dissemination via aerosol spraying and conventional bomb blast. "Effects" refers to the physical, performance, and psychological impact of the attack on humans as well as on the environment. While even a small suitcase nuclear device can cause extensive physical damage to buildings over a relatively large geographical area, the primary effects of other non-conventional weapons is contamination, which may render the structures unusable for long periods of time as discussed. In fact, in some cases, the most cost-effective way of dealing with badly contaminated buildings may be demolition under very cautious and well-defined procedures.

10.6.4 Workers' Compensation Loss

In addition to property damage, terrorism models estimate fatalities under both workers' compensation and life insurance policies, as well as losses from injuries arising from personal accident and other casualty lines. The number of injuries and fatalities, as well as the severity of injuries, is a function of the nature of damage sustained by the structural and non-structural components of buildings and their contents. Figure 10.3 illustrates the process for computing workers' compensation loss.

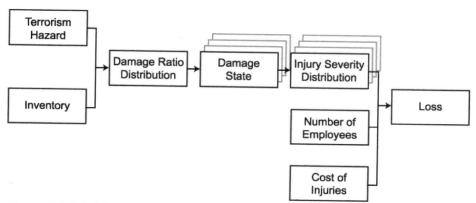

Figure 10.3. Modeling workers' compensation loss.

In estimating workers' compensation loss, models account for variability in damage to individual buildings so that one can estimate the extent of injuries and fatalities. For each level of severity, a mean damage ratio is calculated along with a probability distribution of damage. Because different structural types will experience different degrees of damage, the damage functions vary according to construction materials and occupancy. A distribution of damage for each structure type is mapped to different damage states. These may be, for example, slight, moderate, extensive and complete, as shown in Figure 10.4 for a specific building.

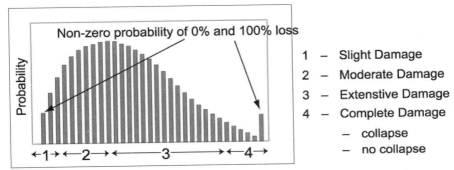

Figure 10.4. Building damage distribution mapped to different damage states.

At the level of complete damage, the building may or may not have collapsed. Complete damage means that the building is not recoverable. Collapse will typically result in more severe injuries and larger numbers of fatalities than if the building is still standing. Estimates of workers' compensation (and other casualty lines) loss are based not only upon the number of people injured, but also on the severity of the injuries, such as minor, moderate, life threatening and fatality. Distributions of injury severity are then developed for each damage state for each building and occupancy type.

By combining information on the number of employees in each damaged building and the cost of injuries, the model generates the total loss distribution for a particular structure. Losses are calculated based on the number of employees in each injury severity level and on the cost of the injury as shown in Figure 10.5. To calculate losses arising from life insurance and personal accident claims, potential losses are calculated for both residential and commercial buildings. These calculations use assumptions about the distribution of the population between these two types of structures at the time of the attack.

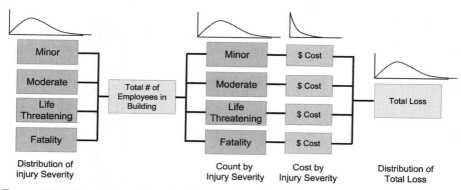

Figure 10.5. Calculation of workers' compensation loss for an individual building.

10.6.5 The ISO Advisory Loss Costs

Loss estimates generated by terrorism models are of interest to all parties. The insureds would like a better understanding of their exposure to potential terrorist attacks in order to determine whether to purchase coverage. Insurers can use model output to develop their pricing, reinsurance needs, and fashion policy conditions such as deductibles, exclusions, and coverage limits. Model output is also of interest to policy makers. In New York City for example, modeled loss estimates have been used to support a request for a larger share of federal funding for homeland security.

Since these terrorism models have been applied to thousands of potential targets, they can provide a picture of the relative risk by state, city, ZIP code and even by individual location. The Insurance Services Office (ISO) used the estimates provided by one of its subsidiaries, AIR Worldwide, to file commercial property advisory average loss costs with the insurance commissioner for each state at the end of 2002.[3] ISO defined three tiers for the country, with certain areas within Washington, DC, New York, Chicago and San Francisco in the highest tier, with assigned loss costs of approximately $0.10 per $100 of property value. A second tier consisted of Boston, Houston, Los Angeles, Philadelphia and Seattle as well as other portions of the highest rated cities; the rest of the country fell into the third tier.

In pre-filing discussions with regulators, ISO's advisory loss costs were challenged by some regulators who felt that such premiums would

---

[3] A *loss cost* is defined by ISO as that portion of a rate that does not include provision for expenses (other than loss adjustment expenses) or profit. It may be used by ISO companies as a starting point to set insurance rates, after reflection of company-specific expenses and profit. Once an ISO advisory loss cost has been approved by a state, an ISO participating insurance company can usually adopt it without having to undertake its own often lengthy and expensive rate filing process.

lead businesses to relocate to other areas (Hsu, 2003). Negotiations ensued and compromises were made. ISO filed loss costs for first-tier cities based on zip code level model results, which differentiated between the higher risk of downtown city centers and the lower risk of properties on the outskirts. But nowhere did the filed loss costs exceed $0.03 per $100 of property value.[4] Thus, while the new official advisory average loss costs no longer adequately reflected the risk in the eyes of the modelers, they became more palatable to other stakeholders. The Departments of Insurance in all 50 states eventually approved these ISO advisory loss costs that covered the years 2003, 2004, and 2005.

10.7 Low Insurance Demand for Terrorism Coverage

When Congress passed the Terrorist Risk Insurance Act (TRIA) in November 2002, the expectation was that it would ease insurers' concerns about suffering large losses from another extreme attack and then enable buyers at risk to purchase coverage at reasonable prices. However, the demand for coverage has been much lower than anticipated even though insurance is now available nationwide under the TRIA requirement (Hsu, 2003; Treaster, 2003).

10.7.1 Empirical Evidence

The Council of Insurance Agents and Brokers (CIAB) undertook the first national survey on the level of demand for terrorism coverage at the beginning of 2003 (CIAB, 2003a). At the time, almost half of its members that handle the largest accounts (customers who pay more than $100,000 annually in commission and fees to the broker) indicated that less than 1 in 5 of their customers had purchased terrorism insurance. The low demand was even more pronounced for smaller companies (less than $25,000 in commission and fees to the broker). Only 65% of the brokers indicated that less than 1 in 5 customers were purchasing insurance against terrorism.

According to another national survey by the CIAB undertaken during the spring of 2003, 72% of the brokers indicated that most of their commercial customers were still not purchasing terrorism insurance coverage even in locations like New York City (CIAB, 2003b). A survey by Marsh Inc. of 2400 of its policyholders revealed that 29.3% of them had purchased terrorism insurance in 2003 (Marsh, 2004). If this level of demand continues, a severe terrorist attack will likely have a more devastating effect on business continuity today than after 9/11.

Although TRIA limits the potential losses to the insurance industry, some insurers are still concerned about the impact of a large terrorist attack on

---

[4]The second tier (third tier) settled at $0.018 ($0.001) per $100 of property value.

the solvency of their firms and their ability to pay. Some businesses are concerned not only with acts of terrorism certified by the federal government, but also by the prospect of "domestic terrorism", such as an attack similar to the Oklahoma City bombings in 1995, which would not be covered by TRIA. The market for domestic terrorism is still mixed with some insurers offering coverage (sometimes at no cost if the risk is perceived to be low) while others simply excluding it (CIAB, 2003a). In the latter case, businesses may prefer not to buy any terrorism coverage than partial protection.

10.7.2 Heuristics and Biases

Since most businesses have little or no information on terrorism risk and no new attack since 9/11 has occurred on U.S. soil at the time this book goes to press, firms may perceive the chances of another event to be extremely low. This behavior has been well documented for natural hazards where many individuals buy insurance after a disaster occurs and cancel their policies several years later if they have not suffered a loss It is hard to convince them that the best return on an insurance policy is no return at all. In other words, there is a tendency for most people to view insurance as an investment rather than as a form of protection (Kunreuther, 2002).

A few years after 9/11, concern with damage from terrorism appears to have taken a back seat. In 2003, most firms believed that if a terrorist attack occurred, it would not affect them, whereas in the first few months after 9/11, they had the opposite belief. The aforementioned CIAB study indicated that more than 90% of the brokers said that their customers eschew terrorism insurance because they think they don't need it (CIAB, 2003b). These firms consider insurance, even at relatively low premiums, to be a bad investment. The expectation that government may financially aid affected businesses whether or not they are covered by insurance, as illustrated by the airline industry following 9/11, may also contribute to limited interest in spending money on coverage.

There seems to be a large difference in the perception of the seriousness of the terrorist threat by those who are potential buyers of insurance and those who are supplying coverage. In these circumstances, TRIA will not solve the problem. To create a market for terrorism insurance, both buyers and sellers need to do a more systematic analysis of the relationship between the price of protection and the implied risk. There is no guarantee that firms will be willing to pay more for coverage or that insurers will greatly reduce their premiums. But there is a much better chance that a larger market for terrorism coverage will emerge than if the status quo is maintained (Kunreuther and Michel-Kerjan, in press).

The U.S. Treasury Department is required by Congress to undertake studies of the supply and demand for terrorism coverage so that more informed decisions on the renewal of TRIA in 2005 may be made. Those studies, launched in December 2003, should contribute to better understanding the current level of demand for terrorism insurance, as well as to suggest possible improvements in the partnership to create a more stable insurance market should another attack occur.

10.8 Future Research Directions

This concluding section suggests future research for dealing with terrorism and other extreme events, such as natural disasters, by focusing on three areas: vulnerability analyses, risk perception and interdependencies.

10.8.1 Vulnerability Analyses

Risk assessment needs to be supplemented by vulnerability analyses that characterize the forms of physical, social, political, economic, cultural, and psychological harms to which individuals and modern societies are susceptible. Modeling events with considerable uncertainty and ambiguity creates discomfort in undertaking risk assessments. Constructing scenarios that may lead to the occurrence of specific events is a useful first step.

A meaningful example of work in this regard is a study undertaken over 25 years ago by Warner North and his colleagues on estimating the likelihood of microbial contamination of Mars from the first Viking mission, where a landing on the planet was planned on July 4, 1976. They first constructed a series of scenarios characterizing how microbes could contaminate Martian soil based on the possible location of microbes on the spacecraft and Martian environmental conditions. They then assigned probabilities of contamination to each of these scenarios and undertook extensive sensitivity analyses to determine how changes in the inputs to these scenarios would lead to changes in these probabilities. On the basis of these analyses, they determined that the probability of contamination was more than one order of magnitude below the predetermined acceptable level of risk of 1 in 10,000. Scientists who had initially expressed concern about the risk of contamination agreed that the mission should proceed without the need for further steps to reduce the microbial burden on the Viking. The Viking successfully landed on Mars in the summer of 1976.

10.8.2 Risk Perception

The terrorist attacks of 9/11 have raised the question as to what should be done to mitigate the consequences of future catastrophes and aid the recovery process should another disaster occur. In order to develop a strategy, incorporating the growing knowledge of how individuals process information on extreme events and then make choices regarding mitigation is necessary.

As illustrated by the examples of Hurricane Andrew and the Northridge earthquake, people are not very concerned about the possibility of catastrophe events before they occur. They want to take protective action only after the event and this concern dissipates over time. To reduce the consequences of natural disasters, safer structures can be built and/or people can move out of harm's way. To mitigate the consequences of chemical accidents, the inventory level and/or production of specific toxins can be reduced to lower the risk of another mishap occurring.

Taking steps to reduce the risk of future terrorist activities is more difficult than for natural disasters or industrial accidents. Considerable uncertainty exists with respect to who the perpetrators are, their motivations, the nature of their next attack and where it will be delivered. Terrorist groups can attack anything, anywhere, at any time, and not everything can be protected. Additionally, there are challenges associated with allocating resources for dealing with terrorism risk. The government may be tempted to invest huge sums of money in protection to provide reassurance for its citizens (i.e., reassuring expenditures). Educating the public on the current likelihood of attacks might reduce such costs. On the other hand, actions taken by government services to curb terrorism might not be publicly revealed to protect national security.

10.8.3 Interdependencies

The antecedents to catastrophes can be quite distinct and distant from the actual disaster, as in the case of the 9/11 attacks, when security failures at Boston's Logan airport led to crashes at the World Trace Center (WTC), Pentagon, and rural Pennsylvania. The same was true in the case of recent power failures in the northeastern US and Canada, where the initiating event occurred in Ohio but the worst consequences were felt hundreds of miles away.

Future research should address the appropriate strategies for dealing with situations where there are interdependencies between agents (persons, organizations, countries). In these situations, there may be a need for the public sector to take the leading role with respect to providing protective measures because the private sector may have few economic incentives to take these steps on their own. Kunreuther and Heal (2003) have addressed this issue by asking the following question: What economic incentives do residents, firms or governments have for undertaking protection if they know that others are not taking these measures and that their failure to do so could cause damage to them?

To illustrate this point, suppose Airline A is considering whether to institute a sophisticated passenger security system knowing that passengers who transfer from other airlines may not have gone through a similar screening procedure and could cause damage to its airplane. If there is no screening process for passengers who transfer from one airline to another and there is a relatively high probability that these dangerous passengers could get on board Airline A due to the failure of other airlines to adopt screening systems, then Airline A will also not want to invest in such a system. The interdependent risks across firms may lead all of them to decide not to invest in protection.

The 9/11 events and the anthrax attacks during the fall of 2001 also demonstrated a new kind of vulnerability. Terrorists can use the capacity of a country's critical infrastructures to have an immediate large-scale impact on the nation by reversing the diffusion capacity of the networks and turn them against the target population so that every aircraft and every piece of mail now becomes a potential weapon (Michel-Kerjan, 2003a). During the anthrax episode, the attackers used the U.S. Postal Service to spread threats throughout the country and abroad. The entire network was potentially at risk as any envelope could have been considered to be contaminated by anthrax (Boin, Lagadec, Michel-Kerjan and Overdijk, 2003).

The emerging vulnerabilities in critical infrastructures raise challenging questions related to strategies for mitigation given the large operating networks associated with the water supply, electricity, transportation networks, telecommunications, banking and finance, energy, emergency, and defense services. The social and economic continuity of a nation's activities critically depend on their operation (OECD, 2003; Michel-Kerjan, 2003a; White House, 2003).

Future research should examine the nature of these interdependencies as well as the appropriate role of regulations, standards, third party inspections, and insurance to encourage individuals and firms to take protective actions. Without some type of coordinating mechanism, or economic incentives such as a fine, subsidy or tax, it may be difficult to convince any individual group to invest in mitigation because they know others may contaminate them.

To better understand these interdependencies at a managerial level, it would be meaningful to organize international strategic debriefings much more systematically after an extreme event or a large-scale threat occurred with senior-executives who were in charge and with academic experts. Every threat offers an opportunity to learn and be collectively prepared (Lagadec and Michel-Kerjan, 2004).

While launching such initiatives requires expertise and commitment by the top-management of organizations, it would help to learn more about these emerging risks and to examine more adequate global security strategies given limited resources. By developing trusted public-private partnerships to deal with interdependencies associated with extreme events substantial benefits can be provided to the affected individuals and firms as well as improving the social welfare.

10.9 References

Adler, M. and Ziglio, E. (eds) (1996). *Gazing Into the Oracle: The Delphi Method and Its Application to Social Policy and Public Health*, London, Kingsley Publishers.

Bantwal, Vivek and Kunreuther, Howard (2000). "A Cat Bond Premium Puzzle?" *Journal of Psychology and Financial Markets*, 1: 76-91.

Boin, A., Lagadec, P., Michel-Kerjan, E., and Overdijk, W. (2003). "Critical Infrastructures under Threat: Learning from the Anthrax Scare" *Journal of Contingencies and Crisis Management,* 11 (3): 99-105.

Central Intelligence Agency (2003). "Terrorist CBRN: Materials and Effects (U)", CIA: Directorate of Intelligence, May 2003, CTC 2003-40058.

Council of Insurance Agents and Brokers (2003a). "Many Commercial Interests Are Not Buying Terrorism Insurance, New CIAB Survey Show" News Release, March 24.

Council of Insurance Agents and Brokers (2003b). "Commercial Market Index Survey" News Release, July 22.

Glasstone, S. and Dolan, P. J. (eds.) (1977). *The Effects of Nuclear Weapons*, Third Edition, 1977, Prepared and published by the United States Department of Defense and the United States Department of Energy.

Hale, D. (2002). "America Uncovered" *Financial Times*, September 12.

Hsu, S. (2003). "D.C. Disputes Insurance Study Raising Rates For Terrorism" *Washington Post*, January 7, page A01.

Insurance Accounting (2003). "Knowledge a Key for Terror Risk Pricing", January 27, 2003, Thomson Media.

Kunreuther, H. and Michel-Kerjan, E. (in press). "Policy Watch: Challenges for Terrorism Risk Coverage in the U.S." *Journal of Economic Perspectives.*

Kunreuther, H. and Heal, G. (2003). "Interdependent Security" *Journal of Risk and Uncertainty,* 26(2/3): 231-249.

Kunreuther, H. (2002). "The Role of Insurance in Managing Extreme Events: Implications for Terrorism Coverage" *Risk Analysis*, 22: 427-437.

Kunreuther, H., Michel-Kerjan, E. and Porter, B. (2003). "Assessing, Managing and Financing Extreme Events: Dealing with Terrorism", *Working Paper 10179*, National Bureau of Economic Research, Cambridge, MA.

Lagadec, P. and Michel-Kerjan, E. (2004). "A Framework for Senior Executives To Meet the Challenge of Interdependent Critical Networks Under Threat: The Paris Initiative, 'Anthrax and Beyond'." Working Paper, WP #2004.28, Center for Risk Management and Decision Processes, The Wharton School, Philadelphia.

Lehmann, Raymond. (2004). "Twin Towers Insured Loss Estimate Drops to Between $30 and $35 Billion", Bestwire, May 10.

Linstone, H. and Turoff, M. (1975). *The Delphi Method. Techniques and Applications.* Addison-Wesly Publishing Company.

Major, J. (2002). "Advanced Techniques for Modeling Terrorism Risk" Journal *of Risk Finance,* 4 (1): 15-24.

Marsh Inc. (2004). "Marketwatch: Property Terrorism Insurance," April 2004.

Michel-Kerjan, E. (2003a). "New Vulnerabilities in Critical Infrastructures: A U.S. Perspective" *Journal of Contingencies and Crisis Management,* 11 (3): 132-140.

Michel-Kerjan, E. (2003b). "Large-scale Terrorism: Risk Sharing and Public Policy" *Revue d'Economie Politique,* 113 (5): 625-648.

Olatidoye, O., Sarathy, S., Jones, G., McIntyre, C., Milligan, L. (1998). "A Representative Survey of Blast Loading Models and Damage Assessment Methods for Buildings Subject to Explosive Blasts", Clark Atlantic University, Department of Defense High Performance Computing Program, CEWES MSRC/PET TR 98-36.

Organisation for Economic Co-operation and Development (2003). *Emerging Systemic Risks in the 21ˢᵗ Century: An Agenda for Action.* Paris: OECD.

Pate-Cornell, E. and Guikema, S. (2002) "Probabilistic Modeling of Terrorist Threats: A Systems Analysis Approach to Setting Priorities Among Countermeasures" *Military Operations Research,* 7: 5-20. December.

Swiss Re (2002). *Natural catastrophes and man-made disasters 2001: man-made losses take on a new dimension,* Sigma No1, Zurich: Swiss Re.

Treaster, J. (2003). "Insurance for Terrorism Still a Rarity" *New York Times,* March 8.

U.S. Department of State (2003). *Patterns of Global Terrorism 2002.* April 2003.

U.S. General Accounting Office (2003). *Catastrophe Insurance Risks. Status of Efforts to Securitize Natural Catastrophe and Terrorism Risk.* GAO-03-1033. Washington, D.C.: September 24.

U.S. General Accounting Office (2002). "Terrorism Insurance: Rising Uninsured Exposure to Attacks Heightens Potential Economic Vulnerabilities", Testimony of Richard J. Hillman Before the Subcommittee on Oversight and Investigations, Committee on Financial Services, House of Representatives. February 27.

White House (2003). *National Strategy for Physical Protection of Critical Infrastructures and Key Assets Washington,* DC, February 2003.

Woo, G. (2002). "Quantitative Terrorism Risk Assessment" *Journal of Risk Finance,* 4 (1): 7-14.

Glossary

AAL: Average Annual Loss, defined as the average or expected loss for an insurance policy or a set of policies per year.

Aleatory Uncertainty: Inherent randomness associated with a future catastrophe; it cannot be reduced by the collection of additional data.

Basis Risk: The imperfect correlation between the actual losses suffered by a company or individual and the payments received from a risk transfer instrument designed to cover these losses.

Blind Thrust Fault: A type of earthquake fault that terminates before it reaches the Earth's surface.

Capital Markets: The markets in which corporate equity and longer-term debt securities are issued and traded.

Capacity: The total limit of liability that a company or the insurance industry can assume, according to generally accepted criteria for solvency.

Catastrophe: An unexpected or unanticipated natural or man-made event that has wide ranging negative socioeconomic impacts; also known as a disaster.

Catastrophe Bond: A corporate bond that requires the purchasers to forgive or defer some or all payments of interest or principal if the actual catastrophe loss surpasses a specified amount or trigger.

Catastrophe Loss: Economic loss resulting from a large-scale disaster.

Catastrophe Model: A computer-based model that estimates losses from natural or man-made hazards, such as earthquakes, floods, hurricanes and acts of terrorism.

Catastrophe Risk: Potential economic loss or other negative impact associated with large-scale disasters.

CEA: The California Earthquake Authority. Established in 1996, it is a state-run agency that manages a fund that provides earthquake insurance coverage to homeowners in California.

Cedant: An insurer transferring all or part of a risk to another party, such as a reinsurer.

Claim: A request by a policyholder for payment for losses covered by insurance.

Coinsurance: The sharing of the losses by an insured party as a way of reducing moral hazard.

Coriolis Force:	A force that results from the Earth's rotation, causing moving objects to be deflected to the right in the Northern Hemisphere and to the left in the Southern Hemisphere.
Correlated Losses:	The simultaneous occurrence of many losses from a single catastrophe or disaster.
Credit Risk:	Risk associated with a reinsurer unable to pay its obligation to a ceding insurance company.
CV:	Coefficient of Variation, an attribute of a probability distribution, calculated as its standard deviation divided by its mean.
Damage Function:	An equation relating the expected damage state of a building to the intensity of an event.
Damage Ratio:	The ratio of repair cost to the replacement cost of a building.
Deductible:	The proportion of an insured loss that the policyholder agrees to pay before any recovery from the insurer.
Demand Surge:	Term used to refer to the sudden increase in construction costs following a natural disaster event.
EERI:	Earthquake Engineering Research Institute, a non-profit organization that strives to improve the understanding and reduce the impact of earthquakes.
Exceedance Probability (EP) Curve:	A graphical representation of the probability that a certain level of risk will be surpassed during a future time period. The most common form of an EP curve is the probability that an economic loss will be surpassed on an annual basis.
Epistemic Uncertainty:	The lack of knowledge associated with a future catastrophe; it can be reduced by the collection of additional data.
Excess of Loss Reinsurance:	A type of reinsurance in which a premium is paid to an insurer to cover losses above a certain threshold or retention.
Exposure:	In a catastrophe model, the properties at risk from a natural or man-made hazard.
FEMA:	The Federal Emergency Management Agency, a U.S. federal agency responsible for developing strategies for mitigation, preparedness, response and recovery from disasters. On March 1, 2003, FEMA became part of the U.S. Department of Homeland Security.
FHCF:	Florida Hurricane Catastrophe Fund. Authorized in 1993, it is a tax-exempt trust fund that covers a portion of natural disaster losses to insurers covering policies in the state of Florida. A

retention level is specified for each year and insurers are reimbursed for losses in excess of that level.

Geocoding:

The process by which one assigns geographic coordinates (latitude and longitude) to a location on the Earth. In catastrophe modeling, geocoding is used to assign coordinates to an exposure at risk, often based on its street address, ZIP code or another location descriptor.

Ground-up Loss:

The total amount of loss sustained by an insurer before any policy deductibles or reinsurance is applied.

Hazard:

One of four catastrophe model components, defining the source, propagation, and site effects for natural perils or defining the likelihood of attacks and attack modes of terrorist activities.

HAZUS:

Hazards, U.S., the U.S.'s nationally applicable standardized methodology and software program for analyzing catastrophes (the federal government's catastrophe model). The model was first introduced in 1997, estimating loss from earthquakes. In 2004, the model was renamed HAZUS-MH (multi-hazard) and wind and flood loss estimation models were added.

Homeowners Insurance:

A comprehensive insurance policy covering an owner-occupied residence for liability, theft, and physical perils.

Indemnity Contract:

A contract in which one insurance company charges a premium to provide funds to another insurance company to cover a stated portion of the loss it may sustain under its insurance policies. See Reinsurance.

Insolvency Risk:

The probability of not having sufficient financial resources to meet financial obligations.

Insurability:

Acceptability to a company of an applicant for insurance, based on certain criteria for an insurable risk.

Inventory:

One of four catastrophe model components, defining exposures at risk from a natural or man-made hazard.

ISO:

Insurance Services Office, Inc. Created in 1971, this company is the leader in supplying industry information to the property/casualty insurance industry in the U.S. It also functions as an insurance advisory organization.

LIBOR:

London Interbank Offered Rate, A risk-free rate that enables one to determine the risk premium associated with securities, such as catastrophe bonds.

Loss:

One of four catastrophe model components, defining the amount of reduction in the value of an asset due to a natural or man-made hazard.

Mitigation:	Loss reduction measure taken to reduce or eliminate damage or loss due to a natural or man-made hazard.
Moral Hazard:	Intentionally careless behavior that increases the risk from an event because the loss is insured. For example, setting a house on fire as a way of collecting an insurance claim is an example of moral hazard.
Natural Disaster:	An event that results in the need for physical and economic assistance from outside sources. A U.S. natural disaster is deemed significant when the economic loss is at least $1 billion and/or over 50 deaths are attributed to the event.
NEHRP:	National Earthquake Hazard Reduction Program, established by the Earthquake Hazards Reduction Act in October of 1977 to reduce the risks to life and property from future earthquakes in the United States.
NFIP:	The National Flood Insurance Program, which provides federal insurance to residents of flood-prone regions.
NOAA:	National Oceanic and Atmospheric Administration. Established in 1970, this federally run organization monitors and predicts the state of the Earth, the oceans and their living resources, and the atmosphere.
Peak Ground Acceleration (PGA):	The maximum absolute magnitude of a ground acceleration time series, as measured during an earthquake event; PGA is often used as an indicator of damage in a catastrophe model.
PML:	Probable Maximum Loss, representing the largest economic loss likely to occur for a given policy or a set of policies when a caatastrophic event occurs.
Portfolio:	The full set of policies covered by an insurance company.
Pro Rata Reinsurance:	A type of reinsurance in which premium and loss are shared by cedant andinsurer on a proportional basis.
Rate Making:	The process by which insurance rates, or the cost per unit of insurance purchased, are established.
Reinsurance:	Purchase of insurance by an insurance (ceding) company from another insurance (reinsurance) company for purpose of spreading risk and reducing the loss from a catastrophe event.
Return Period:	The expected time between a certain magnitude of loss event, defined as the inverse of the annual exceedance probability. For example, a return period of 100 years corresponds to an annual exceedance probability of 1%.

Risk Transfer:	A method by which an individual or company reduces its risk from a natural or man-made hazard by reassigning the risk to another entity.
ROA:	Return on Assets, an indicator of profitability. It is the ratio of net income to total assets.
SBA:	Small Business Administration. Established in 1953 by the U.S. Congress to protect the interests of small businesses and by financially aiding their recovery from natural disasters.
Securitization:	The process by which the economic loss resulting from a catastrophe is guaranteed to be paid. One example of securitization is issuing a catastrophe bond.
Sharpe Ratio:	A relative measure of a portfolio's return-to-risk ratio. It is calculated as the return above the risk-free rate divided by its standard deviation. It is often used to determine the amount of excess return required by investors for an additional unit of risk.
Slip Rate:	The rate at which each side of a fault plane moves relative to the other, in millimeters per year.
Spectral Acceleration:	A measure used as a representation for building response to an earthquake in a catastrophe model.
Underwriting:	The process of selecting risks to insure and determining in what amounts and on what terms the company will accept the risk.
USGS:	United States Geological Survey, an agency of the federal government that collects, monitors, analyzes and provides information about natural resources.
Vulnerability:	One of four catastrophe model components, defining the susceptibility of an inventory to a natural or man-made hazard. Other terms that are often used to characterize vulnerability are damage and fragility.

Index

242

244